AF777867

Reading Essentials® in Science

HEALTHY LIVING

Physical Activity

ALEXANDRA POWE ALLRED

PERFECTION LEARNING®

Editorial Director: Susan C. Thies
Editor: Paula J. Reece
Design Director: Randy Messer
Book Design: Emily J. Greazel
Cover Design: Michael A. Aspengren

To Marc and Karen Powe, who raised me to believe I could fly to the moon, touch the stars, and sail around the world! And thanks, Pooh, for flying and sailing with me.

Image credits:
© Charles Jean Marc/CORBIS SYGMA: p. 12; © Jim Cummins/CORBIS: p. 28 (top left); Northwind Picture Archives: pp. 7, 8, 9 (bottom)

BananaStock: front cover (bottom middle), pp. 11 (foreground), 21 (bottom right); ClipArt.com: pp. 9 (top), 13, 14 (top), 34 (bottom); Corel Professional Photos: pp. 5 (top), 35; CORBIS Royalty-free: pp. 11 (background), 15 (bottom left); Digital Stock: pp. 3, 5 (bottom), 29 (bottom), 30, 33; Image100: pp. 4, 6 (bottom), 16, 26 (bottom), 28 (bottom right), 31 (bottom), 32 (bottom), 40; Library of Congress: p. 19; LifeART © 2003 Lippincott, Williams, & Wilkins: pp. 17, 22, 23 (top left), 23 (bottom left), 24 (top); Perfection Learning: p. 20 (top); PhotoDisc: pp. 24 (bottom), 27, 31 (top), 37; Photos.com: back cover, front cover (main, bottom left, bottom right), pp. 1, 6 (top), 10, 14 (bottom), 15 (top, bottom right), 18, 20 (bottom), 21 (top right, bottom left), 23 (bottom right), 25, 26 (top), 28 (bottom left), 29 (top), 32 (middle), 34 (top)

A special thanks to the following for her scientific review of the book:
Dr. Marcie R. Wycoff-Horn, Assistant Professor, Department of Health Education and Health Promotion, University of Wisconsin-LaCrosse

Text © 2005 by **Perfection Learning®** Corporation.
All rights reserved. No part of this book may be reproduced, stored in a retrieval system, or transmitted in any form or by any means, electronic, mechanical, photocopying, recording, or otherwise, without prior permission of the publisher.

Printed in the United States of America.
For information, contact
Perfection Learning® Corporation
1000 North Second Avenue, P.O. Box 500
Logan, Iowa 51546-0500.
Phone: 1-800-831-4190
Fax: 1-800-543-2745
perfectionlearning.com

1 2 3 4 5 6 PP 09 08 07 06 05 04

ISBN 0-7891-6267-9

Table of Contents

Introduction to Physical Activity

Run, jump, climb, and leap! When you play outside with your friends, you probably only think about all the fun you are having. Did you realize that when you are being active, you are also acting like a scientist—building a machine, creating a strong future for yourself, and learning how to become a better person?

All that from a game of kickball? It sounds crazy, but it is true. **Physical activity** builds strong **bones**, powerful

muscles, and a strong **heart**. Physical activity has become such an important topic that even the president of the United States has asked parents, teachers, and children across the country to start exercising. So what *is* physical activity?

Up for the Challenge?

To find out more about the president's fitness challenge, go to www.presidentschallenge.org.

A physical activity is any sport (like baseball or soccer) or activity (such as freeze tag, climbing a tree, or skipping rope) during which your heart beats a little faster, you sweat, and you begin to feel a little tired. During physical activity, you build stronger muscles and burn **calories**, which burn fat. You also learn better balance and develop speed and quicker **reflexes**.

Physical activity is something that can be done alone or with others.

Physical activity also helps you fight illnesses such as the common cold as well as more serious diseases such as **diabetes** and **high blood pressure**. Because more and more children are not physically active and are becoming **overweight**, these very serious diseases are becoming more common. They can cause great pain and even shorten lives.

The more you **flex** and move, the stronger you make your heart, your muscles, and your mind. When you are physically fit, you will perform better in school and be happier with your friends, family, and yourself. So the next time you jump in the pool or walk with your dog, just think how healthy, smart, and happy you are becoming!

1 How We Used to Live

Today, doctors and health experts are concerned about children and adults in the United States. Why? Because we do not exercise enough to keep our bodies strong and healthy. This is different from the way people used to live. Believe it or not, children did not always have television, video games, or computers. The early American settlers, including the children, worked hard all day long. There was land to be cleared, shelters to be built, and crops to be planted. Being young was no excuse for not working.

Children rose early before school to do chores around the house. They milked cows, gathered eggs, swept floors, sewed, and hauled water from nearby streams or wells. Right after school, children returned home to work until dinnertime. Children were often punished when they complained about having to work. Parents believed that it was the duty of the children to work for the family and help as much as possible.

When the children were able to play, it was not usually quiet play. Their toys were simple in design but required a lot of imagination. Rocks, boards, and pieces of rope were used to make games, and almost every game was played outside. Snowshoeing, sledding, and hockey were played in the winter, while swimming and

Settlers work to build a log cabin.

fishing were fun summertime activities. The children of yesterday were active, imaginative, and fit. From the moment the sun came up until the sun went down, pioneer children hardly sat still.

On a Roll!

One game pioneer children played was "roll the hoop." Children rolled a hoop using a stick while they ran. Races or contests were sometimes held between children.

Pioneer kids spent much of their time outside.

2 How We Live Today

Children used to play outside all day. How times have changed! Today's kids watch an average of 23 hours of TV every week. That's almost one full day! And that doesn't count time spent playing video games or surfing the Internet. In fact, America's children spend more time watching television or playing video games than anything else except sleeping!

Kids used to walk or bike everywhere they wanted to go. Today's kids ride in a car, on the bus, or on the subway. Kids used to be very fit. Most of today's kids are out of condition.

Kids are not only playing outside less than they used to, but **diets** have changed as well. Pioneer families grew their own foods. Meat came from the farm, cooked slowly over a fire. The only choices for drinks were water or milk. Sometimes it would take several hours to cook a fine meal. Compare that with today when families go through the drive through at a fast-food restaurant. They order cheeseburgers, French fries, and soda—all foods high in saturated fats, sugar, and grease. Not only are Americans eating unhealthy foods, but they are also eating bigger meals than ever. This puts them at risk for diseases like diabetes or heart disease.

Because children watch so much television, they are influenced by the food in commercials. Commercials make food look like fun, but often these foods are filled with sugar and are high in fat. Children who watch television all day and eat in fast-food restaurants more than once a week are eating more calories than they are using up in some kind of physical activity. These extra calories are stored as fat. About one in every five kids today is overweight.

Move Over Santa!

Did you know that Ronald McDonald is the second most recognized character around the world, just after Santa Claus?

Children who are overweight and inactive face medical problems. At one time, diabetes was only a problem for overweight adults because few children were overweight. But in the last few decades, doctors

Make Commercials Work for You!

Next time you sit down to watch TV, instead of sitting through the commercials, use that time to put your body to work! See how many exercises you can do before your program comes back on. Here are some exercises to try:

- sit-ups
- push-ups
- running in place
- jumping rope
- shadow boxing

have begun to treat children with **type 2 diabetes**, also known as "adult-onset diabetes." This disease can cause serious health problems including heart disease, blindness, and kidney failure. The best way to avoid diabetes is to exercise and eat well.

A Scary Statistic

Diabetes was the sixth leading cause of death in the United States in 2000.

Today, many schools are working with parents and physicians to teach children how to exercise and eat properly. Even the U.S. government has become involved. The **surgeon general** reports that even children who are overweight and out of shape can become healthier with regular exercise. The surgeon general recommends that children spend 60 minutes in physical activity most days of the week!

So turn off the TV! Get ready, get set, go!

3 Why Run?

The act of running is natural. Since the beginning of time, humans have run to hunt, to play, and to survive. Before there were cars, humans ran on foot to deliver messages. Later, horses were used to help deliver messages or mail, to travel, to work (such as herding cattle), and to play.

How a Horse Got Its Name

The name "quarter horse" came from early American settlers. Horse races were held in small towns as a way to have fun and exercise. The races were a quarter of a mile, and the entire town would turn out to watch!

Running, riding, climbing, and leaping were not only a way of life for early Americans but also a way to stay in shape. The stronger and healthier people were, the more work they were able to do. This was important because their lives were challenging. With no electricity, water, cars, or modern appliances, people had to be strong and work hard. But today we have all kinds of things that make our lives easier—dishwashers and vacuum cleaners and remote controls. So why do we need to run? To stay healthy, that's why.

Our heart is a muscle. In fact, it is the strongest muscle in our body. But that doesn't mean we don't have to exercise it. A happy, healthy heart is always looking to get stronger. Because it can't run or lift weight, it depends on us to exercise it. How? **Aerobic exercise**. Aerobic exercise is any kind of physical activity that makes the muscles in our body—including the heart—use **oxygen**. Since aerobic exercise is repetitive, something we do over and over, our body keeps bringing fresh oxygen to our muscles.

Running is a great form of aerobic exercise. When we run, several things happen. Our heart begins to pump harder. We can feel this when we take our pulse or put our hand on our heart. *Thump, thump, thump!* Our heart muscle is working harder than ever, pumping blood throughout our entire body through **vessels** called **arteries** and **veins**. This helps our **blood circulation**, which carries oxygen from the air

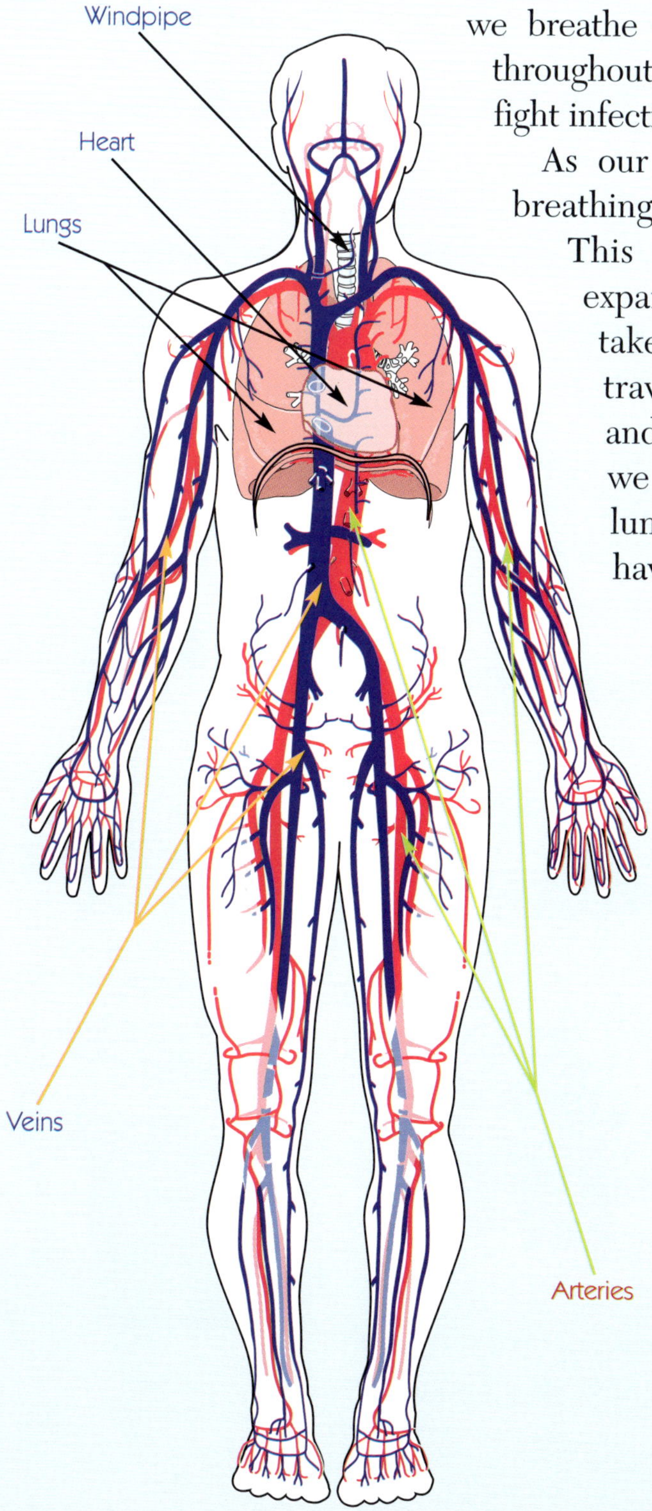

we breathe and healthy foods we eat throughout our entire body. This helps fight infections and keep us strong.

As our heart pumps harder, our breathing gets deeper and deeper. This is because our **lungs** expand, getting bigger as we take gulps of air. Clean air travels down our **windpipe** and into our lungs. The more we exercise, the stronger our lungs become. This makes us have more **endurance**.

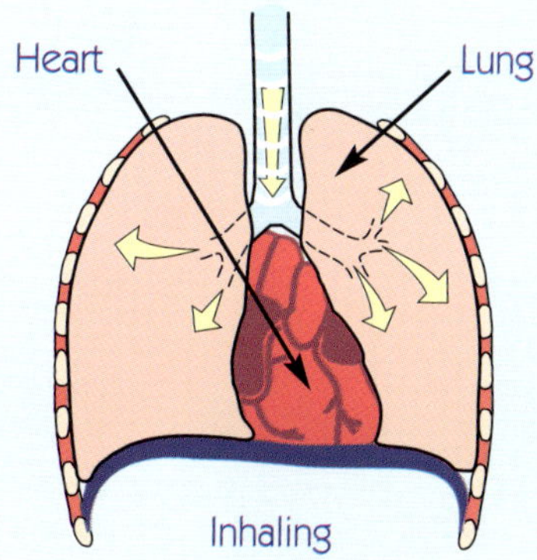

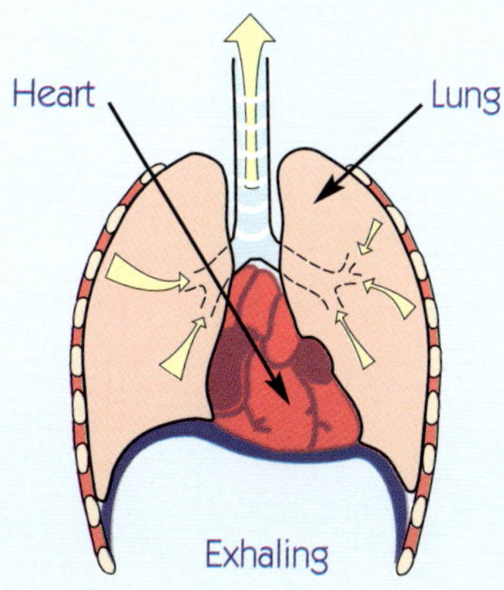

Having more endurance means we can run or play for a longer time. Soccer players and basketball players must have endurance to be able to run for the entire game. They have strong hearts and lungs!

But what if you don't like to run? Well, you're in luck. Running isn't the only form of aerobic exercise. Other excellent ways to exercise your heart and lungs are swimming, playing hockey, walking quickly, rollerblading, jumping rope, or biking. Even dancing is great aerobic exercise! So crank the tunes and get moving!

4

Why Sweat?

Don't you just love to sweat? Don't you? Well, you should. When our body sweats as a result of physical activity, wonderful things happen. The simple definition of sweat is that it is salty water that is produced when we get hot. When we sweat, this water on our skin helps cool us down. Oh, but sweat does so much more than that.

Sweating has been considered so important that it was even discussed in the oldest known medical document. Even then, people knew that sweating was as important to our health as eating and sleeping. As we begin to play a game of soccer or climb a tree, our muscles go to work. They flex and push, making our body warm up. Before we know it, our body is producing sweat.

Sweat It Out!

The oldest known medical document, the Ayurveda, appeared in Sanskrit in 586 B.C. It prescribed a sweat bath and 13 other ways of making sweat for good health.

A Native American medicine man performs a sweat bath ritual.

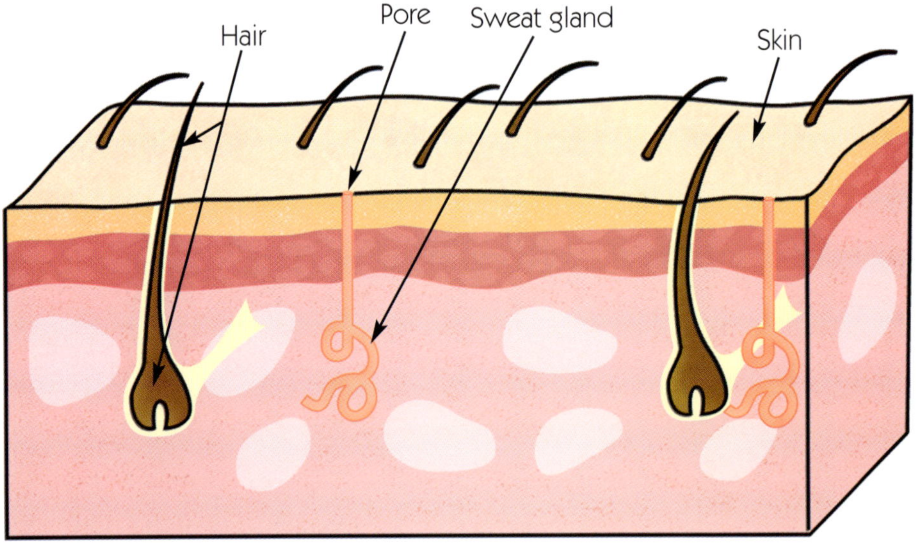

This is great news! Sweat flushes out **toxic metals** that are absorbed into our bodies. With pollution in the air and **toxins** in our water, metals such as copper, zinc, and mercury are absorbed into our body. But sweat flushes all of that out, cleaning our body from the inside out. Eating too many French fries and cheeseburgers may also be toxic, putting too much salt into our body. By sweating, those unwanted wastes are removed too.

Sweat also helps our bodies heal. Have you ever played so hard your muscles were sore the next day? This is because **lactic acid** has built up inside the muscles, causing them to be stiff and sore. We might think the worst thing we could do would be to play hard and make those muscles tired all over again. In truth, physical activity is the best thing we can do. By moving and sweating, the lactic acid is washed out, making us feel stronger and refreshed.

Finally, sweating is great for our skin. Sweating from physical activity cleanses the body by opening the **pores** of the skin. Blood rushes to the skin for a healthier look. It is also true that when we sweat, our body craves more water. Water helps cleanse our body, getting rid of toxins. So the next time someone tells you "Don't sweat it," say, "But I want to!"

5 Why Flex?

Humans have always wanted to be strong. Hunting and building new homes took strength. Long before there were gyms and fitness shows on television, people understood the importance of healthy muscles to keep the **skeletal system** strong.

A baby is born with more than 300 bones. But as we grow, many of the smaller bones grow together to make bigger, stronger bones. This is why it is so important to be physically active. Every time we run, leap, and play, we are building stronger bones and working muscles.

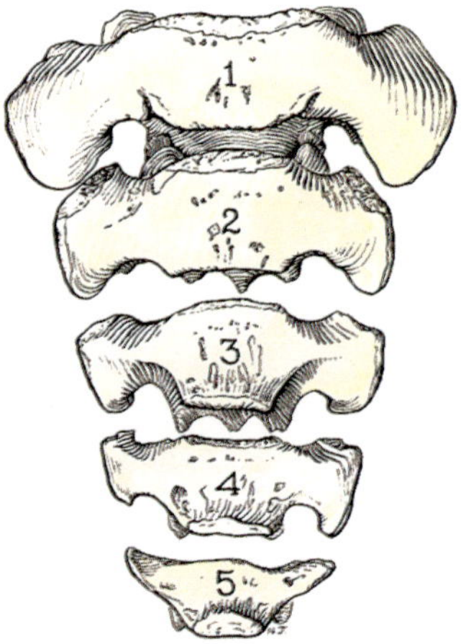

Youth sacrum

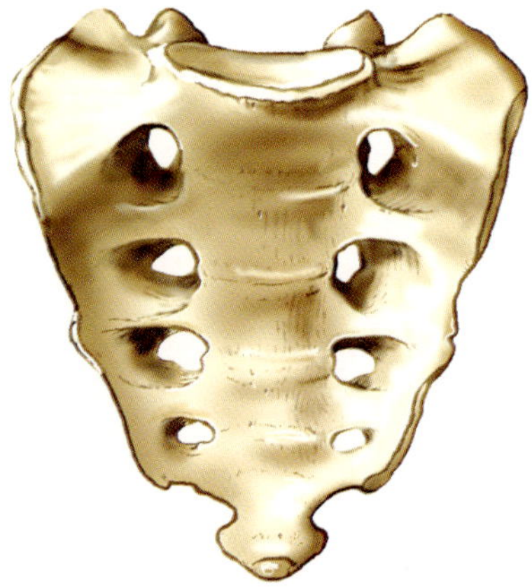

Adult sacrum

When children grow to adults, many of their smaller bones grow together.

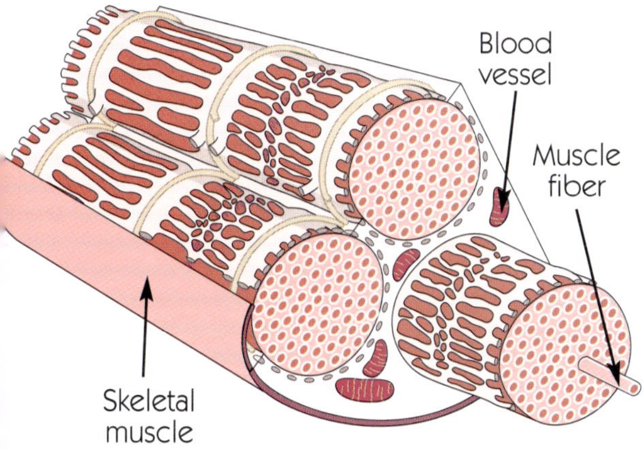

Forty percent of our body is made up of muscle—that's almost half our body! Most of the muscles in our body are skeletal muscles. These are the muscles that work with the bones that make up our skeletal system. Muscles are made up of tiny **fibers** that band together to make the muscles more powerful. The more we flex our muscles, the more fibers are created. Creating new fibers makes us able to run faster and longer, jump higher, and throw farther.

Many, Many Muscles

Did you know that you have a total of 650 muscles in your body?

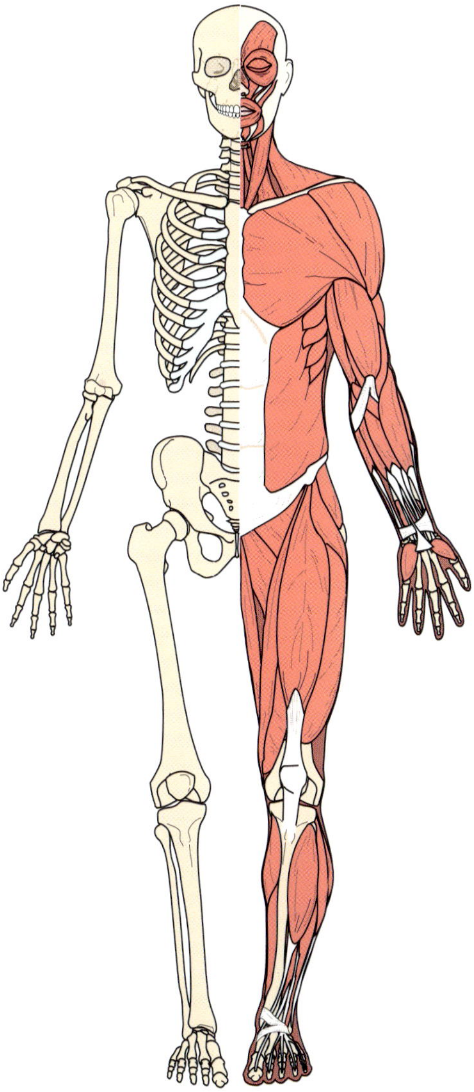

Human skeletal and muscular systems

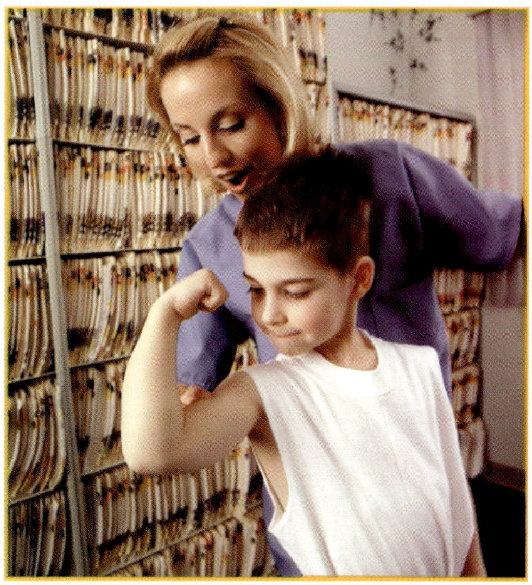

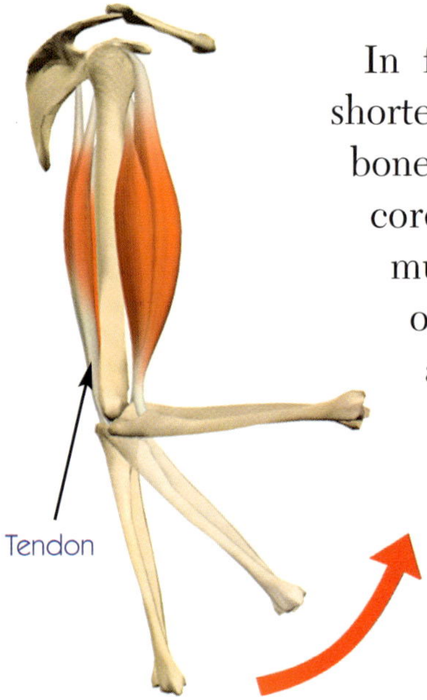

In fact, each time we flex, our muscles get shorter and thicker. That flexing motion moves our bones and strengthens our entire body. White cords called ***tendons*** keep our bones and muscles together. When we contract one of our muscles, the tendon and bone moves along with it. Our tendons allow us to swing a bat, throw a basketball, or lift something heavy.

It's important to let our skeletal muscles and tendons warm up before we work them. If we pull or twist tendons or

muscles before they're warmed up, we can injure them. Take 5 or 10 minutes to stretch before exercising or playing a sport. Your muscles will become larger and stronger—and they will thank you!

What Can You Do?

Want to build up your skeletal muscles? Try doing push-ups or pull-ups, rowing a boat, doing half sit-ups, running, or riding your bike. These exercises and activities will give those skeletal muscles a good workout!

6 Healthy AND Happy

So, being physically active can help our heart, lungs, and muscles. Physical activity can make us healthier and stronger. But did you know that being active can also make us much happier?

When we exercise, **endorphins** are released into our body. Endorphins are chemicals that create a happy feeling in our brain. We feel stronger, healthier, and tend to be happier about everything. But, most importantly, being physically active helps us like ourselves more. And when we like ourselves, other people like us too.

Because we see celebrities everywhere we look—on television, in magazines, on the Internet, and in the movies—it is difficult not to compare ourselves with other people. We wish we had better muscles, longer hair, and a better smile. We wish we were taller or shorter or thinner. But kids who are physically active don't worry so much about these issues.

When we are physically active, something amazing happens. Is it the endorphins? Is it the fun we have with teammates or the praise of a coach? Whatever it is, kids who are physically active like their bodies better, are happier with the way they look and move, and are less critical of others.

Many people think that in order to be physically fit, we must be thin. This is not true. It is also not true that all thin people are physically active and fit. In fact, studies have shown how thin people who do not work out are unhealthier than people who are overweight but very active. So no matter what size or shape you are, exercise is for you!

7 Pass the Test!

How could learning how to hit a ball or dribble a basketball have anything to do with schoolwork? Actually, when our bodies are physically active, our brains become physically active as well. Researchers have found that when kids exercise, it improves the way their brains work. It's true! Physical activity helps blood flow to our brain and spurs **cell** growth. That means our brain, just like all the other muscles in our body, performs better when exercised.

What Are Cells?

Cells are the smallest living units that can carry out basic functions of life. Cells grow. They react to changes in the environment. They change nutrients into energy. They reproduce. Think of them as the building blocks of life. Some of the body's cells die every day, but they are constantly replaced by new cells.

In many states across the United States, schools have reduced the number of gym classes to make more time for other studies. But did you know that when students were tested, it was the kids at schools with daily gym classes and recess who did better on tests? When kids are physically active, their brains are able to better process information (that is, learn better), make decisions more quickly, and remember better. Kids who are physically active are more relaxed, enjoy school more, and tend to like themselves more.

Really? All that from being physically active? Oh, yes, and there is more. Researchers tested kids who were physically active and those who were not active at all. The researchers found that the active kids were less likely to get in trouble at school. They also found that the physically active kids were more likely to have other healthy habits as well. They ate more fruits and vegetables. They watched less television, wore their seatbelts more regularly, and were less likely to smoke when they got older. Wow!

Being physically active keeps us healthy, brainy, and better behaved. "Wow!" is right!

8 Pass the Ball!

It's fun to play a team sport, sharing the wins and losses with teammates. Teammates make exercise more fun, and being part of a team is a great way to make new friends. Playing on a team helps us become a better athlete. But would you believe that it also helps us have better relationships with our family, friends, and teachers? In fact, playing on a team helps us be more successful later in life.

It's true. Most of the successful business leaders in the world say that playing sports as children or young adults taught them important life lessons. They learned how to win and lose, how to get along with others, and how to try hard. These are all skills that helped them become successful.

Team sports and group activities help build lifelong skills.

Every year a list called the Fortune 500 names the most successful business leaders, entertainers, artists, inventors, and scientists. Of that group, more than 70 percent have said that the skills they learned from sports helped them become successful.

Playing at recess is also a healthy form of physical activity. The exercise is good for our body and our brain. Also, playing at recess helps us meet different people, learn how to get along with others, and make new friends. Recess is a great way to have fun and learn skills that you can use to be successful.

No matter what type of physical activity we choose, it should be something that we can continue throughout our lifetimes. As we get older, we become busier. Many times we neglect physical activity to make time for other commitments. Finding a physical activity that we enjoy will make us more likely to fit exercise into our schedule in the future. Start today for a healthy tomorrow!

Internet Connections and Related Readings for *Physical Activity*

BAM! Body and Mind (www.bam.gov)

Maintained by the Centers for Disease Control, this interesting and entertaining site offers information and interactive games and activities on keeping your body and mind fit. Take a quiz to see what types of activities fit your personality. Check out the Activity Cards and get info on all kinds of different physical activities and sports from experts. Read the tips on creating your own fitness plan. Then create your own calendar and get started! Go to the Braggin' Rights page and share stories with other real kids who are trying to improve their bodies and minds—and are succeeding! You can even create your own Kabam! comic.

Kidnetic (www.kidnetic.com)

This site defines *kidnetic energy* as "the energy possessed by a kid who eats right and stays in motion." When you explore this interactive site, you can have fun and learn a ton at the same time. Click on the Inner G page, and match body parts to their proper place in "G." With each body part, you'll get an explanation of what that part does, along with "Bright Papers," related articles to read, and fun recipes that will help keep that body part healthy. The Kore is the game portal. Click on Wet Head Games, and challenge yourself to a game such as Speedy Stairs or Obstacle Fever! Learn how to boogie on down with some new dance moves when you click on the Move Mixer, a dance creation tool. Then race around the house in a wild scavenger hunt that will be sure to get your heart pumping. The Betchacant page allows you to email a dare to a friend, such as how far can you jump, or how many three-point shots can you make. Don't forget to visit the Shout Out page, a message board where you can voice your opinion on health-related topics, along with kids all over the world.

Muscles by Steve Parker. Offers students a comprehensive picture of muscles. Look at Your Body. Millbrook Press, 1997. [RL 5 IL 4–6] (3111106 HB)

Sports for Life: How Athletes Have More Fun by Robin Roberts. This book shows that being a lifelong athlete is a healthy, worthwhile choice that can maintain a girl's natural self-confidence and help her in almost every area of her life. Get in the Game! Millbrook Press, 2000. [RL 4.6 IL 4–8] (3190206 HB)

•RL = Reading Level
•IL = Interest Level
Perfection Learning's catalog numbers are included for your ordering convenience.
HB indicates hardback.

Glossary

aerobic exercise (uhr OH bik EK ser seyez) any activity in which a person's **heart** and **lungs** must work harder, pumping blood throughout the body and sending **oxygen** to the **muscles** (see separate entries)

arteries (AR tuh reez) **vessels** that carry blood away from the **heart** (see separate entries)

blood circulation (bluhd ser kyou LAY shuhn) movement of blood through the body's **vessels**, caused by the **heart's** pumping action (see separate entries)

bones (bohnz) hard, dense parts of the skeleton made of calcium

calories (KAL uh reez) the unit that measures the energy people get from food

cell (sel) the smallest unit of the body that can carry out the basic functions of life

diabetes (deye uh BEE teez) a serious disease that is the result of the body not making enough insulin, a hormone that helps get glucose, or sugar, into the **cells** of the body to be used for energy (see separate entry)

diet (DEYE uht) what a person eats and drinks on a regular basis

endorphins (en DOR fuhnz) a group of hormones with pain-killing and relaxing abilities that are sent to the brain to make the exerciser feel better

endurance (en DUHR uhns) the ability to sustain a lengthy **physical activity** (see separate entry)

fibers (FEYE berz) long connective **cells** of **muscle** tissue (see separate entries)

flex (fleks) to move or tense a **muscle** (see separate entry)

heart (hart) a muscular organ that pumps blood through the **arteries** and **veins**, circulating the blood throughout the entire body (see separate entries)

high blood pressure (heye bluhd PRES sher) too much pressure in the **arteries** (see separate entry)

lactic acid (LAK tik AS uhd) a thick liquid that builds up in **muscles** during exercise, causing the muscles to be stiff and sore (see separate entry)

lungs (luhngz) two spongy, saclike organs located in the chest that inflate and enable **oxygen** to get to the **heart** (see separate entries)

muscle (MUHS uhl) a tissue made up of **fibers** capable of contracting and relaxing as the body moves (see separate entry)

overweight (OH ver wayt) weighing more than is normal or healthy for a body type

oxygen (AWK suh juhn) a colorless, tasteless gas that comes in part from the air humans breathe and is essential for life

physical activity (FIZ uh kuhl ack TIV uh tee) any sport or recreation that causes the **heart** to beat faster and the body to sweat and become tired (see separate entry)

pores (porz) tiny openings on the skin's surface that allow sweat to come out and also let the skin breathe

reflexes (REE fleks uhz) the power of acting or responding with adequate speed

skeletal system (SKEL uh tuhl SIS tuhm) the internal structure made of **bone** and cartilage that protects and supports the softer organs and tissues (see separate entry)

surgeon general (SER juhn JEN uh ruhl) the chief medical officer in the United States Public Health Service

tendons (TEN duhnz) cords of tough tissue that connect **muscle** to the **bone** (see separate entries)

toxic metals (TAWK sik MET uhlz) poisonous metals such as mercury or copper that invade the body

toxins (TAWK sinz) poisonous substances

type 2 diabetes (teyep *2* deye uh BEE teez) also known as adult-onset **diabetes**, it is the most frequently diagnosed type of diabetes, making up 90–95 percent of diagnosed cases (see separate entry)

veins (vaynz) **vessels** that carry blood toward the **heart** (see separate entries)

vessels (VES uhlz) elastic tubes in which blood is carried through the body, specifically **veins** and **arteries** (see separate entries)

windpipe (WIND peyep) a thin-walled tube that carries **oxygen** from the nose and mouth to the **lungs** (see separate entries)

Index

Current Topics in Cardiovascular Disease
Series Editors: R. De Caterina, S. Endres, S. D. Kristensen, E. B. Schmidt

Titles in the series:

Fish Oil and Vascular Disease
Edited by: R. De Caterina, S.D. Kristensen, E.B. Schmidt

n-3 Fatty Acids and Vascular Disease
Edited by: R. De Caterina, S. Endres, S.D. Kristensen, E.B. Schmidt

n-3 Fatty Acids: Prevention and Treatment in Vascular Disease
Edited by: S.D. Kristensen, E.B. Schmidt, R. De Caterina, S. Endres

Acknowledgments: This book contains the proceedings of the oral presentations from the second workshop on ***Preventive Strategies in Vascular Disease: Focus on n-3 Fatty Acids*** held in Cambridge, U.K., April 4 and 5 1995, within the framework of the Annual Meeting of the *European Society for Clinical Investigation,* and was published with a generous grant from Pharmacia, who also supported the Workshop as main sponsor. Contributors to the Workshop were also Norsk Hydro, Norway and Peter Møller, Norway. The Editors wish to acknowledge the dedication, competence and professionalism of the many persons who made it possible, and especially of the individual Authors.
The Editors hope that this book will be a stimulus for further research in the fascinating areas of fatty acids and human biology, and a source of updated reference material. They also look forward to a continuation of the series in 1995.

n-3 Fatty Acids:
Prevention and Treatment in Vascular Disease

Bi & Gi Publishers

AF678266

n-3 Fatty Acids:

Prevention and Treatment in Vascular Disease

- n-3 Fatty Acids and Atherosclerosis
- n-3 Fatty Acids and Ischaemic Heart Disease
- Safety, Preparation and New Indications for n-3 Fatty Acids

EDITED BY: S.D. KRISTENSEN, E.B. SCHMIDT
R. DE CATERINA, S. ENDRES

With 38 figures and 32 tables

Springer-Verlag
London Berlin Heidelberg New York Barcelona Budapest Hong Kong Milan Paris Santa Clara Singapore Tokyo

Bi & Gi Publishers
Verona

S.D. Kristensen - University Department of Cardiology, Skejby Hospital, Aarhus, Denmark
E.B. Schmidt - Department of Internal Medicine, Aalborg Hospital, Aalborg, Denmark
R. De Caterina - Scuola Superiore di Studi Universitari e di Perfezionamento S. Anna and C.N.R. Institute of Clinical Physiology, Pisa, Italy
S. Endres - Medizinische Klinik, Klinikum Innenstadt der Ludwig-Maximilians Universität, München, Germany

Series Editors: R. De Caterina, S. Endres, S.D. Kristensen, E.B. Schmidt

Distribution
Sole distribution rights outside Italy granted to Springer-Verlag.
All orders for this title should be sent to the following addresses:
Italy
Bi & Gi Publishers - Via Ca' di Cozzi, 41 - 37124 Verona Italy
North America
Springer-Verlag New York Inc. - 175 Fifth Avenue, New York, NY 10010, USA
Japan
Springer-Verlag - 37-33 Hongo 3-chome, Bunkyo-Ku, Tokyo 113, Japan
Rest of the world
Springer-Verlag - Heidelberger Platz. 3 - 1000 Berlin 33, Germany

ISBN 88-7651-129-6 Bi & Gi Publishers - Verona
ISBN 3-540-76001-6 Springer-Verlag - Berlin - Heidelberg - New York

British Library Cataloguing in Publication Data
A catalogue record for this book is available from the British Library

©1995 Bi & Gi Publishers s.r.l. All rights reserved. This book is protected by copyright. No part of it may be reproduced, stored in a retrieval system, or transmitted, in any form or by any means, electronic, mechanical, photocopying, recording, or otherwise, without the prior written permission of the publisher.

Typeset by Bi & Gi, Verona, Italy
Printed by Offset Print Veneta, Verona, Italy

Foreword

To Friendship and Friends

As Series Editors for "Current Topics in Cardiovascular Disease", we are happy to have been involved in the publication of this third volume, dedicated, as were the previous two, to n-3 fatty acids.

As in the first two books in this series, the work reported here underlines the importance of *preventive strategies in vascular disease*, which is undoubtedly the most effective way of fighting coronary artery disease, stroke, peripheral ischaemia and the other ominous consequences of atherosclerosis.

This book aims to provide concise, yet authoritative, coverage of the field, by including both basic science and clinical contributions. These will cover important aspects of the mechanism of action of the biological mediators involved in atherosclerosis, as well as the recent medical developments, that are likely to generate clinical indications for n-3 fatty acids in the near future.

The field is rapidly growing, as testified by the increasing number of articles published in this area. Current research draws together medical disciplines as varied as molecular biology, immunology, pathology, lipid metabolism, nutrition, nephrology, developmental pathology and neonatology, epidemiology, and, finally, cardiovascular medicine - including invasive cardiology and electrophysiology.

The Editors have attempted to select, from the many original contributions that have appeared recently in the area, those topics that have evolved most significantly in the last 2 years.

Our ambition has been to produce a book that, besides being a useful update of the most significant literature, is a self-standing contribution to the area. We believe that this volume will prove to be a valuable tool for basic and clinical investigators, by providing new information and an extensive bibliography and by providing a more detailed interpretation and commentary on recently published material. We hope that it will also be a useful primer for the profane willing to master the fascinating and rapidly evolving field of n-3 fatty acids in vascular biology and medicine.

September 1995

Series Editors

Raffaele De Caterina, Stefan Endres, Steen Dalby Kristensen, Erik Berg Schmidt

Preface

'In rebus quibuscumque difficilioribus non expectandum,
ut quis simul, et serat, et metat,
sed praeparatione opus est, ut per gradus maturescant.'
Bacon
Serm. fidel. n. XLV.

The pioneering work by Dyerberg and Bang linking the low incidence of acute myocardial infarction to a high dietary intake of n-3 fatty acids in Greenland Eskimos has stimulated researchers to explore the effects and potential importance of these fatty acids in basic science and clinical medicine. This book is the third in a series edited by ourselves on this subject.

The first book 'Fish Oil and Vascular Disease' focused on the epidemiological background, the mechanism of action of n-3 fatty acids and their effects in lowering blood pressure.

The second book 'n-3 Fatty Acids and Vascular Disease' included chapters on the effects of n-3 fatty acids on lipids and lipoproteins, renal disease, ischaemic heart disease and also a new insight into various mechanisms of action of n-3 fatty acids. These two books included edited and updated chapters written by scientists and doctors, who participated in workshops held within the framework of the European Society of Clinical Investigation in Pisa, Italy in 1991 and in Heidelberg, Germany in 1993.

We are very pleased to be able to publish this third book on the role of n-3 fatty acids in the prevention and treatment of disease. The present book contains contributions from participants of a meeting entitled 'Preventive strategies in vascular disease: focus on n-3 fatty acids' held in Cambridge, UK in April 1995, within the framework of the European Society of Clinical Investigation. It contains chapters on the effect of n-3 fatty acids on cellular events that may be important in atherogenesis, and also focuses on the potential beneficial effects of n-3 fatty acids in experimental atherogenesis, and in the prevention and treatment of ischaemic heart disease, including treatment for patients undergoing coronary by-pass surgery and angioplasty. The potential antiarrhythmic effect of n-3 fatty acids in patients with ischaemic heart disease is also described and discussed. The antiinflammatory effects of n-3 fatty acids are now well recognized and have inspired researchers to investigate the effect of these fatty acids in several other disease states. This book, therefore, also includes chapters on renal medicine and inflammatory bowel disease. Other chapters deal with safety aspects, and describe new formulations and methods of administration of n-3 fatty acids.

We thank Pharmacia, Sweden, for the financial support that has enabled us to publish this book.

S.D. Kristensen
E.B. Schmidt
R. De Caterina
S. Endres

In everything, and in particular in most difficult subjects,
one should not expect to seed and to harvest at the same time,
but it is necessary that a preparation is built up, in order for results to mature gradually.
Bacon
Serm. fidel. n. XLV.

Contents

n-3 Fatty Acids and Ischaemic Heart Disease

Safety, Preparation and New Indications for n-3 Fatty Acids

Contributors

I. Aardestrup
Department of Clinical Chemistry, Aalborg Hospital, Aalborg, Denmark

J. Aarøe
Department of Cardiology, Aalborg Hospital, Aalborg, Denmark

H. Arnesen
Ullevål University Hospital, Oslo, Norway

E.J. Bergstrahl
Mayo Clinic and Foundation, Rochester, MN, USA

H.J.M. Bilo
Renal Transplant Division, Department of Internal Medicine, University Hospital Groningen, The Netherlands

Y.A. Carpentier
L. Deloyers Laboratory for Experimental Surgery, Université Libre De Bruxelles, Brussels, Belgium

J.H. Christensen
Department of Endocrinology, Aalborg Hospital, Aalborg, Denmark

R. De Caterina
Laboratory for Thrombosis and Vascular Research, C.N.R. Institute of Clinical Physiology and Scuola Superiore S. Anna, Pisa, Italy

R.J. Deckelbaum
Institute of Human Nutrition, Columbia University, New York, USA

D.H.W. Dekkers
Department of Biochemistry, Erasmus University, Rotterdam, The Netherlands

J.V. Donadio Jr
Mayo Clinic and Foundation, Rochester, MN, USA

A.J.M. Donker
Renal Transplant Division, Department of Internal Medicine, University Hospital Groningen, The Netherlands

D. Dubois
L. Deloyers Laboratory for Experimental Surgery, Université Libre De Bruxelles, Brussels, Belgium

J. Dyerberg
Medi-Lab a.s., Copenhagen, Denmark

I. El Nakadi
L. Deloyers Laboratory for Experimental Surgery, Université Libre De Bruxelles, Brussels, Belgium

S. Endres
Department of Medicine, Klinikum Innenstadt of Ludwig-Maximilians-University, Munich, Germany

J. Eritsland
Ullevål University Hospital, Oslo, Norway

M.A. Gimbrone Jr.
Vascular Research Division, Department of Pathology, Brigham and Women's Hospital-Harvard Medical School, Boston, MA, USA

E. Gröttrup-Wolfers
Virchow Klinikum, Humboldt University, Berlin, Germany

P. Gustenhoff
Department of Cardiology, Aalborg Hospital, Aalborg, Denmark

J.J. Homan Van Der Heide
Renal Transplant Division, Department of Internal Medicine, University Hospital Groningen, The Netherlands

B.J. Holub
Department of Nutritional Sciences, University of Guelph, Guelph, Ontario, Canada

C. Hübner
Neuropediatric Department, University Clinic of The Charité, Berlin, Germany

E. Jul
Ilulissat Hospital, Ilulissat, Greenland

S.D. Kristensen
University Department of Cardiology, Skejby Hospital, Aarhus, Denmark

E. Korup
Department of Cardiology, Aalborg Hospital, Aalborg, Denmark

J.X. Kang
Department of Medicine, Harvard Medical School, Massachusetts General Hospital, Charlestown, MA, USA

J.M.J. Lamers
Department of Biochemistry, Erasmus University, Rotterdam, The Netherlands

A. Leaf
Department of Medicine, Brockton/West Roxbury VA Medical Center, West Roxbury, MA, USA

H.A. Lehr
Department of Pathology, University of Washington, Seattle, USA

P. Libby
Vascular Medicine and Atherosclerosis Unit, Brigham and Women's Hospital-Harvard Medical School, Boston, MA, USA

K. Loeschke
Institute of Medicine, Klinikum Innenstadt of Ludwig-Maximilians-University, Munich, Germany

R. Luostarinen
Department of Forensic Medicine, University of Uppsala, Sweden

R. Lorenz
Institute of Prophylaxys of Vascular Disease, Klinikum Innenstadt of Ludwig-Maximilians-University, Munich, Germany

P. Madsen
Department of Clinical Chemistry, Aalborg Hospital, Aalborg, Denmark

J.R. van Meegen
Experimental Cardiology, Thoraxcenter, Erasmus University, Rotterdam, The Netherlands

J.L. Mehta
Department of Medicine, University of Florida, Gainesville, Florida, USA

J.P. Middaugh
Department of Health and Social Services, Division of Public Health, State of Alaska, Anchorage, Alaska

J. Møller
Department of Cardiology, Aalborg Hospital, Aalborg, Denmark

G. Mulvad
Queen Ingrid's Hospital, Nuuk, Greenland

W.P. Newman III
Department of Pathology, Louisiana State University Medical Center, New Orleans, Louisiana, USA

S.F. Olsen
Danish Epidemiology Science Centre, State Serum Institute, Artillerivej, Copenhagen, Denmark

H.S. Pedersen
Queen Ingrid's Hospital, Nuuk, Greenland

S. Renaud
Inserm, Unit 63, 22 Avenue Doyen Lépine, Bron Cedex, France

K. Rasmussen
Department of Cardiology, Aalborg Hospital, Aalborg, Denmark

M. Richelle
L. Deloyers Laboratory for Experimental Surgery, Université Libre de Bruxelles, Brussels, Belgium

R.A. Riemersma
Cardiovascular Research Unit, University of Edinburgh, UK

T. Saldeen
Department of Forensic Medicine, University of Uppsala, Sweden

L.M.A. Sassen
Experimental Cardiology, Thoraxcenter, Erasmus University, Rotterdam, The Netherlands

L.M. Scheek
Department of Biochemistry, Erasmus University, Rotterdam, The Netherlands

E.B. Schmidt
Department of Medicine and Endocrinology, Aalborg Hospital, Aalborg, Denmark

V. Siderova
L. Deloyers Laboratory for Experimental Surgery, Université Libre de Bruxelles, Brussels, Belgium

C. Simoens
L. Deloyers Laboratory for Experimental Surgery, Université Libre de Bruxelles, Brussels, Belgium

L.K. Soei
Experimental Cardiology, Thoraxcenter, Erasmus University, Rotterdam, The Netherlands

N. Svaneborg
Department of Medicine and Endocrinology, Aalborg Hospital, Aalborg, Denmark

A.M. Tegzess
Renal Transplant Division, Department of Internal Medicine,University Hospital Groningen, The Netherlands

E. Toft
Department of Cardiology, Aalborg Hospital, Aalborg, Denmark

A. van Tol
Department of Biochemistry, Erasmus University, Rotterdam, The Netherlands

P.D. Verdouw
Experimental Cardiology, Thoraxcenter, Erasmus University, Rotterdam, The Netherlands

S.D. Kristensen, E.B. Schmidt, R. De Caterina, S. Endres
n-3 Fatty Acids: Prevention and Treatment in Vascular Disease
Bi & Gi Publishers, Verona - Springer Verlag, London, 1995

1. An Introduction to n-3 Fatty Acids

E.B. Schmidt[1], S.D. Kristensen[2], S. Endres[3], R. De Caterina[4]

1. *Department of Medicine and Endocrinology, Aalborg Hospital, Denmark*
2. *University Department of Cardiology, Skejby Hospital, Aarhus, Denmark*
3. *Department of Medicine, Klinikum Innenstadt of Ludwig-Maximilians-University, Munich, Germany*
4. *Laboratory for Thrombosis and Vascular Research, C.N.R. Institute of Clinical Physiology and Scuola Superiore S. Anna, Pisa, Italy*

This first chapter aims to give the reader unfamiliar with the area of n-3 (also called omega-3) fatty acids (FA) a general introduction to the subject. This summary also puts the articles in this book into perspective and, together with the first two volumes,[1,2] increases awareness of scientists from other disciplines of the exciting area of n-3 fatty acid research, and its evolving potential in the prevention and treatment of vascular disease.

FA-Types and Physiology

In the Western diet, FA are mainly in the form of n-6 FA, predominantly linoleic acid and to a lesser extent arachidonic acid (AA), and are derived from meat and vegetables. In contrast, eicosapentaenoic acid (EPA) and docosahexaenoic acid (DHA), considered the biologically important long-chained n-3 FA, are derived almost exclusively from seafood. These FA are shown in Figure 1, which also illustrates the nomenclature of FA. Both n-6 and n-3 FA can be metabolized by elongation (increased number of carbon atoms) and desaturation (increased number of double bonds) in the human body, but n-6 and n-3 FA are not interconvertible. Dietary FA are incorporated into cell membranes affecting membrane characteristics, such as membrane fluidity and cellular signal transduction. After appropriate stimulation, FA are liberated from cellular membranes and give rise to prostaglandins (PG), thromboxanes (TX), leukotrienes (LT) and other biologically active compounds.[3] AA is metabolized to TXA_2 in platelets, to LTB_4 in leukocytes and to PGI_2

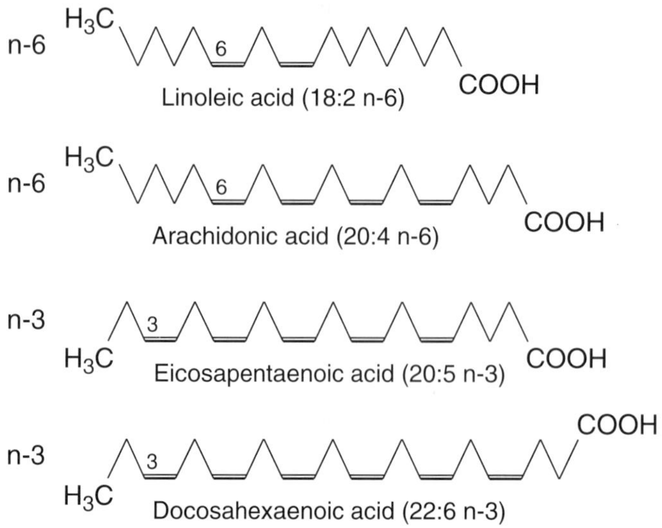

Fig. 1. Some major n-3 and n-6 fatty acids (FA). The number of carbon atoms is given before and the number of double bonds after the colon. The position of the first double bond counted from the methyl end of the fatty acid separates FA into n-3 or n-6 FA.

in endothelial cells, whereas EPA is converted to TXA_3 in platelets, LTB_5 in leukocytes and PGI_3 in endothelial cells. One prevailing hypothesis to explain the different actions of n-6 and n-3 FA relates to dissimilar activities of these metabolites (called eicosanoids). Thus, while the effects of PGI_2 and PGI_3 are considered equal, TXA_2 has proaggregatory, vasoconstrictive actions and LTB_4 has proinflammatory effects far exceeding those of TXA_3 and LTB_5, respectively. However, while eicosanoids are likely to play a role, several other mechanisms probably operate and add to the different biological effects of n-6 and n-3 FA.

Epidemiological Background

Interest in n-3 FA was inspired by studies by Dyerberg and Bang.[4] They undertook five expeditions to the west coast of Greenland in order to investigate the low incidence of coronary heart disease (CHD) in traditional Eskimos (Inuit) living in Greenland. Their main findings were that the Inuit had: first, an antiatherogenic lipid pattern; second, decreased platelet reactivity; and third, a beneficial balance between the antiaggregatory and vasodilatory effects of PGI released from the vessel wall, and the opposite effects of TX released from platelets.[4] These beneficial effects with respect to CHD were believed to be due to the Inuit diet, which is based on seal, whale and other seafood. The major, but not the only, difference between the Inuit and western diets is the exceptionally high intake of n-3 FA by the Inuit.

In 1985, it was reported that a low intake of fish was inversely related to the incidence of CHD in Western populations.[5] More epidemiological studies investigating the association between CHD and fish consumption have now been published (see the chapter by W.P. Newman III *et al.*, pp. 77-84), and although data are inconsistent, there is substantial evidence that intake of low and very large amounts of n-3 FA may reduce CHD.

Intake of n-3 FA-Type and Dose

The daily intake of n-3 FA in the Inuit is approximately 14 g/3000 kcal, whereas the intake of n-3 FA is below 0.5 g/3000 kcal in most Western populations. The approximate content of n-3 FA in various types of seafood is given in Table I, but it should be noticed that this may vary considerably depending on the time of year and the place of capture. It is also evident that a mean daily intake by dietary means of n-3 FA above 1 g is difficult to achieve in most Western countries.

An increased intake of n-3 FA can also be achieved from bottled oils rich in n-3 FA (such as cod liver oil) or from fish oil capsules containing typically 30-85% n-3 FA (mixtures of EPA and DHA) and a total of approximately 1 g fat. It should be emphasized, however, that such concentrates are given as supplements to the habitual diet and not instead of other servings. Most trials with n-3 FA have been performed with fish oil supplements, increasing the daily intake of n-3 FA to between 3 and 6 g. The review by E.B. Schmidt *et al.* (pp. 195-206) suggests that fish-oil concentrates are well tolerated and have a good safety profile.

Potential differences in the absorption of various chemical preparations of n-3

Table I. Content of n-3 fatty acids (FA) in seafood.

Seafood	**n-3 FA content (g)/100 g**
Mackerel	1.8-5.1
Herring	1.2-3.1
Salmon	1.0-1.4
Tuna	0.5-1.6
Trout	0.5-1.6
Oyster	0.4-0.6
Shrimp	0.2-0.5
Crab	0.3-0.4
Cod	0.2-0.3

FA are addressed in the chapter by J. Dyerberg *et al.* (pp. 217-226). Most effects of n-3 FA probably require their incorporation into membrane phospholipids. Recently, however, n-3 FA have become available for parenteral use, and preliminary data from animal studies suggest that platelet and leukocyte reactivity may be modulated within hours following administration of n-3 FA. This calls for studies of parenteral n-3 FA in acute inflammatory disorders and perhaps also acute myocardial ischaemia, as discussed by Y.A. Carpentier *et al.* (pp. 207-216) and J.X. Kang and A. Leaf (pp. 89-96) in later chapters.

Biochemical Effects of n-3 FA

Dietary n-3 FA exert several beneficial effects in healthy subjects and various patient groups,[3] including a reduction in plasma triglycerides, and platelet, neutrophil and monocyte reactivity. In patients with hypertension, n-3 FA also slightly reduce blood pressure. There are indications that n-3 FA may decrease blood viscosity and improve vessel wall function by improving the vasodilatory actions of endothelium-derived relaxing factor (EDRF) and by decreasing production of the vasoconstrictor TX. On the other hand, dietary n-3 FA may impair fibrinolysis by increasing plasma levels of plasminogen activator inhibitor-1 (PAI-1) and could theoretically increase oxidation of low-density lipoproteins (LDL). In general, the effects on n-3 FA are dose-dependent, with the more pronounced effects seen with high doses.

The inhibition of the interaction between leukocytes and the vessel wall by n-3 FA may be of great relevance to atherogenesis, and this is substantiated and discussed in the papers by R. De Caterina and M.A. Gimbrone (pp. 9-24), R. De Caterina and P. Libby (pp. 25-44) and H.A. Lehr and C. Hübner (pp. 45-54). n-3 FA may have a beneficial influence on factors of importance in vascular disease other than those mentioned here; for a discussion of potential mechanisms of action of n-3 FA please consult the two previous books in this series.[1,2]

Clinical Trials

The above-mentioned biochemical effects of n-3 FA and the promising results from the use of n-3 FA in experimental animal models (see later chapter L.K. Soei *et al.* pp. 55-75), have led to several clinical trials in patients with vascular disease. One major study was the Diet and Reinfarction Trial (DART), in which a very modest intake of n-3 FA was shown to reduce mortality by 29% in survivors of myocardial infarction.[6] In a recent study, an increased intake of another n-3 FA, α-linolenic acid, together with other dietary changes, reduced the number of coronary events after myocardial infarction (discussed in the chapter by S. Renaud, pp. 141-154). We recently reviewed the effects of n-3 FA in patients with CHD,[7] while presentations in the two previous books in this series[1,2] and elsewhere[8] have highlighted the effects on n-3 FA in patients with hypertension and various types of dyslipidaemia.

New findings in patients undergoing coronary bypass surgery or coronary angioplasty are presented and reviewed here in the chapter by S.D. Kristensen (pp. 115-124). A new exciting area of research - the potential antiarrhythmic effect on n-3 FA in humans - is discussed, and interesting data are presented by several authors (X.A. Kang and A. Leaf pp. 89-96, R.A. Riemersma pp. 97-106, J.H. Christensen *et al.* pp. 107-114 and T. Saldeen *et al.* pp. 125-138). The effect of n-3 FA on leukocyte function provides a background for the use of n-3 FA as anti-inflammatory agents, so far most clearly demonstrated in patients with rheumatoid arthritis. In this book, a review on the effects on n-3 FA in patients with inflammatory bowel diseases is presented by S. Endres *et al.* (pp. 181-188).

Olsen *et al.* have shown that n-3 FA may increase birth weight by prolonging gestation, possibly caused by effects related to eicosanoids. These findings and the potential usefulness of n-3 FA in pregnancy are reviewed in a later chapter (S.F. Olsen, pp. 189-194).

A new, rapidly developing area is the use of n-3 FA in patients with renal disorders, which was recently reviewed by De Caterina *et al.*[3] Two new important studies are presented in this book. First, the finding that n-3 FA retard the rate at which renal function is lost in patients with IgA nephropathy (reviewed by J.V. Donadio *et al.* pp. 173-180). Second, the finding that n-3 FA improve renal haemodynamics and inhibit rejection episodes in recipients of renal transplants (reviewed by J.J. Homan Van Der Heide *et al.* pp. 157-172).

Recent findings in the n-3 field, including a brief description of major clinical trials (known by us) in progress, are updated in a recent publication.[9]

We hope that this book will be helpful for investigators already working in the area of n-3 FA and will attract scientists from other disciplines to what we consider an exciting field, the findings from which have the potential to reduce vascular disease.

References

1. De Caterina R., Kristensen S.D., Schmidt E.B. (Eds): *Fish Oil and Vascular Disease. Current Topics in Cardiovascular Disease.* Verona; Bi & Gi Publishers, 1992
2. De Caterina R., Endres S., Kristensen S.D., Schmidt E.B. (Eds): *n-3 Fatty Acids and Vascular Disease. Current Topics in Cardiovascular Disease.* Verona; Bi & Gi Publishers, 1993
3. De Caterina R., Endres S., Kristensen S.D., Schmidt E.B.: n-3 fatty acids and renal diseases. Am. J. Kidney Dis. 1994; 24: 397-415
4. Dyerberg J., Bang H.O.: A hypothesis on the development of acute myocardial infarction in Greenlanders. Scand. J. Clin. Lab. Invest. 1982; 42 (Suppl. 161): 7-13

5. Kromhout D., Bosschieter E.B., Coulander CdL: The inverse relation between fish consumption and 20-year mortality from coronary heart disease. N. Engl. J. Med. 1985; 312: 1205-1209
6. Schmidt E.B., Kristensen S.D., De Caterina R., Illingworth D.R.: The effects of n-3 fatty acids on plasma lipids and lipoproteins and other cardiovascular risk factors in patients with hyperlipidaemia. Atherosclerosis 1993; 103: 107-121
7. Burr M.L., Fehily A.M., Gilbert J.F., Rogers S., Holliday R.M., Sweetnam P.M., et al.: Effects of changes in fat, fish, and fibre intakes on death and myocardial reinfarction: Diet and reinfarction trial (DART). Lancet 1989; ii: 757-760
8. Kristensen S.D., De Caterina R., Schmidt E.B., Endres S.: Fish oil and ischaemic heart disease. Br. Heart J. 1993; 70: 212-214
9. Endres S., De Caterina R., Schmidt E.B., Kristensen S.D.: n-3 polyunsaturated fatty acids- update 1995. Eur. J. Clin. Invest. 1995: In press

n-3 Fatty Acids and Atherosclerosis

S.D. Kristensen, E.B. Schmidt, R. De Caterina, S. Endres
n-3 Fatty Acids: Prevention and Treatment in Vascular Disease
Bi & Gi Publishers, Verona - Springer Verlag, London, 1995

2. Leukocyte – Endothelial Interactions and the Pathogenesis of Atherosclerosis

R. De Caterina[1], M.A. Gimbrone Jr.[2]

1. *Laboratory for Thrombosis and Vascular Research, C.N.R. Institute of Clinical Physiology and Scuola Superiore S. Anna, Pisa, Italy*
2. *Vascular Research Division, Department of Pathology, Brigham and Women's Hospital-Harvard Medical School, Boston, MA, USA*

Introduction

A major focus of current research into the pathogenetic mechanisms of atherosclerosis is understanding how vascular endothelium, which comprises the continuous lining of the cardiovascular system, normally controls the traffic of leukocytes into the vessel wall. Atherosclerosis is thus a derangement in the leukocyte traffic homeostasis, with analogies to and differences from similar processes involving increased leukocyte migration outside the blood stream, such as acute and chronic inflammation and special aspects of immune reactions. This review will highlight recent progress in the understanding of atherogenesis in the broader framework of the natural history of the disease. Interpreting atherogenesis as a derangement in leukocyte traffic homeostasis is a significant advancement in the interpretation of the origin of the disease and a stimulating pathophysiological concept that points to new targets for preventive or therapeutic intervention.

Natural History of Atherosclerotic Lesions: the Fatty Streak is the Earliest Stage in Atherogenesis

Atherosclerotic lesions originate at certain points in the arterial vasculature, mainly branch points and bifurcations, and curvature sites, where wall shear stresses are either low or oscillatory,[1] favouring the transport of arterial blood components into the vessel wall and interactions of leukocytes with activated endothelium. Complex lesions, which are usually observed in adults, can take different appearances, reflecting different stages in plaque evolution and perhaps different natural histories in plaque development.[2,3] However, there is now an almost universal agreement that the earliest (although not irreversible) stage in plaque development is a lesion described as the fatty streak.[4-11]

This is clearly the earliest manifestation of atherosclerosis in hypercholesterolemic animal models of different species[4-11] and in mild hypercholesterolemic primates,[8] and has been found at autopsy in the coronary arteries of 50% of young humans between 10 and 14 years of age.[11]

Fatty streaks are areas of focal intimal thickening, sustained by the intimal accumulation of lipid-laden cells (foam cells), surrounded by a loose extracellular matrix and a variable number of lymphocytes.

The relation of the fatty streak to more advanced atherosclerotic lesions has long been disputed.[12-15] However, observations in various animal models,[4-11] particularly the low-level hypercholesterolemic primate *Macaca nemestrina*,[8] have clarified that the fatty streak does indeed precede more advanced atherosclerotic lesions, which evolve in the same critical areas of the arterial vasculature. Therefore, the pathogenesis of the earliest phases of atherosclerosis can now reasonably be reduced to the problem of the pathogenesis of the fatty streak.

Current Theories on the Development of Atherosclerosis

Over the past 20 years, a large body of evidence has been collected supporting the theory that atherosclerosis is a 'response-to-injury' of the vessel wall. In its first formulation, this theory stated that various atherogenic factors, known from epidemiological studies and experimental models, induce the development of lesions through an 'injury' to the endothelial monolayer.[16,17] This injury, which could take many forms, varying from mechanical, to chemical, viral or immunological,[18-21] presumably would compromise the physical integrity of endothelium, resulting in areas of frank desquamation. The exposure of subendothelial matrix components would subsequently cause the interaction of circulating blood elements, in particular platelets, with the vessel wall. The ensuing activation of platelets would cause the release of growth factors able to induce smooth muscle cell migration and proliferation.[19,20,22,23]

Subsequent updated versions of this 'response-to-injury' hypothesis have taken into account new developments.[24] These include: firstly, the evolution of the concept of endothelial damage from focal desquamation, with intimal denudement, to that of endothelial 'dysfunction', a more subtle form of endothelial alteration, not necessarily involving the physical disruption of the endothelial barrier;[25-27] and secondly, a greater appreciation of the role of monocytes and macrophages in the inception and development of the atherosclerotic lesion.

Endothelial Dysfunction and the Origin of the Fatty Streak

Under physiological conditions, vascular endothelium continuously monitors blood-borne and locally generated stimuli and adaptively alters its functional state, thus contributing to normal homeostasis.[27-29] Functional properties of the endothelium are outlined in Table I.

Table I. Functional properties of vascular endothelium.

Property	Mediators
Modulation of thromboresistance	
Antiplatelet	ADPase(s)
	Prostacyclin
	Nitric oxide
Anticoagulant	Heparin-like proteoglycans
	Thrombomodulin
Pro-fibrinolytic	Tissue plasminogen activator, urokinase
Anti-fibrinolytic	Plasminogen activator inhibitor-1
Modulation of vascular tone	Prostacyclin (-)
	Nitric oxide (-)
	Endothelium-derived hyperpolarizing factor (-)
	Angiotensin-converting enzyme (*)
	Endothelin (+)
Modulation of smooth muscle cell growth	Heparin-like molecules (-)
	Nitric oxide (-)
	TGF-β (-)
	Platelet-derived growth factor A/B (+)
Selective permeability barrier	Junctional proteins
	Endocytic receptors
	Cell surface glycocalix
Leukocyte recruitment	Inducible ELAMs (selectins, ICAM-1, VCAM-1)
	Chemoattractant/activators (IL-8, MCP-1, PAF)

Abbreviations: ADPase=adenosine diphosphatase, TGF-β=transforming growth factor-β, ELAMs=endothelial leukocyte adhesion molecules, ICAM-1=intercellular adhesion molecule-1, VCAM-1=vascular cell adhesion molecule-1, IL-8=interleukin-8, MCP-1=macrophage chemoattractant protein-1, PAF=platelet activating factor. +, increase, -, decrease, *catalyzes conversion of angiotensin I into angiotensin II and vasoconstrictor.

They include control of haemostasis (including the function of platelets, the coagulation, and the fibrinolytic system[28]), modulation of vascular tone, endothelial permeability and medial smooth muscle cell growth.[29] Non-adaptive changes in endothelial functional properties provoked by qualitatively or quantitatively abnormal stimuli can result in localized alterations in the interactions between cellular components of the circulating blood and macromolecular components of the vessel wall. Such changes include imbalances in the anti-thrombotic properties of the endothelium, altered vascular tone, altered permeability to plasma lipoproteins, hyperadhesiveness to blood leukocytes, and increased cytokine and growth factor production. These non-adaptive alterations collectively can be termed 'endothelial dysfunction'.[25,27]

The term 'endothelial activation' has been used to designate the functional changes that endothelium may undergo under the influence of various stimuli, the best studied of which are inflammatory cytokines and bacterial endotoxin. The functional changes include the acquisition of new functional and antigenic properties influencing, for example, the interactions with blood leukocytes.[27] Endothelial dysfunction can be considered as a sub-category of endothelial activation, resulting in a pathological alteration of endothelial function in response to excessive or abnormal stimulation. Endothelial dysfunction appears to play an important role in the initiation, progression and clinical complications of atherosclerosis.[25-27] Causes and consequences of endothelial dysfunction, with reference to interactions between the endothelium and leukocytes, will now be considered.

Leukocyte Binding to the Endothelium

Leukocyte binding to the endothelium is a prominent feature of a number of inflammatory and immunological disorders. In acute inflammation, polymorphonuclear leukocytes (PMNs) bind to the endothelium in post-capillary venules. On the other hand, focal adhesion of monocytes, but not of PMNs, to a morphologically intact arterial endothelium is typical of dietary-induced atherosclerosis in animals.[30] Similarly, many features of lymphocyte-selective recirculation, which occurs in a variety of immune reactions, are explained by a preferential binding of lymphocyte subtypes to the specialized endothelium of lymphoid tissues.[31]

Leukocyte binding to cultured endothelial cells *in vitro* has been studied extensively in an attempt to identify and study the mechanisms mediating this cell-cell interaction. It is now clear that activation of the leukocyte, the endothelial cell or both can lead to increased PMN, monocyte or lymphocyte adhesion to the endothelium. Multiple protein families, each with a distinct function, provide 'traffic signals' for leukocytes.

These include: first, the 'selectin' family of adhesion molecules, which appear to recognize a sialylated carbohydrate determinant as their cognate ligand;[32,33]

second, chemoattractants, some of which (N-formyl peptides, complement components, leukotriene B_4 and platelet-activating factor) act broadly, on neutrophils, eosinophils, basophils and monocytes, while newly described 'chemokines' (interleukin (IL)-8 and macrophage chemoattractant protein-1 (MCP-1)) have specificity for discrete leukocyte types;[34,35] and third, the immunoglobulin superfamily members on endothelium, namely, intercellular adhesion molecule (ICAM)-1, ICAM-2, ICAM-3 and vascular cell adhesion molecule (VCAM)-1, recognizing integrin ligands on the leukocyte surface.

For neutrophil recruitment, selectins mediate initial tethering of the circulating leukocyte over the endothelium, allowing it to roll over the endothelium, considerably reducing its speed. Antagonists of L-selectin and E-selectin inhibit neutrophil (and monocyte) influx in response to inflammatory agents.[37,38] The slowing down of leukocytes by selectin-carbohydrate interactions is thought to allow leukocytes to sense the presence of chemotactic gradients and to elicit an event mediated by the chemoattractant receptor, that is, the conformational change and consequent activation of some integrin-type leukocyte ligand, now exhibiting new activation epitopes.[36,39,40] Final firm attachment of leukocytes to the endothelium requires the interaction of integrin ligands on the leukocyte surface with immunoglobulin superfamily members expressed on endothelium, such as ICAM-1, ICAM-2 and VCAM-1.[36,41] The possible sequential interaction of selectins with carbohydrates, chemoattractants with their receptors and immunoglobins with integrins, as first defined for neutrophils and possibly also true for lymphocyte homing, has been termed 'the three step paradigm'.[42] Together with the multiple molecular choices available for each of these ligand-ligand interactions, this model would provide great combinatorial diversity in signals, allowing the selective responses of different leukocyte classes to inflammatory agents, the preferential recirculation of lymphocyte subpopulations, or the selective binding of monocytes to arterial endothelium during early phases of atherogenesis.

The Identification of Monocyte-Specific Adhesion Molecules on Activated Endothelial Cells and the Athero-ELAM Hypothesis

One of the earliest morphologically detectable events in atherogenesis is the adhesion of circulating blood monocytes to a morphologically intact endothelium in large arteries, preceding their transmigration into the intima and the subsequent formation of the fatty streak.[4-6,8] Once in the intima, monocytes/macrophages can accumulate lipids, thus becoming 'foam cells', and can also contribute to lesion progression by the local production of cytokine-growth factors, such as IL-1, tumour necrosis factor (TNF), platelet-derived growth factor (PDGF) and fibroblast growth factor (FGF), reactive oxygen species, procoagulant and fibrinolytic components, and eicosanoids.[43]

As monocyte recruitment into the intima of large arteries is specific for atherosclerosis, it was hypothesized that these localized monocyte-endothelium interactions reflect cell-specific molecular changes in the adhesive properties of the endothelial surface. This leads to endothelial surface expression of 'athero-ELAMs', that is, endothelium-leukocyte adhesion molecules (ELAMs) expressed in the early phases of atherosclerosis. In order to match pathological observations with *in vitro* experimental data, candidate athero-ELAMs should have several properties: first, be able to support mononuclear leukocyte adhesion; second, be inducible, that is, increase their surface expression substantially in the presence of pathophysiological stimuli; and third, be detectable in early atherosclerotic lesions, accompanying and preceding the development of the lesion itself.

The experimental search for such molecules was first undertaken in the rabbit, for which dietary and genetic models of atherosclerosis are well established, using standardized *in vitro* monolayer adhesion assays with cultured rabbit aortic endothelium.[44] Bacterial endotoxin, used as a non-specific endothelial activator to induce gene expression, was added to such endothelial monolayers *in vitro*. This caused a dramatic increase in adhesion of monocytes in a time-dependent and sustained fashion, which was different to the pattern observed for neutrophils and for another inducible ELAM, E-selectin.[45] Some monoclonal antibodies, selectively recognizing endotoxin-activated endothelial cells, exhibited time-dependent binding to these cells in a manner similar to monocyte adhesion to endothelial cells.[44] The binding of monocytes to endothelium could selectively be inhibited by some of these monoclonal antibodies. In further studies, it was shown that specific immunostaining with such antibodies was localized to foam-cell rich lesions in both cholesterol-induced and Watanabe-heritable hyperlipidemic rabbits. Thus, the molecule identified by such antibodies fulfilled all the *a priori* criteria set for the hypothetical athero-ELAM, allowing the first demonstration of lesion-selective ELAM expression in atherosclerosis.

Subsequent work, with a combination of immunochemical and molecular cloning approaches,[44,46,47] revealed the homology between this rabbit molecule and an inducible human leukocyte adhesion molecule, INCAM-110, previously characterized by Rice and co-workers[48] as an endothelial adhesion ligand for lymphocytes. INCAM-110 was cloned by Osborn *et al.* from a cytokine-induced endothelial library and named VCAM-1.[49] This inducible protein, the gene expression of which is upregulated at the transcriptional level by inflammatory cytokines and endotoxin, is a member of the immunoglobulin superfamily, and is expressed on human vascular endothelium in at least two molecular forms (118 and 98 kDa) arising from alternative splicing of unprocessed mRNA.[46,47] Both forms are able to bind a heterodimeric integrin receptor, the very late activation antigen (VLA)-4. The selective expression of this receptor on monocytes and lymphocytes, but not on neutrophils, may explain the selective pattern of inhibition of monocyte *versus* neutrophil adhesion by antibodies directed against VCAM-1 and the selectivity of monocyte recruitment in early atherogenesis.[50] VCAM-1 has also been shown to be expressed in rabbit endothelial cells early during the period of feeding with cholesterol, before the appearance of macrophages/foam cells in the intima of the developing fatty streak, in a temporal pattern consistent with its pathogenetic role in lesion development.[51]

The interaction between VCAM-1 and VLA-4 is only one of the ligand-ligand interactions potentially involved in monocyte recruitment in early atherogenesis. The interactions between the inducible (but also, to a large extent, constitutive) endothelial molecule ICAM-1 and the integrin ligands LFA-1 and Mac-1,[36] between endothelial E-selectin and the monocytic sialylated Lewis-X carbohydrate,[52] between monocytic L-selectin and an, as yet, incompletely characterized inducible endothelial ligand,[53] and between endothelial PECAM-1 and an unknown ligand on monocytes,[54] are likely to contribute to monocyte binding to an activated endothelium. In addition, endothelial monocyte-specific soluble products induced by cytokines and endotoxin, such as MCP-1, which was the first monocyte-specific chemoattractant to be discovered,[55] and macrophage colony-stimulating factor (M-CSF), which promotes activation/maturation of monocytes/macrophages,[56] are likely to be involved in monocyte recruitment in atherogenesis (Table II).

Each of these inducible endothelial products has been detected in atherosclerotic lesions in experimental animals or man.[44,56-59] The relative contribution of each of these adhesion molecules and chemoattractants to monocyte recruitment during early atherosclerotic lesion formation is currently an area of intense experimental study. Nevertheless, given its pattern of early appearance in foam cell lesions and its mononuclear leukocyte-selective adhesive function, VCAM-1 provides a useful marker of endothelial activation in atherogenesis.

Regulation of VCAM-1 Expression in the Broader Context of Endothelial Activation

The expression of the genes encoding VCAM-1, E-selectin, and inducible soluble endothelial products such as MCP-1, M-CSF, IL-6 and IL-8, is augmented several fold in response to bacterial endotoxin and cytokines, such as IL-1 or TNF. Most endothelial products, with the notable exception of ICAM-1, are expressed to a functionally negligible extent in resting, unactivated endothelial cells. Following the interaction of endotoxin or cytokines with their specific endothelial cell surface receptors, a cascade of intracellular events follows,[60] ultimately leading to the appearance on the cell surface or secretion of these products. As most adhesion molecules are not expressed in basal conditions, cytokine activation requires initiation of transcription.[60] Also, expression of different adhesion molecules

Table II. Endothelial molecules involved in endothelial-monocyte interactions.

Endothelial molecules	Category	Monocyte ligand	Category
Surface associated			
E-selectin (ELAM-1)	Selectin	Sialyl Lewis x (sLe^x)	Carbohydrate
P-selectin (PADGEM, GMP-140)	Selectin	Sialyl Lewis x (sLe^x)	Carbohydrate
Mucins	Carbohydrate	L-selectin	Selectin
ICAM-1	Immunoglobulin	CD11a/CD18 (LFA-1)	Integrin
		CD11b/CD18 (Mac-1)	Integrin
ICAM-2	Immunoglobulin	CD11a/CD18 (LFA-1)	Integrin
		CD11b/CD18 (Mac-1)	Integrin
VCAM-1	Immunoglobulin	VLA-4 ($\alpha_4\beta_1$)	Integrin
PECAM-1 (CD31)[54]	Immunoglobulin	Unknown	Unknown
Secreted			
Interleukin-1	Cytokine	IL-1 receptor	-
Tumour necrosis factor	Cytokine	TNF receptor	-
MCP-1	Cytokine	MCP-1 receptor	-
M-CSF	Cytokine	M-CSF receptor	-
PAF	Lipid	PAF receptor	-

Abbreviations: ELAM-1=endothelial leukocyte adhesion molecule, ICAM-1, intercellular adhesion molecule-1, VCAM-1, vascular cell adhesion molecule-1, PECAM=platelet/endothelial cell adhesion molecule-1, LFA-1=leukocyte function associated antigen-1, VLA-4=very late activation antigen-4, IL-1=interleukin-1, TNF=tumour necrosis factor, MCP-1=macrophage chemotactic protein-1, M-CSF=macrophage colony-stimulating factor, PAF=platelet activating factor.

usually proceeds simultaneously, together with other soluble or membrane-bound endothelial products, such as MCP-1, M-CSF, IL-6, IL-8 or tissue factor. This concerted activation of genes following cytokine exposure occurs by the activation of a few transcription factors, including the early-response genes c-*jun* and c-*fos*, and the nuclear factor(NK)-κB system.

This last transcription factor has received increasing attention over the past few years as a common denominator of endothelial activation, causally linked to adhesion molecule expression.[61] Originally discovered in the lymphocyte, where it controls the activation of the genes encoding the κ-chains of immunoglobulins,[62] NF-κB is now appreciated as a much more general control mechanism of cell function.[63] The system consists of a family of transcription factors, present in the cytoplasm as dimeric proteins. Normally, these subunits are inactive because they are bound to an inhibiting protein, I-κB. The separation of one of the 'activating' subunits from I-κB, usually following phosporylation of I-κB, allows the translocation of the activating subunits to the nucleus, where they bind to specific 'consensus' sequences in the promoter region of several genes and initiate mRNA transcription.[61] Nucleotide sequences specifically able to bind NF-κB-like factors ('NF-κB responsive elements') have been identified in many human genes including those encoding the inducible ELAMs, tissue factor, and secretable cytokines.[61] Although many of the fine details of this regulatory system have yet to be elucidated (for example, the cytokine IL-4 is able to selectively increase the expression of VCAM-1 but not ICAM-1 or E-selectin[64]), the NF-κB system provides a final common pathway to explain the coordinated expression of the variety of endothelial genes involved in endothelial activation. As such, it may be a target for mechanisms able to regulate endothelial activation, including atherogenesis, in a global and coordinated fashion.[61]

Pathophysiologically Relevant Stimuli for Adhesion Molecule Expression

VCAM-1, as a paradigm for other endothelial-leukocyte adhesion molecules and cytokine-induced endothelial products, is induced in endothelial cells *in vitro* by IL-1, TNF and IL-4. These cytokines can be produced by monocytes and macrophages, and to some extent by T-lymphocytes, which infiltrate a developing lesion.[43] Such stimuli, therefore, might provide a paracrine mechanism to amplify the local reaction at the site of a fatty streak, enhancing local monocyte recruitment. But what is the initiating stimuli for the whole process of atherogenesis? Some insights into this issue may come from the notion that cholesterol-induced atherosclerosis in rabbits is accompanied by both endothelial activation and the focal expression of VCAM-1 on the one hand,[51] and the focal accumulation of low-density lipoproteins (LDLs) in macrophages, which become foam cells in the arterial intima, on the other.[65]

Therefore, it can be hypothesized that LDLs or some of their biotransformation products may be acting as local stimuli, initiating monocyte recruitment. Indeed, several lines of evidence implicate oxidative modification of LDL as the critical process. This occurs in the arterial intima, in a microenvironment protected from circulating antioxidants, and is able to confer a degree of atherogenicity to LDL much greater than that of native LDL.[66] *In vitro* studies have shown that minimally oxidized LDL or β-very low density lipoprotein (VLDL) can confer hyperadhesive properties to monocytes, and also increase endothelial production of MCP-1.[67,68] Kume *et al.*[69,70] have recently reported that a lysophospholipid associated with oxidized LDL and β-VLDL particles, lysophosphatidylcholine, may be a stimulus able to increase, by itself or in combination with other cytokines or growth factors, the selective expression of certain ELAMs, including VCAM-1 and ICAM-1, in cultured endothelial cells. Lysophosphatidylcholine may be, therefore, one of the pathophysiological stimuli that explains the atherogenic effect of oxidized LDL. Other circulating products or metabolites might act by similar mechanisms, in conditions associated with enhanced atherosclerotic risk, independent of the lipid status. These include the advanced glycosylation end-products (AGEs) associated with diabetes, lipoprotein (Lp)a, a modified LDL particle that appears to be an independent risk factor for atherosclerosis, homocysteine, which is found in patients with homocysteinuria and, possibly, in patients with subtler forms of cistathionine-β-synthase or folate deficiencies. All of these are actively being investigated.

In addition to humoral stimuli, such as cytokines, bacterial products or components of modified lipoproteins, endothelial gene expression also appears to be responsive to haemodynamic forces.[71] In particular, exposure of cultured human endothelial cells to laminar shear stresses in the physiological range, results in a differential pattern of adhesion molecule expression, with selective upregulation of ICAM-1.[72] Interestingly, in cultured murine endothelium, which exhibits high constitutive VCAM-1 levels, VCAM-1 expression appears to be inversely related to the magnitude of applied shear stress.[73] Recent *in vivo* studies,[74] in which blood flow had been altered by surgical manipulations, also showed this correlation of increased VCAM-1 expression with decreased shear, and also an increase in ICAM-1 expression with increased shear. These haemodynamic factors may favour monocyte recruitment in the region of branches and other vessel geometries that are associated with relatively low, time-averaged, wall shear stresses, and thus contribute to the classical predilection of atherosclerotic lesions for these sites.[1]

Downregulation of Cytokine-Induced Endothelial Activation as a Possible Site of Action of Anti-atherogenic Interventions

Cytokine-induced endothelial activation increases the surface expression of ELAMs and the secretion of soluble pro-atherogenic products (*e.g.* MCP-1 and M-CSF) several fold, thus creating the potential for downregulation by certain stimuli. We hypothesized that an important, lipid status-independent, site of action of n-3 fatty acids, which are associated epidemiologically with protection from atherosclerosis, might be the vessel wall itself, through an effect on endothelial activation. We therefore investigated the effect of various saturated, monounsaturated and polyunsaturated fatty acids on IL-1- or TNF-induced surface expression of VCAM-1 in human saphenous vein endothelial cells.[75,76]

We found that one n-3 fatty acid, docosahexaenoic acid (DHA), is able to reduce cytokine-induced expression of VCAM-1 by up to 50%. Conversely, linoleic acid and arachidonic acid (both n-6 fatty acids) and, surprisingly, eicosapentaenoic acid

(EPA), did not exert any effect on stimulated VCAM-1 expression (see also the chapter in this book by R. De Caterina and P. Libby, pp. 25-44). Oleic acid and ricinoleic acid, which are both monounsaturates, showed a moderate effect, but this was not as pronounced as that seen with DHA.[77,78] In another set of studies, we demonstrated that different nitric oxide (NO) donors were also able to reduce the cytokine-inducible, coordinated expression of adhesion molecules and secretable endothelial products,[79,80] thus indicating a potential role for NO as an endogenous anti-atherogenic substance. Sources of NO in the vasculature include both endothelial cells (by means of both the constitutive and the inducible NO synthase) and other cell types, such as monocytes, macrophages and smooth muscle cells (mostly by means of the cytokine-inducible NO synthase). Thus, regulation of endothelial activation may occur by a substance, NO, which can itself be produced by the vessel wall. This adds further complexity to the entire picture of the control of monocyte recruitment in the origin of the fatty streak.

In a broader sense, the notion that adhesion molecule expression is subject to downregulation could provide a novel explanation for the action of protective factors in atherosclerosis. Thus, one may speculate that nutritional interventions may act by counteracting the effects of pro-atherogenic stimuli at the level of the vessel wall, and of endothelial cells in particular.

By the same token, it is conceivable that other known protective factors, such as oestrogens, may act at the level of endothelial activation, influencing leukocyte-endothelial interactions and the very beginning of the vessel wall response to pro-atherogenic factors. Thus, once more, endothelium acts as a multifunctional unit able to integrate different blood-borne stimuli and convey an integrated response, influencing both circulating blood components and other cell types within the vessel wall. These advancements in our understanding of endothelial cell biology and of the initial phases of atherosclerosis are potentially able to link biological observations with epidemiology, and generate hypotheses for developing or better using preventive and, possibly, therapeutic approaches to this disease.

Acknowledgements

Original research by the authors was supported by grants from the Italian Ministry of the University and Scientific Research, and the Italian National Research Council (to Dr. De Caterina) and grants PO1-HL-35028 and PO1-HL-48743 from the National Institutes of Health (to Dr. Gimbrone). Part of the research described has been obtained during a 2-year sabbatical leave of Dr. De Caterina at the Vascular Medicine and Atherosclerosis Unit, Cardiovascular Division, Department of Medicine (Director: Dr. Peter Libby) and partly sponsored by NIH grant HL-48743 to Dr. Libby. Dr. Gimbrone is a recipient of an unrestricted research award from the Bristol-Myers Squibb Research Institute.

Summary

The earliest morphological change in atherosclerosis is a focal attachment of monocytes to a morphologically intact endothelium, followed by the accumulation of monocyte-derived macrophages in the arterial intima and their subsequent transformation into lipid-laden cells (foam cells). This sequence of events leads to the appearance of the fatty streak, which precedes the development of more advanced (raised) lesions. The molecular mechanisms by which endothelial cells, which are normally not reactive towards circulating monocytes, support monocyte adhesion, are beginning to be unravelled. Stimulation of endothelial cells *in vitro* with bacterial endotoxin, interleukin-1 (IL-1), IL-4, or tumour necrosis factor, elicits a programmed set of endothelial responses involving the activation of gene transcription. These genes encode an array of molecules, which control different phases of leukocyte braking ('rolling') in the proximity of the endothelial surface - arrest, spreading and diapedesis. A pivotal factor in this process is the synthesis of endothelial-leukocyte adhesion molecules, which tether and stably attach leukocytes onto the vascular endothelium, and of leukocyte-specific chemoattractants, which elicit leukocyte movement towards a chemotaxis gradient. Thus, the origin of atherosclerosis can be viewed as a site- and cell-specific type of inflammatory reaction. The type of endothelium involved (*e.g.* arterial endothelium at particular sites), the nature of the stimulus involved (*e.g.* oxidized low-density lipoproteins, advanced glycosylation end-products), the secondary mediators elicited (*e.g.* specific cytokines) and the set of adhesion molecules and chemoattractants produced by endothelial cells may explain the localization and the type of local reaction initiated. Endothelial activation (*i.e.* the process by which endothelial cells, which are normally not reactive towards circulating leukocytes, acquire the ability to support leukocyte attachment) appears to be a novel site of mechanistic action for risk factors of atherosclerosis and for nutritional and pharmacological strategies in preventing this disease, including the action of n-3 fatty acids.

References

1. Ku D.N., Giddens D.P., Zarins C.K., Glagov S.: Pulsatile flow and atherosclerosis in the human carotid bifurcation: positive correlation between plaque location and low and oscillating shear stress. Arteriosclerosis 1985; 5: 293-302
2. Stary H.C.: Evolution and progression of atherosclerotic lesions in coronary arteries of children and young adults. Arteriosclerosis 1989; 88 (Suppl 1): 1-32
3. Fuster V., Badimon L., Badimon J.J., Chesebro J.H.: The pathogenesis of coronary artery disease and the acute coronary syndromes (first of two parts). N. Engl. J. Med. 1992; 326: 242-251
4. Gerrity R.G.: The role of the monocyte in atherogenesis: I. Transition of blood-borne monocytes into foam cells in fatty lesions. Am. J. Pathol. 1981; 103: 181-190
5. Joris I., Znad T., Nunnari J.J., Krolikowski F.J., Majno G.: Adhesion and emigration of mononuclear cells in the aorta of hypercholesterolemic rats. Am. J. Pathol. 1983; 113: 341-358
6. Faggiotto A., Ross R., Harker L.: Studies of hypercholesterolemia in the nonhuman primate. I. Changes that lead to fatty streak formation. Arteriosclerosis 1984; 4: 323-340
7. Rosenfeld M.E., Tsukada T., Gown A.M., Ross R.: Fatty streak initiation in Watanabe heritable hyperlipemic and comparably hypercholesterolemic fat-fed rabbits. Arteriosclerosis 1987; 7: 9-23
8. Masuda J., Ross R.: Atherogenesis during low level hypercholesterolemia in the nonhuman primate. I. Fatty streak formation. Arteriosclerosis 1990; 10: 164-177
9. Faggiotto A., Ross R.: Studies of hypercholesterolemia in the nonhuman primate. II. Fatty streak conversion to fibrous plaque. Arteriosclerosis 1984; 4: 341-356

10. Masuda J., Ross R.: Atherogenesis during low level hypercholesterolemia in the nonhuman primate. II. Fatty streak conversion to fibrous plaque. Arteriosclerosis 1990; 10: 178-187
11. Stary H.C.: Macrophage, macrophage-foam cell, and eccentric intimal thickening in the coronary arteries of young children. Atherosclerosis 1987; 64: 91-108
12. Mitchell J.R.A., Schwartz C.J.: *Arterial Disease*. Oxford; Blackwell Scientific Publishers, 1965
13. Smith E.B., Slater R.S.: Lipids and low-density lipoproteins in intima in relationship to its morphological characteristics. In: *Atherogenesis: Initiating Factors*. Ciba Foundation Symposium No. 12. Amsterdam; Elsevier Publishing Co, 1973: 39-51
14. Smith E.B., Slater R.S., Crothers D.X.: Quantitative interrelationships between plasma constituents and normal and atherosclerotic human intimal tissue. In: Schletter D., Weizel A. (Eds.) *Atherosclerosis III*. Berlin; Springer-Verlag, 1974: 96-102
15. Panganamala R.V., Geer J.C., Sharma H.A., Cornwell D.G.: The gross and histologic appearance and the lipid composition of normal intima and lesions from human coronary arteries and aorta. Atherosclerosis 1974; 20: 93-100
16. Ross R., Glomset J.: The pathogenesis of atherosclerosis. Part I. N. Engl. J. Med. 1976; 295: 369-377
17. Ross R., Glomset J.: The pathogenesis of atherosclerosis. Part II. N. Engl. J. Med. 1976; 295: 420-425
18. Mustard J.F.: Increased activity of the clotting mechanism during alimentary lipemia: its significance with regard to thrombosis and atherosclerosis. Can. Med. Assoc. J. 1957; 77: 308-317
19. Haust M.D., More R.H., Movat H.Z.: The role of the smooth muscle cell in the fibrogenesis of atherosclerosis. Am. J. Pathol. 1960; 37: 377-383
20. Ross R., Glomset J.: Atherosclerosis and the arterial smooth muscle cell. Science 1973; 180: 1332-1339
21. Harker L., Ross R., Slichter S.J., Scott C.R.: Homocystine-induced atherosclerosis: the role of endothelial cell injury and platelet response in its generation. J. Clin. Invest. 1976; 58: 731-741
22. Geer J.C.: Fine structure of human atherosclerotic lesions. Am. J. Pathol. 1961; 38: 263-287
23. Wissler R.W.: The arterial medial cell, smooth muscle or multifunctional mesenchyme? J. Atheros. Res. 1968; 8: 201-212
24. Ross R: The pathogenesis of atherosclerosis: an update. N. Engl. J. Med. 1986; 314: 488-500
25. Gimbrone M.A., Jr.: Endothelial dysfunction and the pathogenesis of atherosclerosis. In: Fidge N., Nestel P.L., (Eds.) *Atherosclerosis VII*. New York; Elsevier, 1986: 367-369
26. Gimbrone M.A. Jr., Kume N., Cybulsky M.I.: Vascular endothelial dysfunction and the pathogenesis of atherosclerosis. In: Weber P., Leaf A., (Eds.) *Atherosclerosis Reviews*. New York; Raven Press, 1993: vol. 25
27. Gimbrone M.A. Jr.: Vascular endothelium in health and disease. In: Haber E., (Ed.) *Molecular Cardiovascular Medicine*. New York; Scientific American Medicine, 1995: 49-61
28. Gimbrone M.A. Jr., (Eds.) *Vascular Endothelium in Hemostasis and Thrombosis*. Edinburgh; Churchill Livingstone, 1986
29. Gimbrone M.A. Jr., Bevilacqua M.P.: Vascular Endothelium: functional modulation at the blood interface. In: Simionescu N., Simionescu M., (Eds.) *Endothelial Cell Biology in Health and Disease*. New York; Plenum Press, 1988: 255-273
30. Cybulsky M.I., Gimbrone M.A. Jr.: Endothelial leukocyte adhesion molecules in acute inflammation and atherogenesis. In: Simionescu N., Simionescu M., (Eds.) *Endothelial Cell Dysfunctions*. New York; Plenum Press, 1992: 129-140
31. Mackay C.R.: Migration pathways and immunologic memory among T-lymphocytes. Semin. Immunol. 1992; 4: 51-58

32. Lasky L.A.: Selectins: interpreters of cell-specific carbohydrate information during inflammation. Science 1992; 258: 964-969
33. Rosen D.S.: Cell surface lectins in the immune system. Semin. Immunol. 1993; 5: 237-247
34. Oppenheim J.J., Zachariae C.O.C., Mukaida N., Matsushima K.: Properties of the novel proinflammatory supergene 'intercrine' cytokine family. Annu. Rev. Immunol. 1991; 9: 617-648
35. Miller M.D., Krangel M.S.: Biology and biochemistry of the chemokines: a family of chemotactic and inflammatory cytokines. CRC Crit. Rev. Immunol. 1992; 12: 17-46
36. Springer T.A.: Adhesion receptors of the immune system. Nature 1990; 346: 425-434
37. Mulligan M.S., Varani J., Dame M.K., Lane C.L., Smith C.W., Anderson D.C., Ward P.A.: Role of endothelial-leukocyte adhesion molecule-1 (ELAM-1) in neutrophil-mediated lung injury in rats. J. Clin. Invest. 1991; 88: 1396-1406
38. Picker L.J., Butcher E.C.: Physiological and molecular mechanisms of lymphocyte homing. Annu. Rev. Immunol. 1992; 10: 561-591
39. Landis R.C., Bennett R.I., Hogg N.: A novel LFA-1 activation epitope maps to the I domain. J. Cell. Biol. 1993; 120: 1519-1527
40. Diamond M.S., Springer T.A.: A subpopulation of Mac-1 (CD11b/CD18) molecules mediates neutrophil adhesion to ICAM-1 and fibrinogen. J. Cell. Biol. 1993; 120: 545-556
41. Chan B.M.C., Elices M.J., Murphy E., Hemler M.E.: Adhesion to vascular cell adhesion molecule 1 and fibronectin: comparison of a_4b_1 (VLA-4) and a_4b_7 on the human B cell line J.Y. J. Biol. Chem. 1992; 267: 8366-8370
42. Springer T.A.: Traffic signals for lymphocyte recirculation and leukocyte emigration: the multistep paradigm. Cell 1994; 76: 301-314
43. Clinton S.K., Libby P.: Cytokines and growth factors in atherogenesis. Arch. Pathol. Lab. Med. 1992; 116: 1292-1300
44. Cybulsky M.I., Gimbrone M.A. Jr.: Endothelial expression of a mononuclear leukocyte adhesion molecule during atherogenesis. Science 1991; 251: 788-791
45. Bevilacqua M.P., Stengelin S., Gimbrone M.A. Jr, Seed B.: Endothelial leukocyte adhesion molecule 1: an inducible receptor for neutrophils related to complement regulatory proteins and lectins. Science 1989; 243: 1160-1165
46. Cybulsky M.I., Fries J.W.U., Williams A.J., Sultan P., Gimbrone M.A. Jr., Collins T.: Gene structure, chromosomal location, and basis for alternative mRNA splicing of the human VCAM-1 gene. Proc. Natl. Acad. Sci. USA 1991; 88: 7859-7863
47. Cybulsky M.I., Fries J.W.U., Williams A.J., Sultan P., Davis V.M., Gimbrone M.A. Jr, Collins T.: Alternative splicing of human VCAM-1 in activated vascular endothelium. Am. J. Pathol. 1991; 138: 815-820
48. Rice G.E., Munro J.M., Bevilacqua M.P.: Inducible cell adhesion molecule 110 (INCAM-110) is an endothelial receptor for lymphocytes: A CD11/CD18 independent adhesion mechanism. J. Exp. Med. 1990; 171: 1369-1374
49. Osborn L.: Leukocyte adhesion to endothelium in inflammation. Cell 1990; 62: 3-6
50. Bochner B.S., Luscinskas F.W., Gimbrone M.A. Jr., *et al.*: Adhesion of human basophils, eosinophils, and neutrophils to interleukin-1-activated human vascular endothelial cells: contribution of endothelial cell adhesion molecules. J. Exp. Med. 1991; 173: 1553-1556
51. Li H., Cybulsky M.I., Gimbrone M.A. Jr., Libby P.: An atherogenic diet rapidly induces VCAM-1, a cytokine-regulatable mononuclear adhesion molecule, in rabbit aortic endothelium. Arterioscler. Thromb. 1993; 13: 197-204
52. Erbe D.V., Wolitzky B.A., Presta L.G. *et al.*: Identification of an E-selectin region critical for carbohydrate recognition and cell adhesion. J. Cell. Biol. 1992; 119: 215-227

53. Spertini O., Luscinskas F.W., Kansas G.S, Munro J.M., Griffin J.D., Gimbrone M.A. Jr, Tedder T.F.: Leukocyte adhesion molecule-1 (LAM-1, L-selectin) interacts with an inducible endothelial cell ligand to support leukocyte adhesion. J. Immunol. 1991; 147: 2565-2573
54. Muller W., Weigl S., Deng X., Phillips D.: PECAM-1 is required for transendothelial migration of leukocytes. J. Exp. Med. 1993; 178: 449-460
55. Rollins B.J.: JE/MCP-1: an early response gene encodes a monocyte-specific cytokine. Cancer Cells 1991; 3: 517-524
56. Clinton S.K., Underwood R., Sherman M.L., Kufe D.K., Libby P.: Macrophage-colony stimulating factor gene expression in vascular cells and in experimental and human atherosclerosis. Am. J. Path. 1992; 140: 301-316
57. Poston R.N., Haskard D.O., Coucher J.R., Gall N.P., Johnson-Tiedy R.R.: Expression of intercellular adhesion molecule-1 in atherosclerotic plaques. Am. J. Pathol. 1992; 140: 665-673
58. Nelken N.A., Coughlin S.R., Gordon D., Wilcox J.N.: Monocyte chemoattractant protein-1 in human atheromatous plaques. J. Clin. Invest. 1991; 88: 1121-1127
59. Page C., Rose M., Yacoub M., Pigott R.: Antigenic heterogeneity of vascular endothelium. Am. J. Pathol. 1992; 141: 673-683
60. Kishimoto T., Taga T., Akira S.: Cytokine signal transduction. Cell 1994; 76: 253-262
61. Collins T.: Endothelial nuclear factor-kB and the initiation of the atherosclerotic lesion. Lab. Invest. 1993; 68: 499-508
62. Bauerle P.A.: The inducible transcription activator NF-kB: regulation by distinct protein subunits. Biochim Biophys. Acta 1991; 1072: 63-80
63. Lenardo M.J., Baltimore D.: NFkB: a pleiotropic mediator of inducible and tissue specific gene control. Cell 1988; 58: 227-229
64. Luscinskas F.W., Kansas G.S., Ding H., *et al.*: Monocyte rolling, arrest and spreading on IL-4-activated vascular endothelium under flow is mediated via sequential action of L-selectin, b_1-integrins, and b_2-integrins. J. Cell. Biol. 1994; 125: 1417-1427
65. Schwenke D.C., Carew T.E.: Initiation of atherosclerotic lesions in cholesterol-fed rabbits. II. Selective retention of LDL vs. selective increases in LDL permeability in susceptible sites of arteries. Arteriosclerosis 1989; 9: 908-918
66. Witztum J.L.: The role of monocytes and oxidized LDL in atherosclerosis. In: Leaf A., Weber P. (Eds.) *Atherosclerosis Reviews, vol. 21: Prevention and Noninvasive Therapy of Atherosclerosis.* New York; Raven Press, 1990: 59-69
67. Berliner J., Territo M.C., Sevanian A., Ramin S., Kim J.A., Bamshad B., Esterson M., Fogelman A.M.: Minimally modified low density lipoprotein stimulates monocyte endothelial interactions. J. Clin. Invest. 1990; 85: 1260-1266
68. Territo M.C., Berliner J.A., Almada L., Ramirez R., Fogelman A.M.: b-VLDL pretreatment of endothelial monolayers increases monocyte but not neutrophil adhesion. Arteriosclerosis 1989; 9: 824-828
69. Kume N., Cybulsky M.I., Gimbrone M.A. Jr.: Lysophosphatidyl-choline, a component of atherogenic lipoproteins, induces mononuclear leukocyte adhesion molecules in cultured endothelial cells. J. Clin. Invest. 1992; 90: 1138-1144
70. Kume N., Gimbrone M.A. Jr.: Lysophosphatidylcholine transcriptionally induces growth factor gene expression in cultured human endothelial cells. J. Clin. Invest 1993; 93: 907-911
71. Resnik N., Collins T., Atkinson W., Bonthron D.T., Dewey C.F.J., Gimbrone M.A. Jr.: Platelet-derived growth factor B chain promotor contains a cis-acting fluid shear-stress-responsive element. Proc. Natl. Acad. Sci. USA. 1993; 90: 4591-4595
72. Nagel T., Resnick N., Atkinson W.J., Dewey C.F.J., Gimbrone M.A. Jr.: Shear stress selectively upregulates intercellular adhesion molecule-1 expression in cultured human vascular endothelial cells. J. Clin. Invest. 1994; 94: 885-891

73. Ando J., Tsuboi H., Korenaga R., Takada Y., Yoyama-Sorimachi N., Miyasaka M., Kamiya A.: Shear stress inhibits adhesion of cultured mouse endothelial cells to lymphocytes by downregulating VCAM-1 expression. Am. J. Physiol. 1994; 267: C679-C687
74. Walpola P.L., Gotlieb A.I., Cybulsky M.I., Langille B.L.: Expression of ICAM-1 and VCAM-1 and monocyte adherence in arteries exposed to altered shear stress. Arterioscler. Thromb. Vasc. Biol. 1995; 15: 2-10
75. De Caterina R., Cybulsky M.L., Gimbrone M.A. Jr., Clinton S.K., Libby P.: Docosahexaenoic acid and expression of endothelial leukocyte adhesion molecules. Circulation 1993; 88: I-77 (Abstract 402)
76. De Caterina R., Cubulsky M.I., Clinton S.K., Gimbrone M.A., Jr., Libby P.: The omega-3 fatty acid docosahexaenoate reduces cytokine-induced expression of proatherogenic and proinflammatory proteins in human endothelial cells. Arterioscler. Thromb. 1994; 14: 1829-1836
77. De Caterina R., Nakagawa T., Hauptman P.J., Tanaka H.: Cyclosporin-A vehicle inhibits basal vascular cell adhesion molecule-1 in coronary artery endothelium and cultured endothelial cells. Circulation 1994; 90: I-83 (Abstract 440)
78. De Caterina R., Tanaka H., Nakagawa T., Hauptman P.J., Libby P.: The direct effect of injectable cyclosporine and its vehicle cremophor on endothelial VCAM-1 expression. Transplantation 1995; In press
79. De Caterina R., Shin W.S., Liao J.K., Libby P.: Nitric oxide inhibits cytokine-induced expression of endothelial leukocyte adhesion molecules. Circulation 1994; 90: I-29 (Abstract 144)
80. De Caterina R., Libby P., Rajavashisth T., Shin W.S., Gimbrone M.A. Jr., Liao J.K.: Nitric oxide decreases cytokine-induced endothelial activation. Nitric oxide selectively reduces endothelial expression of adhesion molecules and proinflammatory cytokines. J. Clin. Invest. 1995; 96:60-68

S.D. Kristensen, E.B. Schmidt, R. De Caterina, S. Endres
n-3 Fatty Acids: Prevention and Treatment in Vascular Disease
Bi & Gi Publishers, Verona - Springer Verlag, London, 1995

3. n-3 Fatty Acids and Atherogenesis: Effects on Leukocyte-Endothelial Interactions

R. De Caterina[1], P. Libby[2]

1. *Laboratory for Thrombosis and Vascular Research, C.N.R. Institute of Clinical Physiology and Scuola Superiore S. Anna, Pisa, Italy*
2. *Vascular Medicine and Atherosclerosis Unit, Brigham and Women's Hospital-Harvard Medical School, Boston, MA, USA*

Introduction

The epidemiological association between dietary n-3 polyunsaturated fatty acids (n-3 FA) and protection from cardiovascular disease[1-8] results, at least in part, from the decreased incidence of atherosclerosis in populations with a high intake of n-3 FA.[9] A recent study of n-3 FA supplementation after coronary bypass surgery indicated that such treatment also reduces vein graft stenosis significantly.[10]

The adhesion of circulating leukocytes, in particular monocytes, to the endothelium, and their subsequent transendothelial migration are early events in the development of fatty streaks.[11-18] Recruitment of monocytes to the subendothelium depends on the expression by endothelial cells of adhesion molecules, such as vascular cell adhesion molecule-1 (VCAM-1), E-selectin and intercellular adhesion molecule-1 (ICAM-1),[19-21] and on the production of monocyte chemoattractants.[22]

We have hypothesized that n-3 FA may modulate atherogenesis by affecting such processes of 'endothelial activation' (described extensively in the chapter of this book by R. De Caterina and M. Gimbrone, pp. 9-24). Human adult saphenous vein endothelial cells (HSVEC), activated by cytokines, have been used as an *in vitro* model of the early steps of atherogenesis. The effects of various n-3 FA on the surface expression of endothelial leukocyte adhesion molecules have been assessed, and the mechanisms and functional relevance of such effects have subsequently been characterized.

Methods

The methods used are described in detail in our recent paper,[23] and are summarized briefly here.

Cells

HSVEC were harvested from saphenous veins left over after coronary bypass surgery, using type II collagenase, and were cultured in medium 199 containing HEPES (25 mmol/l), heparin (1%), endothelial cell growth factor (50 μg/ml), L-glutamine (2 mM), penicillin, streptomycin, fungizone and fetal calf serum (FCS; 5%), as described.[24-26] Cells were used within passage 4 after primary culture.

Fatty acids

The following fatty acids, representing the most abundant esterified species in cell phospholipids, were used: oleic acid (18:1 n-9), linoleic acid (18:2 n-6), arachidonic acid (AA; 20:4 n-6), eicosapentaenoic acid (EPA; 20:5 n-3) and docosahexaenoic acid (DHA; 22:6 n-3); all fatty acids were >99% pure, and in the form of sodium salts (Nu-Check). In control experiments, DHA was also used in free acid form (obtained from Aldrich Chemicals and Calbiochem-Behring). Free acid was dissolved in a small volume of ethanol, and then in medium before use.

Cytokines

The following human recombinant cytokines were used: interleukin (IL)-1α (Hoffman-La Roche), IL-1β, tumour necrosis factor α (TNFα) and IL-4 (all from Genzyme). *Escherichia coli* bacterial lipopolysaccharide (LPS), indomethacin, aspirin, (+)-α-tocopherol acid succinate (vitamin E) and butylated hydroxytoluene (BHT) were purchased from Sigma. Vitamin E and BHT were first dissolved in ethanol and then in medium before use. Whenever appropriate, ethanol was used as a control at appropriate dilutions.

Assays

- *Surface associated molecules* were detected by either cell-surface enzyme immunoassays (EIAs) or by flow cytometry, using a panel of mouse anti-human monoclonal antibodies against VCAM-1 (E1/6), E-selectin (H18/7), ICAM-1 (HU5/3), major histocompatibility complex class I (MHC-I, W6/32)[27] or the monoclonal antibody E1/1, which recognizes a constitutive and non-cytokine inducible endothelial cell antigen.[28]

EIAs were performed by sequential incubations, first with the monoclonal antibody against the target molecule, then with a secondary anti-mouse biotinylated IgG (Vector), and finally with streptavidin-alkaline phosphatase (Zymed). Three washing steps were performed after each incubation. The surface expression of the target molecule was quantified spectrophotometrically, after the addition of the chromogenic substrate paranitrophenylphosphate, by assessing the optical density of the wells at 410 nm, as described.[27] For flow cytometry, a suspension of HSVEC in Hanks' buffered saline containing EDTA (3 mmol/l) was incubated with the specific primary monoclonal antibody, and then with a fluoresceine-conjugated goat anti-mouse $F(ab\ )_2$ from IgG (H+L) (Caltag). Cells were washed and fixed in formaldehyde (1%), and the cell suspension was analysed using a Becton-Dickinson FACScan analyser (10,000 cells counted in each analysis).

- *Fatty acid incorporation into cellular lipids:* relative amounts of the individual chemical species of the n-3 and n-6 classes were quantified by integration of peaks obtained by gas-liquid chromatographic separation of fatty acids from HSVEC monolayers. After chloroform-methanol (2:1) extraction, total cellular lipids were subjected to acidic transmethylation. Fatty acid methyl esters were then analysed by flame-ionization capillary gas liquid chromatography (on a Hewlett-Packard model 5890 apparatus) using a 30 m Supelcowax 10 2-4079 column (0.25 mm internal diameter, 0.25 μm film thickness). A temperature gradient from 170 to 225°C was used, at a rate of 1°/minute. The hydrogen, air and carrier (helium) pressures were 0.8, 0.9-1 and 0.6 bar, respectively. Individual peaks were integrated automatically using a Hewlett-Packard integrator, and identified by comparison with retention times of known fatty acid standards (these analyses were kindly performed through Dr A. Leaf, Massachusetts General Hospital, Boston, MA).

- *Total protein synthesis:* HSVEC were cultured in 12-well plates in the presence or absence of DHA for 24-96 hours, and were subsequently stimulated with IL-1α for periods of up to 24 hours. At the time of IL-1α addition, ^{3}H-leucine (New England Nuclear, 0.2 μCi/10^4 cells) was also added. Total protein synthesis was then evaluated by counting radioactivity after cold trichloroacetic acid precipitation of supernates and of total cell extracts at various time points, as described.[29]

- *Assays for prostacyclin:* IL-6 and IL-8 were carried out using commercially available EIAs for the stable hydrolytic product of prostacyclin, 6-keto-prostaglandin (PG)$F_{1\alpha}$ (Cayman), or for IL-6 and IL-8 (R & D). Assays were conducted directly in HSVEC supernates.

- *Isolation of RNA and Northern analysis:* cultured HSVEC were harvested using trypsin/EDTA and were lysed in guanidinium isothiocyanate. RNA was purified by ultracentrifugation through CsCl.[30] The concentration and purity of RNA were determined from the A_{260} and A_{260}/A_{280} ratio, respectively. RNA quality was confirmed by gel electrophoresis prior to Northern analysis. Cellular RNA (20 µg/lane) was separated on an agarose-formaldehyde gel (1.2%, 2.2 mol/l), transferred to a nylon membrane (Hybond-N, Amersham, Arlington Heights, IL) and immobilized by short-wave ultra-violet illumination. Membranes were prehybridized for at least 4 hours, prior to hybridization with a DNA probe for VCAM-1 or α-actin, labeled with ^{32}P by random hexanucleotide priming (Pharmacia-Inc., Piscataway, NJ) to a specific activity >10^8 cpm/µg DNA.

Monocyte isolation

Human peripheral blood monocytes were obtained from the white blood cell-rich fraction (leukopek), which is a by-product of the local platelet pheresis program (Dana Farber Cancer Institute, Boston, MA). Cells were obtained by centrifugation on a Ficoll-Hypaque density gradient at 15°C (LMS, Organon Teknika), followed by counterflow centrifugation elutriation in a Beckman J2-21 M/E centrifuge, using a JE-6 elutriation rotor and a 6 ml Sanderson chamber (Beckman). A modification of Doherty's method was used: the elutriation buffer was Dulbecco's modified phosphate-buffered saline (DPBS, Gibco), supplemented with EDTA (3 mmol/l) and human serum albumin (HSA, Sigma, 0.25%). The mononuclear cell fraction, isolated at the Ficoll-plasma interface, was loaded at 14 ml/minute onto the elutriator centrifuge rotor head (2500 rpm at 10°C), and fractions of elutriated cells were collected. Monocytes were eluted at 21.5 ml/minute. Using this technique, the suspension obtained contained 89±4% monocytes, 8% lymphocytes, <2% granulocytes, and essentially no free platelet contamination, as determined by light scatter (FACScan, Becton Dickenson) and cell surface antigen analysis with a monoclonal antibody directed to CD14. Monocytes were resuspended in cold DPBS containing Ca^{2+} (0.75 mmol/l) and Mg^{2+} (0.75 mmol/l) and HSA (0.2%). U937 cells were obtained from American Tissue Culture Collection, and were grown in RPMI 1640 medium (Gibco), containing FCS (10%). Both monocytes and U937 cells were concentrated by centrifugation at 1 x 10^6 cells/ml. For the adhesion assays, HSVEC were grown to confluence in six-well tissue culture plates in the presence or absence of DHA (10 µmol/l) for 96 hours. IL-4 (50 ng/ml) or IL-1α (10 ng/ml) was then added for an additional 24 hours to induce the expression of VCAM-1. Control monolayers were treated with a mouse anti-human monoclonal antibody (E1/6) against VCAM-1. The adhesion assay was performed by adding 1 ml of the concentrated monocyte or U937 cell suspension to each monolayer under rotating conditions (63 rpm in an orbital shaker) at 21°C.[31-33] After 10 minutes, non-adherent cells were removed by gentle washing with medium 199, and monolayers were fixed in paraformaldehyde (1%). The number of adherent cells was determined by counting six different fields, using an ocular grid and a 20 x field (0.16 mm^2/field). Fields were selected randomly at a half-radius distance from the centre of the monolayers; counts were performed blindly by two independent observers, with an inter-observer variability of less than 8%. Separation of blood monocytes was performed through Dr Francis W. Luscinskas, Brigham and Women's Hospital, Boston, MA.

Experimental design

Cultured HSVEC were pre-incubated for 0-96 hours with various unsaturated fatty acids, and were then stimulated with cytokines (IL-1α, IL-1β, TNFα, or IL-4) or LPS for an additional 0-24 hours in the continued presence of fatty acid or in control conditions. The expression of endothelial surface molecules (detected by cell surface EIA and/or flow cytometry), endothelial secreted products (detected by EIA), mRNA encoding adhesion molecules (detected by Northern blot analysis) or parameters of cell viability (morphology, number, total protein synthesis) were subsequently assessed, or the adhesion was measured.

Statistics

Multiple comparisons were performed by one-way analysis of variance (ANOVA); individual differences were tested by the Fisher's protected least significance difference test after the demonstration of significant inter-group differences by ANOVA. The Student's t-test for unpaired data was used to compare the IL-1-stimulated production of IL-6 and IL-8 with or without DHA pre-incubation. The distribution of fluorescence intensities obtained by flow cytometry was compared using Kolgomorov-Smirnov's statistics. The significance level was set at $p<0.05$. Results are expressed as mean ± standard error of the mean (SEM), unless otherwise indicated.

Results

A cell surface enzyme immunoassay for VCAM-1 was used to assess and compare the effects of various fatty acids on the surface expression of this protein after stimulation with either IL-1α or TNFα. In the absence of stimulating cytokines, surface expression of VCAM-1 is virtually absent. However, stimulation with cytokines increases the level of expression more than 50-fold. AA, EPA and linoleic acid had no effect on cytokine stimulated-expression of VCAM-1 in

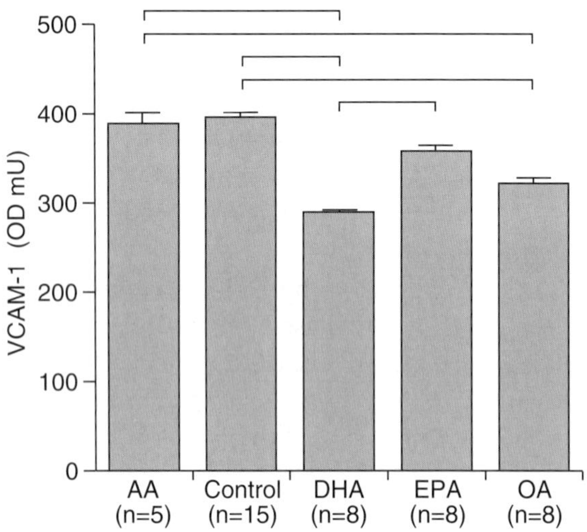

Fig. 1. Surface expression of vascular cell adhesion molecule (VCAM)-1 by human adult saphenous vein endothelial cells (HSVEC) 6 hours after stimulation with human recombinant tumour necrosis factor (TNF)α (1 ng/ml), following a 24-hour pre-incubation with arachidonic acid (AA), docosahexaenoic acid (DHA), eicosapentaenoic acid (EPA) or oleic acid (OA) (all at 10 μmol/l), or medium containing no added fatty acids (control). VCAM-1 expression was measured in milliunits of optical density (OD mU) following a cell surface enzyme immunoassay. Data represent the mean ± SEM. Baseline expression of VCAM-1 (without TNFα) was 5±3 mU. Horizontal lines join groups of treatment for which significant ($p<0.05$) differences were found after ANOVA. Similar findings were obtained following different periods of TNFα stimulation and when interleukin (IL)-1 was used as a stimulus. Increased VCAM-1 expression was seen in the presence of DHA and, to a lesser extent, with OA, but no effect was seen in the presence of AA or EPA (nor of linoleic acid in other experiments, data not shown) (partially modified from De Caterina *et al.*[23] with permission of American Heart Association).

a number of experiments. In contrast, DHA and, to a lesser extent, oleic acid, significantly reduced VCAM-1 expression. One example of such an experiment is shown in Figure 1.

In this study, the effect of DHA was examined in suboptimal conditions, as a more prolonged incubation with DHA prior to cytokine stimulation induced a larger effect (see below). However, these experiments demonstrated a significant and unexpected difference in the potency of DHA *versus* EPA, and some effect of oleic acid, which differs considerably from DHA in chain length, position and number of unsaturations (double bonds). Although ineffective *per se* in this system, EPA potentiated the effect of DHA. Compared with DHA alone, IL-1-stimulated VCAM-1 expression was inhibited 35% (±7%) by DHA (10 μmol/l) and 47% (±8%) by DHA (10 μmol/l) and EPA (10 μmol/l) in combination.

Figure 2 shows the time-dependence of the reduction in expression of VCAM-1 induced by DHA after stimulation with either IL-1α or TNFα. A similar effect on

VCAM-1 expression was seen in the presence of another cytokine-inducible endothelial leukocyte adhesion molecule, E-selectin, which, like VCAM-1, exhibits little or no cell surface expression before cytokine stimulation. Although the time-course of surface expression of these two molecules was quite different (E-selectin expression was rapid and transient, whereas VCAM-1 expression was slower and more persistent), DHA inhibited the expression of these proteins at all time points studied (Fig. 2).

Inhibition of VCAM-1 expression by DHA was also demonstrated by flow cytometry. This technique is also based on the recognition of VCAM-1 by antibodies, but can be used to identify the cellular distribution of the target antigen. DHA reduced the median of the flow-cytometric distribution of fluorescence intensity *versus* cell number after IL-1 stimulation (Fig. 3).

In addition, DHA slightly, but significantly, increased the spread of the distribution (indicated by the increased SEM in Fig. 3). This may have been due to the appearance of a population of endothelial cells with an nonhomogeneous pattern of VCAM-1 expression.

In addition to VCAM-1 and E-selectin, other molecules were also affected by DHA, although to a different extent. A comparison of the inhibition of VCAM-1 and ICAM-1 by DHA in response to TNFα is shown in Figure 4.

ICAM-1 expression was affected much less than VCAM-1, although the extent of inhibition was still significant. A modest, but significant, inhibition in baseline expression of ICAM-1 was also seen. Furthermore, production of two soluble cytokines, IL-6 and IL-8, released by endothelial cells in response to IL-1, was inhibited by DHA (Fig. 5), demonstrating that the effect of DHA was not restricted to adhesion molecules. DHA, however, lacked nonspecific, toxic effects. DHA had no effect on cell number (assessed by direct counting), viability (by trypan blue exclusion), expression of constitutively expressed membrane molecules, such as major histocompatibility class I antigen, or the antigen recognized by the antibody E1/1 (a common antigen for endothelial cells, which is not affected by cytokine stimulation) (data not shown).

Similarly, the level of total cell-associated and secreted proteins, estimated by the incorporation of ^{14}C-leucine into trichloroacetic acid precipitable proteins, was indistinguishable in DHA-treated and control endothelial cells at various time points (Fig. 6). The selectivity of the action of DHA for cytokine-induced molecules and the lack of any effect on various parameters of cell viability, provided evidence of a specific effect.

The inhibition by DHA of cytokine-induced expression of the molecules tested required prolonged incubation times, and the extent of inhibition increased progressively for up to 48-96 hours (Fig. 7). The increase in the magnitude of this inhibition paralleled an increase in the incorporation of DHA into total cellular lipids, and a corresponding decrease in the percentage of total n-6 fatty acid (Fig. 7).

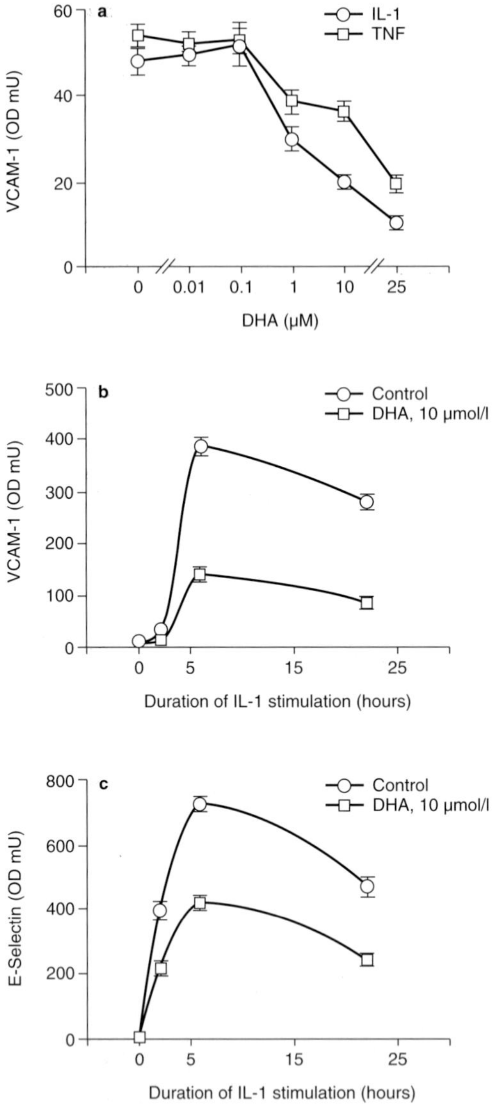

Fig. 2. Inhibition of cytokine-induced expression of vascular cell adhesion molecule (VCAM)-1 and E-selectin in human adult saphenous vein endothelial cells (HSVEC) by docosahexaenoic acid (DHA). HSVEC monolayers were incubated in 96-well plates for 96 hours in medium 199 containing fetal calf serum (FCS; 5%) and the sodium salt of DHA. Cytokines were added for a further 24 hours (a) or for 0-24 hours (b and c) to induce surface expression of endothelial-leukocyte adhesion molecules. Expression was assessed by cell-surface enzyme immunoassays. (a) VCAM-1 expression, in milliunits of optical density (OD mU), as a function of the concentration of DHA, after stimulation with interleukin (IL)-1α or tumour necrosis factor (TNF)α (both 10 ng/ml). (b) and (c) The time-course of VCAM-1 and E-selectin expression, respectively, after addition of IL-1α (10 ng/ml) in the absence or presence of DHA (10 μmol/l). Data are presented as mean±SEM.

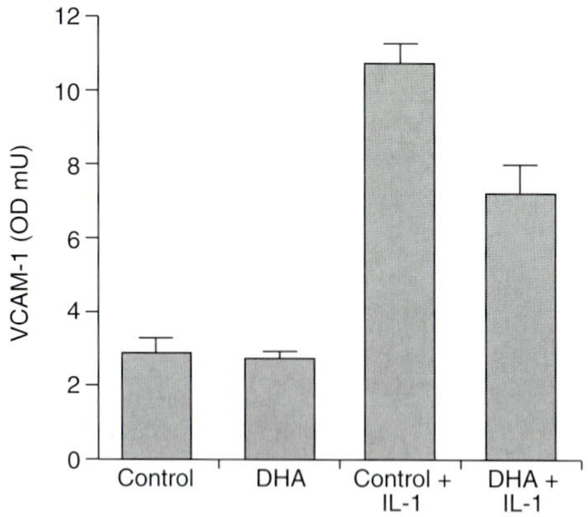

Fig. 3. Flow-cytometric analysis of the effect of docosahexaenoic acid (DHA) (10 μmol/l, 48 hours of pre-incubation) on the expression of vascular cell adhesion molecule (VCAM)-1 by human adult saphenous vein endothelial cells (HSVEC). Bars represent the median±SEM of the distribution of fluorescence intensity *versus* cell number, derived from flow-cytometric histograms. Fluorescence intensity increased after interleukin (IL-1) stimulation. Addition of docosahexaenoic acid (DHA) significantly inhibited ($p<0.01$) and spread out the fluorescence distribution. Baseline fluorescence in unstimulated conditions was the same as that obtained using a non-binding antibody, indicating the virtual absence of baseline expression of VCAM-1 in HSVEC. Addition of an antibody (E1/1) directed against a constitutive and non-cytokine-inducible endothelial antigen shifted the distribution to the right compared with that obtained in the presence of a non-binding antibody. This distribution was not modified by either cytokines or DHA (data not shown), indicating the presence of a non-cytokine-inducible antigen on the cell surface.

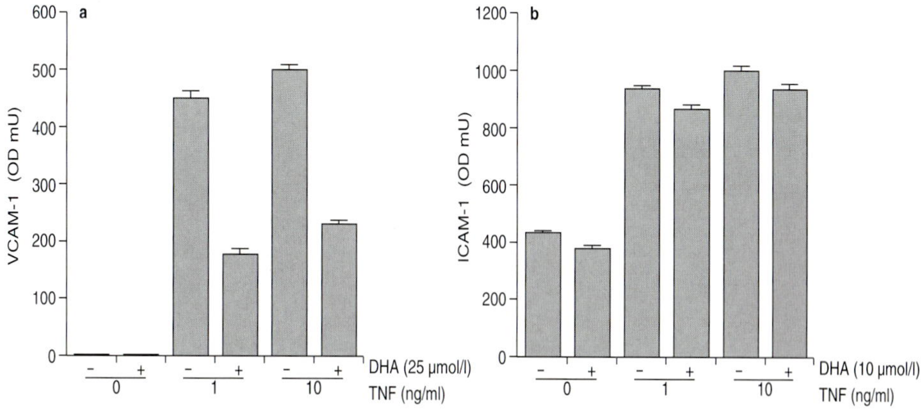

Fig 4. Surface expression of vascular cell adhesion molecule (VCAM)-1 (a) and intercellular adhesion molecule (ICAM)-1 (b) measured in milliunits of optical density (OD mU) in the presence or absence of docosahexaenoic acid (DHA) (pre-incubation for 96 hours). Baseline expression and expression following a further 24-hour stimulation with tumour necrosis factor (TNF)α (1 and 10 ng/ml) are shown. Data represent means±SEM. DHA significantly inhibited expression at both TNFα concentrations used, but the degree of inhibition was much greater for VCAM-1 compared with ICAM-1. There was also a small, but significant, reduction in the constitutive expression of ICAM-1 by DHA.

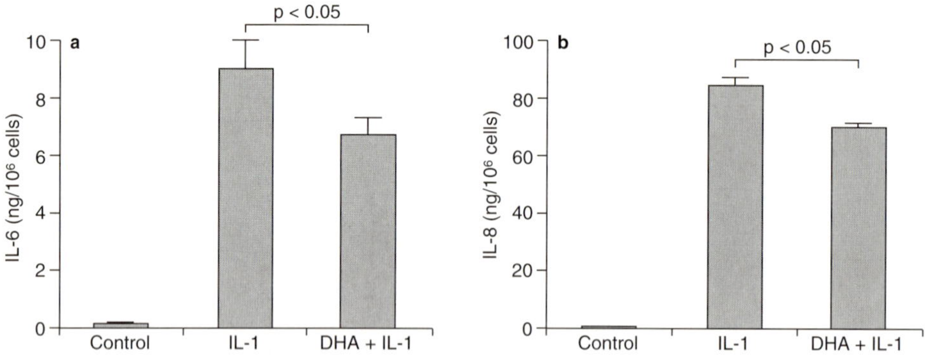

Fig. 5. Production of interleukin (IL)-6 (a) and IL-8 (b) in the absence of endothelial activation (control), after 24-hour stimulation with IL-1α (10 ng/ml) and after treatment with docosahexaenoic acid (DHA) (10 mmol/l, 48 hours alone plus 24 hours with IL-1α). IL-6 and IL-8 were measured in the supernatant of endothelial cell cultures. A significant decrease in IL-1α- stimulated production of both IL-6 and IL-8 after DHA pre-incubation is apparent.

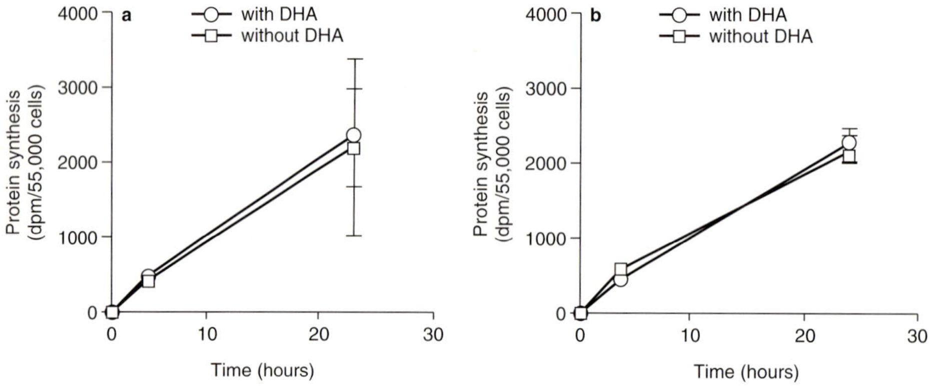

Fig. 6. Measurement of cumulative protein synthesis associated with cells (a) or secreted (b) in the presence or absence of docosahexaenoic acid (DHA) (25 μmol/l for 96 hours) as a function of time after the addition of ^{3}H-leucine (0.2 μCi/10^4 cells). Total protein synthesis was measured by counting the radioactivity after protein precipitation with trichloracetic acid. Data represent mean±SD.

^{14}C-labelling revealed that DHA was initially incorporated preferentially into the neutral lipid pool and following subsequent rearrangements, was distributed predominantly in the phosphatidylethanolamine pool (Fig. 8), as assessed by two-dimensional thin layer chromatography.

Indomethacin and aspirin - well-known blockers of the cyclooxygenase metabolism of AA and of EPA - had no effect on the inhibition of VCAM-1 by DHA (Fig. 9). The main product of AA in endothelial cells is prostacyclin, the levels of which can be estimated from its stable hydrolytic product, 6-keto-PGF$_{1\alpha}$. At the concen-

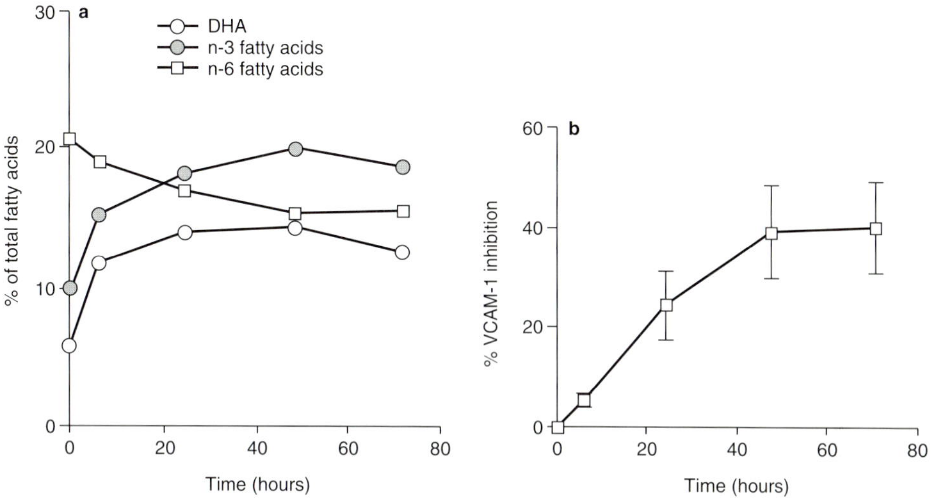

Fig. 7. Changes in fatty acid incorporation into total cellular lipids (a) and in interleukin (IL)-1-stimulated vascular cell adhesion molecule (VCAM)-1 inhibition (b) as a function of time following incubation of human adult saphenous vein endothelial cells (HSVEC) with docosahexaenoic acid (DHA) (10 μmol/l). A parallel increase in DHA and total n-3 fatty acids occurred, whereas the level of total n-6 fatty acids decreased. These changes parallel the progressive increase in VCAM-1 inhibition after IL-1 stimulation.

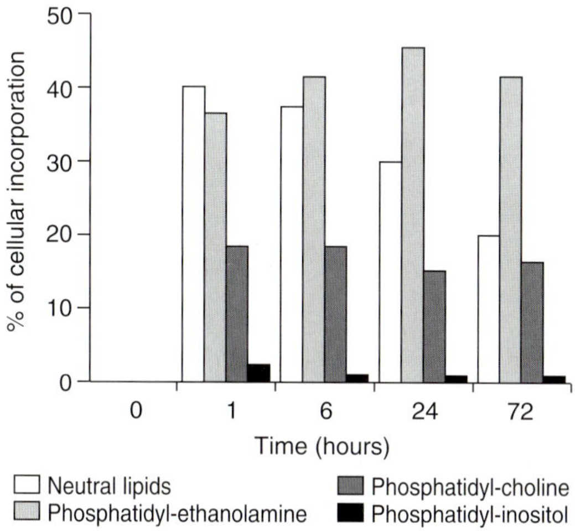

Fig. 8. Lipid class distribution of ^{14}C-docosahexaenoic acid (DHA) as a function of time in human adult saphenous vein endothelial cells (HSVEC). Major neutral lipids and phospholipid classes were resolved by two-dimensional thin layer chromatography, and quantified by counting the radioactivity after scraping the silica plate in areas corresponding to migration of authentic phospholipid standards. A preferential accumulation of DHA into neutral lipids occurred, followed by the redistribution of DHA into phospholipid classes, with the greatest accumulation in the phosphatidyl-ethanolamine pool.

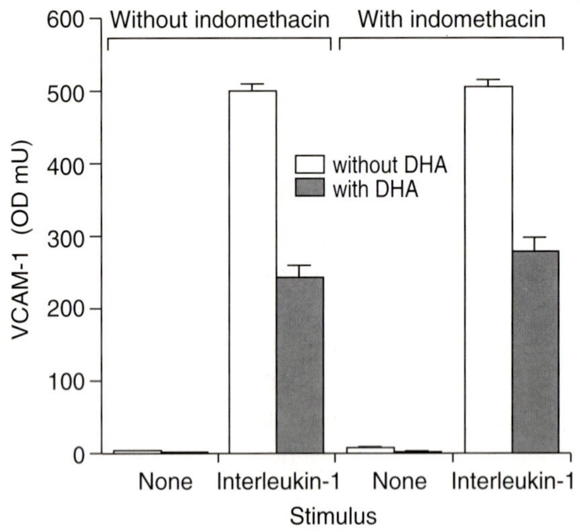

Fig. 9. Inhibition of vascular cell adhesion molecule-1 (VCAM-1) expression, measured in milliunits of optical density (OD mU) by docosahexaenoic acid (DHA) in the absence or presence of indomethacin (5 μmol/l). Inhibition of VCAM-1 expression by DHA was totally unaffected by indomethacin. Data represent mean±SEM.

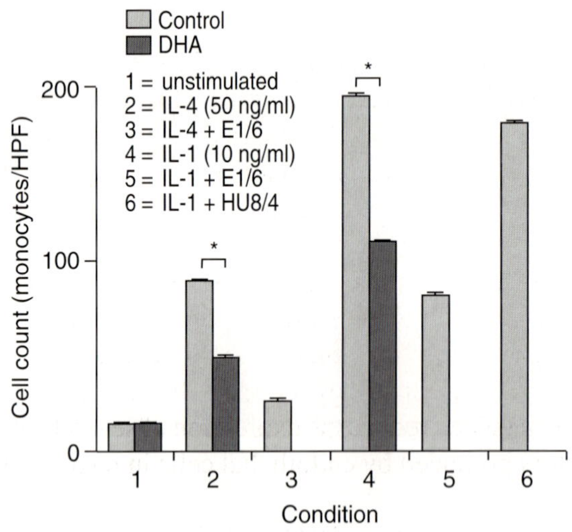

Fig. 10. The effect of docosahexaenoic acid (DHA) on adhesion of monocytes to human adult saphenous vein endothelial cells (HSVEC) after stimulation with interleukin (IL)-4 or IL-1, in a typical experiment performed under rotation (63 rpm). Monocyte adhesion in the presence of IL-4 was more dependent on VCAM-1 expression (assessed by the extent of inhibition obtained in the presence of the anti-VCAM-1 antibody, E1/6) than in the presence of IL-1. The lack of a response to the control antibody HU8/4 is also shown. DHA significantly inhibited both IL-4 and IL-1-induced monocyte adhesion. Data represent mean±SEM. HPF=high-power field.*$p<0.05$.

trations of indomethacin used, the level of 6-keto-PGF$_{1\alpha}$ in the supernatant of endothelial cells, stimulated for 48 hours with IL-1α, decreased from 21±5 ng/ml to undetectable levels, indicating the efficacy of the cyclooxygenase blockade. Northern analysis of VCAM-1 mRNA at various time points after the addition of either IL-1 or TNFα to DHA-treated and control HSVEC cultures, revealed a decrease in steady state levels, consistent with the observed reduction in VCAM-1 protein expression (data not shown). The extent of inhibition of VCAM-1 expression, as determined by densitometry of Northern blots 6-9 hours after cytokine stimulation, was 40±10% in four different experiments.

In parallel with its effects on the surface expression of adhesion molecules, DHA inhibited the adhesion of monocytes and cells of the monocytoid line U937 to HSVEC. The results obtained using human peripheral blood monocytes are shown in Figure 10. Monocyte adhesion after IL-4 stimulation was almost totally dependent on the expression of VCAM-1, as indicated by its virtual suppression following treatment of HSVEC monolayers with the anti-VCAM-1 monoclonal antibody E1/6. Conversely, adhesion was less dependent on VCAM-1 expression after IL-1 stimulation. However, in both cases, the inhibition of monocyte adhesion by DHA was significant.

Discussion

Inhibition of atherogenesis appears to be one of the modes by which n-3 FA may prevent vascular disease. Newman and coworkers have reported a decrease in the percentage of fatty streaks and raised lesions in the intima of Alaskan natives with a high n-3 FA dietary intake, *versus* non-natives.[9] In this study, the magnitude of the difference in fatty streak development appeared to be larger in younger age groups, suggesting that diet mainly affects the early events leading to fully developed atherosclerotic lesions. As the early events of atherogenesis are now beginning to be unravelled in molecular detail, we sought to determine the effects of n-3 FA on the expression of endothelial leukocyte adhesion molecules implicated in early monocyte recruitment over endothelial cells. This study shows that one n-3 FA, DHA, can indeed reduce the expression of several adhesion molecules and soluble mediators produced by endothelial cells in response to inflammatory cytokines.

The difference in potency between DHA and EPA in our system was remarkable and unexpected. The findings reported here are not absolute, as EPA could potentiate the effect of DHA to a certain extent. However, the present finding is one of the first descriptions of a selective effect of DHA *versus* EPA on a biological system that may be pertinent in atherosclerosis and inflammation. Previous reports have described selective (DHA *versus* EPA) effects of n-3 FA.[34-40] However, the link demonstrated here between biochemical observations and the biological phenomenon of monocyte adhesion should foster further research into the effects of FA in atherogenesis. In addition, the observation that oleic acid, which is structurally unrelated to DHA, may share with DHA the ability to inhibit VCAM-1 expression could offer a potential link between the relative abundance of this dietary component and the cardiovascular protection ascribed to a 'Mediterranean diet' (see the paper by S. Renaud in this book, pp 141-152). Clearly, further investigation is required to elucidate structure-activity relationships more fully.

The time-course of inhibition of IL-1-stimulated adhesion molecule expression by DHA clearly shows a delayed effect, parallel to the incorporation of DHA into the total cellular lipid pool, and consistent with the slow occurrence of most biological effects of n-3 FA.[41-44]

The magnitude of the inhibition of VCAM-1 and E-selectin expression by DHA ranged between 30% and 60%. Several arguments suggest that such a degree of inhibition may be of physiological relevance. First, effective DHA concentrations were in the low micromolar levels, within the range reported to occur *in vivo* after administration of marine lipids with a high content of n-3 FA, both by pharmacological[45,46] and dietary intervention.[47] Second, the effect appeared to be a general 'blunting' of endothelial cell responses to a variety of different stimuli, including IL-1, TNFα, IL-4 or LPS. It would appear, therefore, that an increase in the incorporation of DHA into cellular lipids would limit the activity of an entire array of proteins induced during endothelial cell 'activation'.

Third, the effect was accompanied by a significant and quantitatively similar decrease in the functional end-point of monocyte adhesion, which appears to be an important pathogenetic step in the development of atherosclerosis. Furthermore, the observed effect was consistent with the order of magnitude demonstrated for most effects of n-3 FA in epidemiological studies or experimental models of atherosclerosis,[41] suggesting a role for n-3 FA as agents "that will tactfully nudge the body back into healthful rather than self-destructive applications of its normal homeostatic responses".[48] Finally, since the spectrum of cytokine-inducible molecules affected by DHA is comprised of molecules implicated in neutrophil recruitment (E-selectin, ICAM-1, IL-8)[18,49-51] or in the amplification of tissue responses (IL-6),[52] our findings may contribute to the recognized anti-inflammatory effects of n-3 FA.[42]

We have partially addressed the mechanisms by which DHA exerts its effects on endothelial activation. As inhibition of adhesion molecule expression by DHA is independent of the stimulus used, and is relatively selective, it is reasonable to exclude a generalized 'membrane' effect. The reduction in VCAM-1 steady-state mRNA, demonstrated by Northern analysis, indicates that the effect is pre-translational. Therefore, DHA must act in the cytokine signal transduction pathway, at a point sufficiently downstream to involve a mechanism common to different cytokines, or in the activation of cytokine-induced transcription factors, or, alternatively, by affecting mRNA stability. The expression of cytokine-induced adhesion molecules appears to be regulated mainly at the transcriptional level, through the activation of transcription factors of the nuclear factor (NF)κB family.[53] An action at this level is conceivable, but needs to be demonstrated by specific experiments. In any case, the effects of DHA appear to be independent of the generation of prostanoid; which is still quoted as one of the main explanations for many biological effects of n-3 fatty acids.[54,55] This theory is supported by the lack of any interference in DHA-induced VCAM-1 inhibition by aspirin or indomethacin, and the finding that, despite some retroconversion of DHA to EPA (demonstrated by fatty acid analysis), the immediate precursor of n-3 eicosanoids, EPA, was ineffective *per se* in our system.

An issue that remains to be addressed is whether oxidative products of DHA may mediate the effects observed, a theory suggested by Fox and DiCorleto to explain their reported inhibition of platelet-derived growth factor (PDGF)-like molecules by endothelial cells.[56] Preliminary experiments using BHT and vitamin E as lipid-soluble antioxidants, did not reveal changes in the magnitude of the effects of DHA (data not shown).

However, the absence of a direct measurement of the antioxidant efficacy of these compounds in the system used precludes a firm conclusion. The action of oleic acid, which is less likely to undergo oxidation than DHA, would also point against such a mechanism. Our findings are limited mainly to the effects on cytokine-induced stimulation. Recent evidence suggests that some FA *per se* are selective inducers of VCAM-1 gene expression in the absence of stimulating cytokines, and that this effect is not shared by oleic acid.[57] In view of our findings, an assessment of the effect of EPA and DHA in this system is also warranted.

Conclusions

In summary, we have shown that one n-3 FA, DHA, can modulate the response of endothelial cells to inflammatory cytokines in an anti-atherogenic and anti-inflammatory fashion, thus providing a novel mechanism by which quantitatively minor dietary lipid components may influence cell physiology and the pathogenesis of certain ‘inflammatory’ diseases, including atherosclerosis.

Future avenues of research in this area may include the investigation of other endothelial proteins induced by cytokines, such as monocyte-chemoattractant protein-1 (MCP-1), which is the most powerful chemoattractant for monocytes identified to date, cyclooxygenase II,[58-60] and the inducible form of nitric oxide synthase.[61] The expression of all these genes appears to be regulated in a similar manner to that of adhesion molecules.[22]

An effect on cyclooxygenase II could explain the effects of n-3 FA on eicosanoids independently of the currently prevailing hypothesis of substrate substitution,[54] while an effect on nitric oxide production could provide an additional mechanistic explanation of our findings. In this regard, we have reported that nitric oxide donors may affect endothelial activation in a similar manner to DHA, via a specific action on NFκB.[62,63]

Finally, an extension of the concept of specific n-3 FA as 'general dampeners' of the responsiveness of cells to cytokines to other cell types may provide a general interpretative framework for a number of previously described and, as yet, unconnected events that follow *in vivo* supplementation with n-3 FA. Examples of such events include: first, the reduced production of IL-1 and TNFα by monocytes stimulated with LPS;[64] second, the reduced expression of tissue factor activity by monocytes;[65] third, the reduced accumulation of PDGF mRNA in mononuclear cells;[66] and finally, the reduced *in vivo* adhesion of leukocytes to the vessel wall in hamsters.[67]

Our observations may therefore offer a general insight into how minor dietary components affect cell function and cell-cell interactions.

Acknowledgments

This work was supported by NIH grant HL-48743 (to Dr P. Libby), and grants by SPA-Pharmaceuticals, Milan, Italy, and the Italian National Research Council (to Dr R. De Caterina). The co-authors of the original paper (Arterioscler. Thromb. 1994; 14: 1829-1836) in which most of the findings reported here were first described, namely Dr Myron I. Cybulsky and Dr M.A. Gimbrone, Vascular Research Division, Department of Pathology, at Brigham and Women's Hospital, Boston, and Dr S.K. Clinton, at the Dana Farber Cancer Institute, Boston, MA, are acknowledged with gratitude. Thanks also to Dr A. Leaf for conducting the fatty acid analyses; Dr C.N. Serhan for advice on thin layer chromatography; Dr F.W. Luscinskas for help in adhesion experiments and to Dr M. Muszynski D.V.M., for help with cell culture experiments. We thank all of our colleagues at the Vascular Medicine and Atherosclerosis Unit, Brigham and Women's Hospital and Harvard Medical School in Boston, for providing a most stimulating and friendly environment for the pursuit of these studies.

Summary

Dietary long-chain n-3 polyunsaturated fatty acids may influence several steps in the natural history of vascular disease, from its inception (the beginning of the atherosclerotic lesion), to its progression (plaque growth), its complications (thrombosis and alterations in vascular tone), and finally the susceptibility of the tissue/organ to ischaemic damage. Early events in atherosclerotic vascular disease involve the adhesion of monocytes to a morphologically intact endothelium and their subsequent transendothelial migration, leading to the formation of the fatty streak. Such events occur because of a critical interaction between endothelial cells in large and medium-size arteries and circulating monocytes. Such an interaction is largely mediated by the *de novo* or increased expression of endothelial-leukocyte adhesion molecules on vascular endothelial cells, which are able to tether and stably bind monocytes to the vessel wall, and by the production of monocyte-specific chemoattractants. Such endothelial changes are generally referred to as 'endothelial activation'. Here we show that one particular n-3 fatty acid, docosahexaenoic acid (DHA), at nutritionally achievable concentrations, can modulate endothelial activation *in vitro* in response to inflammatory cytokines. The production of vascular cell adhesion molecule-1 (VCAM-1), E-selectin, intercellular adhesion molecule-1 (ICAM-1), interleukin (IL)-6 and IL-8, in response to IL-1, IL-4, tumour necrosis factor or bacterial endotoxin, can all be reduced by previous incubation with DHA, which parallels the degree of increased incorporation of this fatty acid into cellular phospholipids. Accompanying this reduced surface expression of adhesion molecules, DHA reduces the adhesion of human monocytes and of monocyte U937 cells to cytokine-stimulated endothelial cells. These effects are accompanied by a quantitatively consistent reduction in VCAM-1 mRNA, indicating pre-translational control of adhesion molecule gene expression. These newly recognized properties of DHA may contribute to the antiatherogenic and anti-inflammatory effects of n-3 fatty acids and demonstrate a previously unknown qualitative difference in activity among various n-3 fatty acids.

References

1. Kromann N., Green A.: Epidemiological studies in the Upernavik district, Greenland. Acta Med. Scand. 1980; 208: 401-406
2. Bang H.O., Dyerberg J., Hjorne N.: The composition of food consumed by Greenland Eskimos. Acta Med. Scand. 1976; 200: 69-73
3. Kagawa Y., Nishizawa M., Suzuki M.: Eicosapolyenoic acid of serum lipids of Japanese islanders with low incidence of cardiovascular diseases. J. Nutr. Sci. Vitaminol. (Tokyo) 1982; 28: 441-453
4. Hirai A., Hamazaki T., Terano T.: Eicosapentaenoic acid and platelet function in Japanese. Lancet, 1980; ii: 1132-1133
5. Arthaud B.: Cause of death in 339 Alaskan natives as determined by autopsy. Arch. Pathol. 1970; 90: 433-438
6. Middaugh J.P.: Cardiovascular deaths among Alaskan natives 1980-1986. Am. J. Public Health 1990; 80: 282-285
7. Kromhout D., Bosschieter E.B., De Lezenne Coulander C.: The inverse relation between fish consumption and 20-year mortality from coronary heart disease. N. Engl. J. Med. 1985; 312: 1205-1209
8. Shekelle R., Missel L., Paul O., MacMillan-Schryock A., Stamler J.: Fish consumption and mortality from coronary heart disease (Letter). N. Engl. J. Med. 1985; 313: 820
9. Newman W.P., Middaugh J.P., Propst M.T., Rogers D.R.: Atherosclerosis in Alaska natives and non-natives. Lancet 1993; 341: 1056-1057
10. Eritsland J., Arnesen H., Grønseth K., Field N.B., Abdelnoor M.: Effect of supplementation with n-3 fatty acids on graft patency in patients undergoing coronary artery bypass operation. Results from the SHOT study. Eur. Heart J. 1994; 15: 29 (Abstract 351)
11. Gerrity R.G.: The role of the monocyte in atherogenesis: I. Transition of blood-borne monocytes into foam cells in fatty lesions. Am. J. Pathol. 1981; 103: 181-190
12. Joris I., Znad T., Nunnari J.J., Krolikowski F.J., Majno G.: Adhesion and emigration of mononuclear cells in the aorta of hypercholesterolemic rats. Am. J. Pathol. 1983; 113: 341-358
13. Faggiotto A., Ross R., Harker L.: Studies of hypercholesterolemia in the nonhuman primate. I. Changes that lead to fatty streak formation. Atherosclerosis 1984; 4: 323-340
14. Rosenfeld M.E., Tsukada T., Gown A.M., Ross R.: Fatty streak initiation in Watanabe heritable hyperlipemic and comparably hypercholesterolemic fat-fed rabbits. Atherosclerosis 1987; 7: 9-23
15. Masuda J., Ross R.: Atherogenesis during low level hypercholesterolemia in the nonhuman primate. I. Fatty streak formation. Atherosclerosis 1990; 10: 164-177
16. Faggiotto A., Ross R.: Studies of hypercholesterolemia in the nonhuman primate. II. Fatty streak conversion to fibrous plaque. Atherosclerosis 1984; 4: 341-356

17. Masuda J., Ross R.: Atherogenesis during low level hypercholesterolemia in the nonhuman primate. II. Fatty streak conversion to fibrous plaque. Atherosclerosis 1990; 10: 178-187
18. Simionescu N., Simionescu M.: Endothelial cell dysfunctions. New York; Plenum Press, 1992
19. Cybulsky M.I., Gimbrone M.A. Jr.: Endothelial expression of a mononuclear leukocyte adhesion molecule during atherogenesis. Science 1991; 251: 788-791
20. Bevilacqua M., Pober J., Mendrick D., Cotran R., Gimbrone M.A. Jr.: Identification of an inducible endothelial-leukocyte adhesion molecule. Proc. Natl. Acad. Sci. USA 1987; 84: 9238-9242
21. Springer T.A.: Adhesion receptors of the immune system. Nature 1990; 346: 425-434
22. Rollins B.J.: JE/MCP-1: an early response encodes a monocyte-specific cytokine. Cancer Cells 1991; 3: 517-524
23. De Caterina R., Cybulsky M.I., Clinton S.K., Gimbrone M.A. Jr, Libby P.: The omega-3 fatty acid docosahexaenoate reduces cytokine-induced expression of pro-atherogenic and pro-inflammatory proteins in human endothelial cells. Arterioscler. Thromb. 1994; 14: 1829-1836
24. Warner S.J., Auger K.R., Libby P.: Interleukin-1 induces interleukin-1. II. Recombinant human interleukin 1 induces interleukin 1 production by adult human vascular endothelial cells. J. Immunol. 1987; 139: 1911-1917
25. Libby P., Ordovas J.M., Birinyi L.K., Auger K.R., Dinarello C.: Inducible interleukin-1 gene expression in human vascular smooth muscle cells. J. Clin. Invest. 1986; 78: 1432-1438
26. Libby P., Ordovas J.M., Auger K.R., Robbins A.H., Birinyi L.K., Dinarello C.A.: Endotoxin and tumor necrosis factor induce interleukin-1 gene expression in adult human vascular endothelial cells. Am. J. Pathol. 1986; 124: 179-185
27. Warner S.J.C., Friedman G.B., Libby P.: Regulation of major histocompatibility gene expression in human vascular smooth muscle cells. Atherosclerosis 1989; 9: 279-288
28. Pober J.S., Gimbrone M.A. Jr, Lapierre L.A., Mendrick D.L., Fiers W., Rothlein R., Springer T.A.: Overlapping patterns of activation of human endothelial cells by interleukin 1, tumor necrosis factor, and immune interferon. J. Immunol. 1986; 137: 1893-1896
29. Fox P.L., Di Corleto P.E.: Regulation of production of a platelet-derived growth factor-like protein by cultured bovine aortic endothelial cells. J. Cell Physiol. 1984; 121: 298-308
30. Chirgwin J.M., Przybyla A.E., MacDonald R.J., Rutter W.J.: Isolation of biologically active ribonucleic acid from sources enriched in ribonuclease. Biochemistry 1979; 18: 5294-5299
31. Luscinskas F.W., Kansas G.S., Ding H., Pizcueta P., Schleiffenbaum B.E., Tedder T.F., Gimbrone M.A. Jr: Monocyte rolling, arrest and spreading on IL-4-activated vascular endothelium under flow is mediated via sequential action of L-selectin, b1-integrins, and b2-integrins. J. Cell Biol. 1994; 125: 1417-1427
32. Spertini O., Luscinskas F.W., Gimbrone M.A. Jr, Tedder T.F.: Monocyte attachment to activated human vascular endothelium *in vitro* is mediated by leukocyte adhesion molecule-1 (L-selectin) under nonstatic conditions. J. Exp. Med. 1992; 175: 1789-1792
33. Schleimer R.P., Sterbinsky S.A., Kaiser J., Bickel C.A., Klunk D.A., Tomioka K., Newman W., Luscinskas F.W., Gimbrone M.A., McIntyre B.W., *et al.*: IL-4 induces adherence of human eosinophils and basophils but not neutrophils to endothelium. J. Immunol. 1992; 148: 1086-1092
34. Weber C., Aepfelbacher M., Lux I., Zimmer B., Weber P.C.: Docosahexaenoic acid inhibits PAF and LTD4 stimulated Ca^{2+} increase in differentiated monocytic U937 cells. Biochim. Biophys. Acta. 1991; 1133: 38-45
35. Holian O., Nelson R.: Action of long-chain fatty acids on protein kinase C activity: comparison of omega-6 and omega-3 fatty acids. Anticancer Res. 1992; 12: 975-980
36. Hrelia S., Biagi P.L., Turchetto E., Rossi C.A., Bordoni A.: Protein kinase C activity in neonatal cultured rat cardiomyocytes supplemented with docosahexaenoic acid. Biochem. Biophys. Res. Commun. 1992; 183: 893-898

37. Shikano M., Masuzawa Y., Yazawa K.: Effect of docosahexaenoic acid on the generation of platelet-activating factor by eosinophilic leukemia cells, Eol-1. J. Immunol. 1993; 150: 3525-3533
38. Scheurlen M., Kirchner M., Clemens M.R., Jaschonek K.: Fish oil preparations rich in docosahexaenoic acid modify platelet responsiveness to prostaglandin-endoperoxide/thromboxane A2 receptor agonists. Biochem. Pharmacol. 1993; 46: 245-249
39. Bates E.J., Ferrante A., Harvey D.P., Nandoskar M., Poulos A.: Docosahexaenoic acid (22:6, n-3) but not eicosapentaenoic acid (20:5, n-3) can induce neutrophil-mediated injury of cultured endothelial cells: involvement of neutrophil elastase. J. Leukoc. Biol. 1993; 54: 590-598
40. Willumsen N., Hexeberg S., Skorve J., Lundquist M., Berge R.K.: Docosahexaenoic acid shows no triglyceride-lowering effects but increases the peroxisomal fatty acid oxidation in liver of rats. J. Lipid Res. 1993; 34: 13-22
41. Leaf A., Weber P.C.: Cardiovascular effects of n-3 fatty acids. N. Engl. J. Med. 1988; 318: 549-557
42. Simopoulos A.P.: Omega-3 fatty acids in health and disease and in growth and development. Am. J. Clin. Nutr. 1991; 54: 438-463
43. Schmidt E.B., Kristensen S.D., De Caterina R., Illingworth R.: The effects of n-3 fatty acids on plasma lipids and lipoproteins and other cardiovascular risk factors in patients with hyperlipidemia. Atherosclerosis 1993; 103: 107-121
44. De Caterina R., Giannessi D., Mazzone A., Bernini W., Lazzerini G., Maffei S., Cerri M, Salvatore L., Weksler B.: Vascular prostacyclin is increased in patients ingesting omega-3 polyunsaturated fatty acids before coronary artery bypass surgery. Circulation 1990; 82: 428-438
45. Bønaa K.H., Bjerve K.S., Straume B., Gram I.T., Thelle D.: Effect of eicosapentaenoic and docosahexaenoic acids on blood pressure in hypertension. N. Engl. J. Med. 1990; 322: 795-801
46. Harris W.S., Connor W.E., McMurry M.P.: The comparative reductions of the plasma lipids and lipoproteins by dietary polyunsaturated fats: salmon oil *versus* vegetable oil. Metabolism 1983; 32: 179-184
47. Burr M.L., Fehily A.M., Gilbert J.F., Rogers S., Holliday R.M., Sweetnam P.M., Elwood P.C., Deadman N.M.: Effects of changes in fat, fish, and fibre intakes on death and myocardial reinfarctions: diet and reinfarction trial (DART). Lancet 1989; ii: 757-761
48. Leaf A.: Cardiovascular effects of fish oils - beyond the platelet. Circulation 1990; 82: 624-628
49. Oppenheim J.J., Zachariae C.O., Mukaida N., Matsushima K.: Properties of the novel proinflammatory supergene 'intercrine' cytokine family. Annu. Rev. Immunol. 1991; 9: 617-648
50. Taub D.D., Oppenheim J.J.: Review of the chemokine meeting: the Third International Symposium of Chemotactic Cytokines. Cytokine 1993; 5: 175-179
51. Rot A.: Endothelial cell binding of NAP-1/IL-8: role in neutrophil emigration. Immunol. Today 1992; 13: 291-294
52. Van Snick J.: Interleukin-6: an overview. Annu. Rev. Immunol. 1990; 8: 253-278
53. Collins T.: Endothelial nuclear factor-kB and the initiation of the atherosclerotic lesion. Lab. Invest. 1993; 68: 499-508
54. Dyerberg J., Bang H.O., Stofferson E., Moncada S., Vane J.R.: Eicosapentaenoic acid and prevention of thrombosis and atherosclerosis. Lancet 1978; ii: 117-119
55. Lee T.H., Hoover R.L., Williams J.D., Sperling R.I., Ravalese J. 3rd, Spur B.W., Robinson D.R., Corey E.J., Lewis R.A., Austen K.F.: Effect of dietary enrichment with eicosapentaenoic and docosahexaenoic acids on *in vitro* neutrophil and monocyte leukotriene generation and neutrophil function. N. Engl. J. Med. 1985; 312: 1217-1224
56. Fox P.L., Di Corleto P.E.: Fish oils inhibit endothelial cell production of platelet-derived growth factor-like protein. Science 1988; 241: 453-456

57. Khan B.V., Olbrych M.T., Parthasarathy S.S., Alexander R.W., Medford R.M.: Polyunsaturated fatty acids are selective, redox-sensitive regulators of VCAM-1 gene expression in human vascular endothelial cells. Circulation 1994; 90: 1-82 (Abstract 436)
58. Maier J.A., Hla T., Maciag T.: Cyclooxygenase is an immediate-early gene induced by interleukin-1 in human endothelial cells. J. Biol. Chem. 1990; 265: 10805-10808
59. Habib A., Creminon C., Frobert Y., Grassi J., Pradelles P., Maclouf J.: Demonstration of an inducible cyclooxygenase in human endothelial cells using antibodies raised against the carboxyl-terminal region of the cyclooxygenase-2. J. Biol. Chem. 1993; 268: 23448-23454
60. Hla T., Neilson K.: Human cyclooxygenase-2 cDNA. Proc. Natl. Acad. Sci. USA 1992; 89: 7384-7388
61. Kilbourn R.G., Belloni P.: Endothelial cell production of nitrogen oxides in response to interferon in combination with tumor necrosis factor, interleukin-1, or endotoxin. J. Natl. Cancer Inst. 1990; 82: 772-776
62. De Caterina R., Shin W.S., Liao J.K., Libby P.: Nitric oxide inhibits cytokine-induced expression of endothelial leukocyte adhesion molecules. Circulation 1994; 90: 1-29 (Abstract 144)
63. De Caterina R., Libby P., Thannickal V.I., Peng H-B., Rajavashisth T., Gimbrone M.A. Jr, Shin W.S., Liao J.K.: Nitric oxide decreases cytokine-induced endothelial activation. J. Clin. Invest. 1995; 96: 60-68
64. Endres S., Ghorbani R., Kelley V.E., Georgilis K., Lonnemann G., van der Meer J.W., Cannon J.G., Rogers T.S., Klempner M.S., Weber P.C., *et al.*: The effect of dietary supplementation with n-3 polyunsaturated fatty acids on the synthesis of interleukin-1 and tumor necrosis factor by mononuclear cells. N. Engl. J. Med. 1989; 320: 265-271
65. Hansen J.B., Olsen J.O., Wilsgard L., Østerud B.: Effects of dietary supplementation with cod liver oil on monocyte thromboplastin synthesis, coagulation and fibrinolysis. J. Intern. Med. 1989; 225 (Suppl): 133-139
66. Kaminski W.E., Jendraschak E., Kiefl R., von Schacky C.: Dietary omega-3 fatty acids lower levels of platelet-derived growth factor mRNA in human mononuclear cells. Blood 1993; 81: 1871-1879
67. Lehr AH., Hübner C., Finckh B., Nolte D., Beisiegel U., Kohlschutter A., Messmer K.: Dietary fish oil reduces leukocyte/endothelium interaction following systemic administration of oxidatively modified low density lipoproteins. Circulation 1991; 84: 1725-1731

S.D. Kristensen, E.B. Schmidt, R. De Caterina, S. Endres
n-3 Fatty Acids: Prevention and Treatment in Vascular Disease
Bi & Gi Publishers, Verona - Springer Verlag, London, 1995

4. Effect of n-3 Fatty Acids on Oxidized Low-Density Lipoprotein-Induced Leukocyte Adhesion

H.A. Lehr[1], C. Hübner[2]

1. Department of Pathology, University of Washington, Seattle, USA
2. Neuropediatric Department, University Clinic of the Charité, Berlin, Germany

Introduction

The first observations of leukocyte participation in atherogenesis were made by Anitchkow in 1933.[1] In this survey, it was suggested that foam cells originate from blood-borne monocytes entering the vessel wall from the luminal side. The presence of adherent leukocytes at random sites in the arterial tree - preferentially over early atherosclerotic lesions - was later repeatedly described in various animal models of diet-induced atherogenesis (reviewed in Ross[2] and Lehr *et al.*[3]) and in heritable hyperlipidaemic in rabbits,[4] as well as in coronary arteries obtained from human hearts explanted during cardiac transplantation.[5] Adherent leukocytes were found mostly in areas of increased macromolecular permeability,[6,7] suggesting a temporal and/or causal interrelation between leukocyte adhesion and endothelial cell dysfunction.

Several Authors described the subsequent transendothelial migration of adherent leukocytes, their accumulation in the intima, the differentiation of monocytes into macrophages and the uptake of cholesterol esters, giving rise to the formation of lipid-engorged foam cells and fatty streak lesions (reviewed in Ross[2] and Lehr *et al.*[3]). In addition to providing the morphological basis for the formation of foam cells and fatty streak lesions, emigrated leukocytes have been shown to secrete toxic substances, such as reactive oxygen metabolites and hydrolytic enzymes, which inflict damage on neighbouring cells, and cytokines and growth factors that are capable of inducing far-reaching metabolic and functional changes. These events set the stage for further changes that culminate in the proliferative lesions of atherosclerosis (reviewed in Ross[2]).

While investigating leukocyte attractant and adhesion-promoting factors, Alderson *et al.* and others have demonstrated that exposure of cultured endothelial cells to human low-density lipoprotein (LDL) or to very low density lipoprotein (VLDL) from cholesterol-fed animals enhanced their adhesiveness for monocytes.[8,9] This effect was ascribed to the peroxidative damage of membrane phospholipids and/or cholesterol transfer into endothelial cell membrane bilayers, leading to alterations in the cholesterol:phospholipid molar ratio and thus to pronounced changes in biophysical membrane properties. It was later found that the adhesion-promoting effect of LDL on endothelial cells can be markedly increased by prior *in vitro* oxidation of LDL particles.[10] This finding is consistent with the observation that oxidized LDL (oxLDL) exerts direct chemotactic effects on monocytes.[11] Liao *et al.*[12] reported that in mice, minimally modified LDL - a form of oxLDL more likely to be found in human plasma or atherosclerotic lesions - induces the synthesis of mRNA for *JE*, equivalent to human monocyte chemoattractant protein-1 (MCP-1), and significantly increases monocyte adhesion to cultured endothelial cells.[13]

On the basis of these findings, we have used an intravital microscopic approach in unanaesthetized hamsters and mice to provide *in vivò* evidence for a leukocyte chemoattractive and adhesion-promoting role of oxLDL, and to study the mechanisms involved in this phenomenon.

In Vivo Model of oxLDL-Induced Leukocyte Adhesion

A detailed description of the animal model and the individual experimental approaches is given in Lehr *et al.*[14] and in the references listed in Figure 1. Briefly, observation chambers were implanted surgically into the dorsal skinfold of pento-barbital-anaesthetized hamsters and mice. A recovery period of 48-72 hours between the chamber implantation and the experiments was allowed in order to eliminate the effects of anaesthesia and surgical trauma on the microvasculature contained within the observation chamber. Leukocyte-endothelium interaction, vessel diameters and red cell velocities were assessed in five postcapillary venules (diameter, 20-60 mm) and five arterioles (diameter, 20-60 mm) in each observation chamber. The identical vessel segments were examined before and over the time course after injection of native oxLDL (via indwelling catheters in the jugular vein) using a computer-controlled, stepping-motor-driven platform. Leukocytes were stained *in vivo* with acridine orange, 0.5 mg/kg/minute intravenously (i.v.), and classified by fluorescence microscopy according to their interaction with the endothelial lining (adherent, rolling or free-flowing). Lipoproteins were isolated using density gradient centrifugation from the blood of healthy human subjects and oxidized *in vitro* by copper, as described previously.[14] LDL oxidation was verified by fatty acid determination of native LDL and oxidized LDL, as well as by assessment of the electrophoretic mobility of LDL particles on an agarose gel.[14] These experiments were performed in untreated control animals and in animals pretreated with pharmacological agents or by dietary means aimed at the inhibition of inflammatory mediators and/or leukocyte adhesion molecules (Fig. 1).

Under normal conditions, represented by baseline values, the majority of leukocytes did not interact with the microvascular endothelium; however, injection of oxLDL elicited the immediate onset of leukocyte rolling along the endothelial lining and their subsequent firm adhesion to the endothelium of postcapillary venules and arterioles (Fig. 1). Leukocyte adhesion reached a maximum 15-30 minutes after injection of oxLDL and then gradually declined until it reached baseline levels 60 minutes after injection. For reasons of space and clarity, only the 15-minute values are shown in Figure 1 for each experimental condition tested. No increase in leukocyte-endothelium interactions was observed after injection of native LDL. Electron micrographs showed that the adhesion-promoting effect of oxLDL involved all leukocyte subpopulations[14] and was not confined to the microcirculation, but was also apparent on the aortic endothelium.[15] This effect was

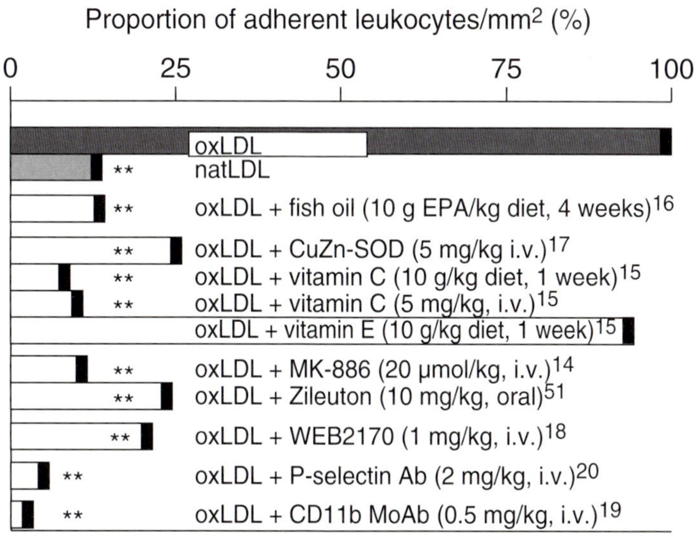

Fig. 1. Mediators and receptor molecules involved in oxidized low-density lipoprotein (oxLDL)-induced leukocyte adhesion to the arteriolar endothelium. Leukocyte adhesion was assessed by intravital fluorescence microscopy in five arterioles and five venules (not shown) in each animal. Data are expressed as percentage of the oxLDL control at 15 minutes after intravenous injection of oxLDL. All pharmacological agents were administered 10-30 minutes before oxLDL injection. Ab=antibody, MoAb=monoclonal antibody, CuZnSOD=copper-zinc superoxide dismutase, PAF=platelet activating factor, natLDL=natural LDL. n=7 animals per group, **p<0.01 *versus* oxLDL.

not due to local microhaemodynamic changes as blood pressure, heart rate, vessel diameter and red cell velocity were not affected by oxLDL injection. As a response to the generalized leukocyte sequestration in the micro- and macrocirculation, the total leukocyte count dropped by almost 50% 15 minutes after injection of oxLDL (but not native LDL), and remained low throughout the entire follow-up period.[14]

Mediator Interplay in oxLDL-Induced Leukocyte Adhesion

The mechanisms involved in oxLDL-induced leukocyte adhesion were investigated by inhibiting well-known mediators of leukocyte adhesion to determine if this interfered with oxLDL-induced adhesion. Pretreatment of animals with pharmacological and dietary inhibitors demonstrated the involvement of several factors in this phenomenon: first, oxygen radicals;[15,16] second leukotrienes;[14,17] third, the receptor for platelet activating factor (PAF);[18] and fourth, a set of well-characterized leukocyte adhesion molecules (Fig. 1).[19,20] Of particular interest was the finding that pretreatment of the animals with dietary fish oil significantly inhibited oxLDL-induced leukocyte adhesion - to an extent comparable with either of the specific pharmacological inhibitors alone (Fig. 1). The 4-week pretreatment of the hamsters with a dietary supplement of n-3 fatty acids (a fish oil concentrate containing 18% eicosapentaenoic acid (EPA) and 12% docosahexaenoic acid, which comprised 5% of the total weight of the diet) had resulted in a significant decrease in the ratio of arachidonic acid (AA) to EPA in leukocyte total lipids (Fig. 2). These observations are comparable with changes observed in human subjects after consumption of dietary fish oil.[21-24]

The individual contributions of each mediator to the overall degree of leukocyte adhesion add up to considerably more than 100%, suggesting interactions in the form of a cascade system or a self-amplifying circuit. These findings are in agreement with earlier reports demonstrating that inhibitors of either leukotriene biosynthesis, superoxide radical action and/or PAF-receptors significantly attenuate leukocyte adhesion in response to diverse pathophysiological stimuli, such as acute or chronic inflammation as well as ischaemia-reperfusion injury.

In vitro studies have revealed complex cross-reactivity between oxygen radicals, leukotrienes and PAF, both in respect to their biosynthesis and their action on target cells.[25-28] These reports have recently been supplemented by an elegant *in vitro* study which showed that the PAF receptor binds not only to authentic PAF, but also to numerous phospholipid fragments, generated through uncontrolled peroxidation of membrane phospholipids catalysed by oxygen radicals.[29]

The demonstration that these so-called PAF-like lipids not only bind to the PAF receptor, but also induce leukocyte activation and adhesion to gelatin-coated plastic may imply that, in our experiments, oxLDL-induced leukocyte adhesion to the microvascular endothelium involves not necessarily authentic PAF, but also the

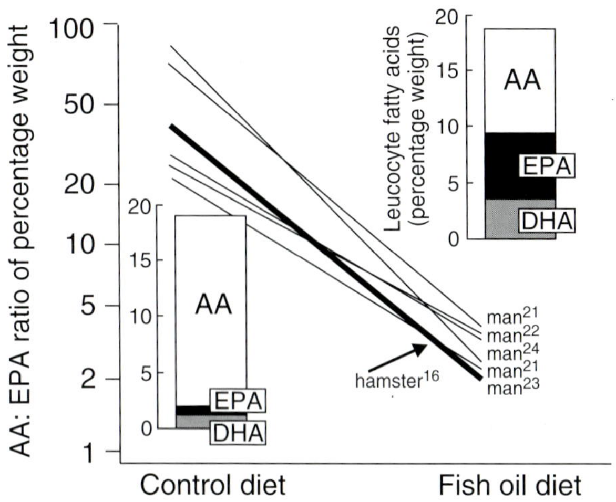

Fig. 2. Fatty acid composition of leukocyte total lipids in control and fish-oil-fed hamsters. Fatty acids in blood samples taken from control hamsters and from hamsters after 4 weeks of dietary supplementation with 5% of a fish oil concentrate (containing 18% eicosapentaenoic acid (EPA)) were identified using capillary gas chromatography.[17] Results are expressed as a percentage weight. AA=arachidonic acid, DHA=docosahexaenoic acid. AA:EPA ratios for hamster leukocytes are depicted by the bold line. AA:EPA ratios for human subjects are taken from the literature.[21-24]

oxygen radical-induced generation of PAF-like lipids from membrane phospholipids. It is also conceivable that oxLDL may have exerted PAF-like activity *per se*. In agreement with these considerations, we propose that injection of oxLDL into hamsters induces the radical-dependent peroxidation of membrane phospholipids and the generation of PAF or PAF-like lipids, which then bind to PAF-receptors on the leukocyte surface and stimulate leukocyte adhesion through a leukotriene-dependent mechanism.[25] On the basis of these considerations, we presume that leukocyte adhesion *in vivo* in response to oxLDL and other pathophysiological stimuli is a consequence of a complex network of amplificatory interrelations between these mediator systems (a cascade system or a circuit).

Effect of Fish Oil on oxLDL-Induced Leukocyte Adhesion

The finding that dietary fish oil significantly inhibited oxLDL-induced leukocyte adhesion is of interest as n-3 fatty acids exert diverse inhibitory effects on several of the mediator systems described above.

First, fish oil has been found to inhibit the generation of biologically active leukotrienes of the four series, particularly the adhesion-promoting leukotriene (LT)B_4.[21-23] In fact, the drop in the AA:EPA percentage weight ratio observed in the hamster fed fish oil in our study[17] (Fig. 2) corresponds well with the differences in

AA:EPA ratios observed in Danes eating a Western diet compared with Greenland Eskimos,[30] and between healthy American males before and after 6 weeks of eating a fish-oil diet. This drop in the AA:EPA ratio was found to lead to a marked inhibition of leukotriene biosynthesis and leukocyte function.[21-23] In addition to inhibiting leukotriene generation, dietary fish oil has also been shown to reduce the responsiveness of leukocytes to LTB_4,[21] presumably through effects of LTB_4 receptor expression.[31]

Second, dietary fish oil has been found to significantly reduce the capacity of leukocytes to generate superoxide anions,[32] which play a key role in leukocyte adhesion under a variety of pathophysiological conditions, including oxLDL-induced leukocyte adhesion (Fig. 1).

Third, the production of PAF by leukocytes is markedly inhibited when n-3 fatty acids are incorporated in their membrane phospholipids, replacing AA in alkyl phosphatidylcholine, the precursor for PAF.[33]

Fourth, fish oil may not only attenuate leukocyte-endothelium interaction through the inhibition of adhesion-promoting mediators, but also through enhanced generation of anti-adhesive forces. Among these, prostacyclin has been shown to protect against leukocyte adhesion to the endothelium.[34] A diet rich in fish oil increases prostacyclin formation by adding the active trienoic prostaglandin $(PG)I_3$ to PGI_2,[35] which remains unchanged or is increased *per se*.[36] In pigs given fish oil, the formation and release by endothelial cells of another potent antagonist of leukocyte adhesion, the endothelial-derived relaxing factor (nitric oxide),[37] are increased and this is associated with a significant attenuation of hypercholesterolaemia-induced coronary atherosclerosis.[38,39] Indeed, an intravital microscopic study of the rat mesentery has shown recently that the adhesion-promoting effect of oxLDL *in vivo* can be, at least to a major degree, ascribed to the inhibition of nitric oxide generation and/or action.[40]

Finally, we demonstrated that oxLDL-induced leukocyte adhesion involves CD11b/CD18 and P-selectin. These are both preformed adhesion molecules that are translocated to the cell surface in response to adequate stimuli and mediate the earliest phase of leukocyte-endothelium interaction following pathophysiological stimuli (reviewed in Zimmerman *et al.*[41] and Smith[42]). It has been demonstrated that LTB_4 induces leukocyte adhesion to the microvascular endothelium through the upregulation of CD11b/CD18 adhesion receptors on the leukocyte surface.[43] Compared with LTB_4, LTB_5, derived from EPA,[44] is about twofold less potent in upregulating CD11b/CD18.[44] While the leukocyte-confined adhesion receptor CD11b/CD18 is upregulated by LTB_4 and PAF (both of which are susceptible to n-3 fatty acids), its endothelial counterparts are upregulated by the action of interleukin-1 and tumour necrosis factor,[45,46] the generation of which has also been found to be suppressed by dietary fish oil.[23]

These observations suggest that fish oil may attenuate leukocyte-endothelium interactions through effects on adhesion receptors on the cell membranes of both leukocytes and endothelial cells.

The conclusion drawn from the present study, that dietary fish oil may exert its preventive effects on atherogenesis through the inhibition of leukocyte-endothelium interactions, is in agreement with and extends recent reports demonstrating that dietary fish oil significantly reduces the excessive number of leukocytes attached to the arterial endothelium in cholesterol-fed pigs[47] and reduces the numbers of monocytes/macrophages within atherosclerotic lesions in cholesterol-fed rhesus monkeys.[48] Although caution should be exercised in extrapolating the data obtained from acute animal experiments to the clinical situation, the results obtained in our intravital microscopic studies suggest that inhibition of leukocyte adhesion to the vascular endothelium may be one of the mechanisms by which fish oil exerts its protective effects on experimental and clinical atherogenesis.[47-51]

Summary

The interaction between leukocytes and the endothelium is essential during acute inflammatory responses and tissue repair. In addition, leukocyte adhesion to the endothelium has been observed during a number of pathophysiological conditions, including reperfusion after local or systemic ischaemia, allograft rejection and atherogenesis. Studies conducted *in vitro* indicate that oxidized low-density lipoprotein (oxLDL) promotes leukocyte adhesion to the vascular endothelium, which is a feature of early atherosclerotic lesions. Thus, oxLDL has been implicated in the development of atherogenesis. In this study, intravital microscopy has been conducted in hamsters and mice using a dorsal skinfold chamber model, in order to demonstrate the adhesion-promoting effect of oxLDL on leukocytes, platelets, and endothelial cells *in vivo*.

OxLDL (4 mg/kg body weight, administered intravenously) of both hamster and human origin was oxidized *in vitro* by 7.5 mM Cu^{2+} or by incubation with macrophages. OxLDL, but not native LDL, stimulated the adhesion of leukocytes to both venous and arterial endothelia (assessed by intravital microscopy) and also to the aortic endothelium (assessed by scanning electron microscopy). This adhesion-promoting effect was observed in all leukocyte subpopulations (assessed by differential leukocyte counts and electron microscopy). OxLDL also induced the formation of leukocyte/platelet aggregates (assessed by intravital and scanning electron microscopy). The effect was maximal 20-30 minutes after injection of oxLDL. OxLDL-induced leukocyte/platelet/endothelium interactions were significantly inhibited by pretreatment of animals with inhibitors of leukotriene biosynthesis (MK-886, AA-64077), superoxide dismutase, a receptor antagonist to platelet-activating factor (PAF) and with blocking monoclonal antibodies directed against a variety of adhesion molecules, including CD11b/CD18 and P-selectin. These results suggest that leukotrienes, reactive oxygen species, PAF or PAF-like lipids, and well-characterized adhesion molecules may be involved in oxLDL-induced interactions. OxLDL-induced leukocyte adhesion was significantly inhibited by supplementing the diet with fish oil, which affects the generation of biologically active leukotrienes, superoxide radicals and PAF, and which significantly attenuates the upregulation of CD11b/CD18 adhesion molecules on activated leukocytes. These results establish oxLDL as a mediator of the interaction between leukocytes and the endothelium *in vivo*. The implication of oxLDL in atherogenesis is still based on indirect evidence. However, data presented here suggest that inhibition of oxLDL-induced leukocyte adhesion may help to explain the observation made in large epidemiological surveys and clinical trials, that dietary fish oil can help to prevent cardiovascular diseases.

References

1. Anitschkow N.: Experimental arteriosclerosis in animals. In: Cowdry E.V., (Ed.): *Arteriosclerosis: A Survey of the Problem.* New York; MacMillan, 1933: 271
2. Ross R.: Atherosclerosis: a defense mechanism gone awry. Am. J. Pathol. 1993; 143: 987-1002
3. Lehr H.A., Hübner C., Menger M.D., Messmer K.: Mechanisms and mediators of leukocyte/endothelium interaction during atherogenesis. Atheroscler. Rev. 1993; 25: 49-56
4. Rosenfeld M.E., Tsukada T., Gown A.M., Ross R.: Fatty streak initiation in Watanabe heritable hyperlipemic and comparably hypercholesterolemic fat-fed rabbits. Arteriosclerosis 1987; 7: 9-23
5. Davies M.J., Woolf N., Rowles P.M., Pepper J.: Morphology of the endothelium over atherosclerotic plaques in human coronary arteries. Br. Heart J. 1988; 60: 459-464
6. Jørgensen L., Packham M.A., Rowsell H.C., Mustard J.F.: Deposition of formed elements of blood on the intima and signs of intimal injury in the aorta of rabbit, pig, and man. Lab. Invest. 1972; 27: 341-350
7. Gerrity R.G.: The role of the monocyte in atherogenesis: I. Transition of blood-borne monocytes into foam cells in fatty lesions. Am. J. Pathol. 1981; 103: 181-190
8. Alderson L.M., Endemann G., Lindsey S., Pronczuk A., Hoover R.L., Hayes K.C.: LDL enhances monocyte adhesion to endothelial cells *in vitro*. Am. J. Pathol. 1986; 123: 334-342
9. Pritchard Jr. K.A., Schwartz S.M., Medow M.S., Stemerman M.B.: Effect of low-density lipoprotein on endothelial cell membrane fluidity and mononuclear cell attachment. Am. J. Phyisol. 1991; 260: C43-49
10. Frostegard J., Nilsson J., Haegerstrand A., Hamsten A., Wigzell H., Gidlund M.: Oxidized low density lipoprotein induces differentiation and adhesion of human monocytes and the monocytic cell line U937. Proc. Natl. Acad. Sci. USA 1990; 87: 904-908
11. Quinn M.T., Parthasarathy S., Steinberg D.: Lysophosphatidylcholine: A chemotactic factor for human monocytes and its potential role in atherogenesis. Proc. Natl. Acad. Sci. USA 1988; 85: 2805-2809
12. Liao F., Berliner J.A., Mehrabian M., Navab M., Demer L.L., Lusis A.J., Fogelman A.M.: Minimally modified low density lipoprotein is biologically active *in vivo* in mice. J. Clin. Invest. 1991; 87: 2253-2257
13. Berliner J.A., Territo M.C., Sevanian A., Ramin S., Kim J.A., Bamshad B., Esterson M., Fogelman A.M.: Minimally modified low density lipoprotein stimulates monocyte endothelial interactions. J. Clin. Invest. 1990; 85: 1260-1266
14. Lehr H.A., Hübner C., Finckh B., Angermüller S., Nolte D., Beisiegel U., Kohlschütter A., Messmer K.: Role of leukotrienes in leukocyte adhesion following systemic administration of oxidatively modified human low density lipoprotein in hamsters. J. Clin. Invest. 1991; 88: 9-14
15. Lehr H.A., Frei B., Carew T.E., Olofsson A.M., Arfors K.E.: Protection from oxidized LDL-induced leukocyte adhesion to micro- and macrovascular endothelium *in vivo* by vitamin C, but not by vitamin E. Circulation 1995; 91: 1525-1532
16. Lehr H.A., Becker M., Marklund S.L., Hubner C., Arfors K.E., Kohlschütter A., Messmer K.: Superoxide-dependent stimulation of leukocyte adhesion by oxidatively modified LDL *in vivo*. Arterioscler. Thromb. 1992; 12: 824-829
17. Lehr H.A., Hübner C., Finckh B., Nolte D., Beisiegel U., Kohlschütter A., Messmer K.: Dietary fish oil reduces leukocyte/endothelium interaction following systemic administration of oxidatively modified human low density lipoprotein. Circulation 1991; 84: 1725-1731

18. Lehr H.A., Seemüller J., Hübner C., Menger M.D., Messmer K.: Oxidized LDL-induced leukocyte/endothelium interaction *in vivo* involves the receptor for platelet-activating factor. Arterioscler. Thromb. 1993; 13: 1013-1018
19. Lehr H.A., Kröber M., Hübner C., Vajkoczy P., Menger M.D., Nolte D., Kohlschütter A., Messmer K.: Stimulation of leukocyte/endothelium interaction by oxidized low-density lipoprotein in hairless mice. Lab. Invest. 1993; 68: 388-395
20. Lehr H.A., Olofsson A.M., Carew T.E., Vajkoczy P., von Andrian U.H., Hübner C., Berndt M.C., Steinberg D., Messmer K., Arfors K.E.: P-selectin mediates the interaction of circulating leukocytes with platelets and microvascular endothelium in response to oxidized lipoprotein *in vivo*. Lab. Invest. 1994; 71: 380-386
21. Lee T.H., Hoover R.L., Williams J.D., Sperling R.I., Ravalese III J., Spur B.W., Robinson D.R., Corey E.J., Lewis R.A., Austen K.F.: Effect of dietary enrichment with eicosapentaenoic and docosahexaenoic acids on *in vitro* neutrophil and monocyte leukotriene generation and neutrophil function. N. Engl. J. Med. 1985; 312: 1217-1224
22. Strasser T., Fischer S., Weber P.C.: Leukotriene B_5 is formed in human neutrophils after dietary supplementation with eicosapentaenoic acid. Proc. Natl. Acad. Sci. USA 1985; 82: 1540-1543
23. Endres S., Ghorbani R., Kelley V.E., Georgilis K., Lonnemann G., van der Meer J.W.M., Cannon J.G., Rogers T.S., Klempner M.S., Weber, P.C., Schaefer E.J., Wolff S.M., Dinarello C.A.: The effect of dietary supplementation with n-3 polyunsaturated fatty acids on the synthesis of interleukin-1 and tumour necrosis factor by mononuclear cells. N. Engl. J. Med. 1989; 320: 265-271
24. Payan D.G., Wong M.Y.S., Chernov-Rogan T., Valone F.H., Pickett W.C., Blake V.A., Gold W.M., Goetzl E.J.: Alterations in human leukocyte function induced by ingestion of eicosapentaenoic acid. J. Clin. Immunol. 1986; 6: 402-410
25. Chilton F.H., O'Flaherty J.T., Walsh C.E., Thomas M.J., Wyke R.L., DeChatelet L.R., Waite B.M.: Platelet-activating factor: stimulation of the lipoxygenase pathway in polymorphonuclear leukocytes by 1-O-alkyl-2-O-acetyl-sn-glycero-3-phosphocholine. J. Biol. Chem. 1982; 257: 5402-5407
26. McIntyre T.M., Zimmerman G.A., Prescott S.M.: Leukotrienes C_4 and D_4 stimulate human endothelial cells to synthesize platelet-activating factor and bind neutrophils. Proc. Natl. Acad. Sci. USA 1986; 83: 2204-2208
27. Lewis M.S., Whatley R.E., Cain P., McIntyre T.M., Prescott S.M., Zimmerman G.A.: Hydrogen peroxide stimulates the synthesis of platelet-activating factor by endothelium and induces endothelial cell-dependent neutrophil adhesion. J. Clin. Invest. 1988; 82: 2045-2055
28. Stewart A.G., Dubbin P.N., Harris T., Dusting G.J.: Platelet-activating factor may act as a second messenger in the release of eicosanoids and superoxide anions from leukocytes and endothelial cells. Proc. Natl. Acad. Sci. USA 1990; 87: 3215-3219
29. Smiley P.L., Stremler K.E., Prescott S.M., Zimmerman G.A., McIntyre T.M.: Oxidatively fragmented phosphatidylcholines activate human neutrophils through the receptor for platelet-activating factor. J. Biol. Chem. 1991; 266: 11104-11110
30. Dyerberg J., Bang H.O., Stoffersen E., E., Moncada S., Vane J.R.: Eicosapentaenoic acid and prevention of thrombosis and atherosclerosis. Lancet 1978; i: 117-119
31. Georgilis K., Klempner M.S.: *In vitro* effects of n-3 fatty acids on neutrophil intracellular calcium homeostasis and receptor expression for fMLP and LTB_4. Inflammation 1988; 12: 475-490
32. Fisher M., Upchurch K.S., Levine P.H., Johnson M.H., Vaudreuil C.H., Natale A., Hoogasian J.J.: Effects of dietary fish oil supplementation on polymorphonuclear leukocyte inflammatory potential. Inflammation 1986: 10: 387-392
33. Sperling R.I.: Effects of dietary fish oil on leukocyte leukotriene and PAF generation and on neutrophil chemotaxis. World Rev. Nutr. Diet 1991; 66: 391-400

34. Boxer L.A., Allen J.M., Schmidt M., Yoder M., Baehner R.L.: Inhibition of polymorphonuclear leukocyte adherence by prostacyclin. J. Lab. Clin. Med. 1980; 95: 672-678
35. Fischer S., Weber P.C.: Prostaglandin I_3 is formed *in vivo* in man after dietary eicosapentaenoic acid. Nature, 1984; 307: 165-168
36. De Caterina R., Giannessi D., Mazzone A., Bernini W., Lazzerini G., Maffei S., Cerri M., Salvatore L., Weksler B.: Vascular prostacyclin is increased in patients ingesting n-3 polyunsaturated fatty acids before coronary artery bypass graft surgery. Circulation 1990; 82: 428-438
37. Kubes P., Suzuki M., Granger D.N.: Nitric oxide: an endogenous modulator of leukocyte adhesion. Proc. Natl. Acad. Sci. USA 1991; 88: 4651-4655
38. Shimokawa H., Vanhoutte P.M.: Dietary cod liver oil improves endothelium-dependent responses in hypercholesterolemic and atherosclerotic porcine coronary arteries. Circulation 1988; 78: 1421-1430
39. Lawson D.L., Mehta J.L., Saldeen K., Mehta P., Saldeen T.G.: Omega-3 polyunsaturated fatty acids augment endothelium-dependent vasorelaxation by enhanced release of EDRF and vasodilator prostaglandins. Eicosanoids 1991; 4: 217-223
40. Liao L., Granger D.N.: Modulation of oxidized low density lipoprotein-induced microvascular dysfunction by nitric oxide. Am. J. Physiol. 1995; 268: H1643-H1650
41. Zimmerman G.A., Prescott S.M., McIntyre T.M.: Endothelial cell interactions with granulocytes: tethering and signalling molecules. Immunol. Today 1992; 13: 93-100
42. Smith C.W.: Endothelial adhesion molecules and their role in inflammation. Can. J. Physiol. Pharmacol. 1993: 71: 76-87
43. Lindström P., Lerner R., Palmblad J., Patarroyo M.: Rapid adhesive responses of endothelial cells and of neutrophils induced by leukotriene B_4 are mediated by leukocytic adhesion protein CD18. Scand. J. Immunol. 1990; 31: 737-744
44. Lee T.H., Sethi T., Crea A.E.G., Peters W., Arm J.P., Horton C.E., Walport M.J., Spur B.W.: Characterization of leukotriene B_3: comparison of its biological activities with leukotriene B_4 and leukotriene B_5 in complement receptor enhancement, lysozyme release and chemotaxis of human neutrophils. Clin. Sci. 1988; 74: 467-475
45. Pober J.S., Bevilacqua M.P., Mendrick D.L., Lapierre L.A., Fiers W., Gimbrone M.A.: Two distinct monokines, interleukin 1 and tumor necrosis factor, each independently induce biosynthesis and transient expression of the same antigen on the surface of cultured human vascular endothelial cells. J. Immunol. 1986; 136: 1680-1687
46. Pohlman T.H., Stanness K.A., Beatty P.G., Ochs H.D., Harlan J.M.: An endothelial cell surface factor(s) induced *in vitro* by lipopolysaccharide, interleukin 1, and tumor necrosis factor α increases neutrophil adherence by a CDw18-dependent mechanism. J. Immunol. 1986; 136: 4548-4553
47. Kim D.N., Schmee J., Thomas W.A.: Dietary fish oil added to a hyperlipidemic diet for swine results in reduction in the excessive number of monocytes attached to arterial endothelium. Atherosclerosis 1990; 81: 209-216
48. Davis H.R., Bridenstine R.T., Vesselinovitch D., Wissler R.W.: Fish oil inhibits development of atherosclerosis in rhesus monkeys. Atherosclerosis 1987; 7: 441-449
49. Weiner B.H., Ockene I.S., Levine P.H., Cuenoud H.F., Fisher M., Johnson B.F., Daoud A.S., Jarmolych J., Hosmer D., Johnson M.H., Natale A., Vaudreuil C., Hoogasian J.J.: Inhibition of atherosclerosis by cod-liver oil in a hyperlipidemic swine model. N. Engl. J. Med. 1986; 315: 841-846
50. von Schacky C.: Prophylaxis of atherosclerosis with marine n-3 fatty acids: a comprehensive strategy. Ann. Int. Med., 1987; 107: 890-899
51. Lehr H.A., Becker M., Seemüller J., Kress E., Nolte D., Hübner C., Menger M.D., Mebmer K.: Microvascular events during the development of atherogenesis: mediator crosstalk in oxidized LDL-induced leukocyte/endothelium interaction. Prog. Appl. Microcirc. 1995; 21: 79-89

S.D. Kristensen, E.B. Schmidt, R. De Caterina, S. Endres
n-3 Fatty Acids: Prevention and Treatment in Vascular Disease
Bi & Gi Publishers, Verona - Springer Verlag, London, 1995

5. Fish Oil: A Modulator of Experimental Atherosclerosis in Animals

L.K. Soei[1], J.M.J. Lamers[2], L.M.A. Sassen[1], A. van Tol[2], L.M. Scheek[2], D.H.W. Dekkers[2], J.R. van Meegen[1], P.D. Verdouw[1]

1. *Experimental Cardiology, Thoraxcenter, Erasmus University, Rotterdam, The Netherlands*
2. *Department of Biochemistry, Erasmus University, Rotterdam, The Netherlands*

Introduction

In the early 1970s, Bang and Dyerberg reported that the prevalence of and mortality from cardiovascular disease were lower in an Inuit population (Eskimos living on the west coast of Greenland) than in an equivalent population of Danes.[1] They also found that these Greenland Eskimos had a favourable plasma lipid profile, with low levels of triglycerides, plasma cholesterol and very low-density lipoproteins (VLDL) and high levels of high-density lipoproteins (HDL). From this epidemiological study, it was concluded that the diet of the Inuit population, which contains large amounts of fish and seals, could contribute to these findings. Fish and seals are rich in long-chain polyunsaturated n-3 fatty acids, which are presumed to be a major factor responsible for the supposedly beneficial effect of fish oil. However, one should not forget that other cardiovascular risk factors, such as hypertension and diabetes, are also uncommon among Inuit people.

The report by Dyerberg *et al.*[1] spurred many investigators to perform epidemiological studies in other countries, and several of these have confirmed that a regular intake of fish oil is associated with a lower prevalence of cardiovascular events in man.[2-4] From the design of these epidemiological studies, however, it was not possible to conclude that less severe atherosclerosis was responsible for the decreased incidence of cardiovascular events.

The mechanisms by which n-3 fatty acids may exert their potentially beneficial effects are not yet fully elucidated. Epidemiological studies have established that ingestion of n-3 fatty acids is negatively correlated with levels of blood cholesterol, arterial blood pressure and platelet aggregation and thrombosis, but the possible mechanisms underlying these relationships could not be determined from these studies. Many investigators have therefore used animal models to elucidate the mechanisms by which n-3 fatty acids may prevent or even cause regression of atherosclerosis. In these models, atherosclerosis is usually induced by highly controlled diets rich in cholesterol, and by endothelial injury. In this chapter we will review the rationale for studying the effects of fish oil on the progression and regression of experimentally induced atherosclerosis, and will compare the results of our studies on pigs with those of other investigators.

Biochemical Processes Modulated by n-3 Fatty Acids

Oils obtained from marine life have high concentrations of long-chain polyunsaturated n-3 fatty acids. This is not surprising, as n-3 fatty acids, such as eicosapentaenoic acid (EPA; 20:5 n-3), docosapentaenoic acid (DPA; 22:5 n-3) and docosahexaenoic acid (DHA; 22:6 n-3), are synthesized mainly by algae and phytoplankton. These microorganisms are eaten by larger marine animals; thus, n-3 fatty acids enter the food chain and eventually reach humans. This pathway is responsible for the bulk of the n-3 fatty acids in humans. Synthesis can also occur by conversion of α-linolenic acid (18:2 n-3), but under normal conditions, when the 20- and 22-chain length n-3 polyunsaturated fatty acids are present in sufficient amounts in the diet, the contribution of 20- and 22-chain n-3 polyunsaturated fatty acids derived from α-linolenic acid is negligible.

In mammals, an increased intake of n-3 fatty acids leads to a change in the function of various cell types and in the plasma concentrations of some blood constituents (Table I).[5,6] Some effects of n-3 fatty acids can be attributed to alteration of eicosanoid production in cells by interference of n-3 fatty acids with the metabolism of arachidonic acid (20:4 n-6). Arachidonic acid is produced from dietary linoleic acid (18:2 n-6) by elongation and desaturation. Competition by n-3 fatty acids for the active sites of the elongation and desaturation enzymes can explain the reduction of arachidonic acid formation in the presence of excessive amounts of n-3 fatty acids. Furthermore, EPA and, to a lesser extent, DHA not only compete with arachidonic acid for the (re)acylation of membrane (lyso)-phospholipids, but also for the formation of eicosanoids by cyclooxygenase and lipoxygenase. This interference with the formation of eicosanoids occurs by two mechanisms. First, the rate of conversion by cyclooxygenase and lipoxygenase is lower when these enzymes use n-3 fatty acids as substrate. Secondly, eicosanoids derived from n-3 fatty acids are different from those derived from n-6 fatty acids. Moreover, the eicosanoids derived from n-3 fatty acids are biologically less active than those derived from n-6 fatty acids. For instance, in platelets, the weak agonist

Table I. Biochemical effects of n-3 fatty acids on cell functions and blood constituents involved in atherosclerosis.

	Intimal hyperplasia and lipid infiltration	**Platelet aggregation**	**Vascular smooth muscle tone**	**Inflammation**
Platelets	Factor 4 ↓; ß-thromboglobulin ↓; PAF ↓; platelet survival ↑	TXA_2 ↓; TXA_3 ↑; platelet count ↓; bleeding time ↓↑	TXA_2 ↓; TXA_3 ↑	
Endothelial cell	PDGF ↓	PGI_3 ↑; PGI_2 preserved; EDRF effect ↑	PGI_3 ↑; EDRF effect ↑	
Lipoproteins	VLDL ↓; triglycerides ↓; LDL ↓↑=; HDL ↓↑=; change in lipoprotein size; apoprotein content; physical properties; lipoprotein metabolism; lipid peroxidation			
Monocyte	IL-1; TNF ↓	PAF ↓		LTB_4 ↓; LTB_5 ↑
Neutrophil	LTB_4 ↓; LTB_5 ↑; free radical synthesis ↓; chemotaxis ↓			LTB_4 ↓; LTB_5 ↑; adhesion and chemotaxis ↓
Vascular smooth muscle cell			Blood pressure ↓↑; response to noradrenaline ↓	
Coagulation factors		Fibrinogen = ↓↑; PAI-1 ↓↑; Factor VII = ↑ Antithrombin = ↓; tPA ↑=; von Willebrand factor =		

Abbreviations: PAF=platelet activating factor, TX=thromboxane, PDGF=platelet-derived growth factor, PG=prostaglandin, EDRF=endothelium-derived relaxing factor, VLDL=very low density lipoprotein, LDL=low-density lipoprotein, HDL=high-density lipoprotein, IL=interleukin, TNF=tumour necrosis factor, LT=leukotriene, PAI=plasminogen activator inhibitor, tPA=tissue plasminogen activator. Effect of fish oil: =, unchanged; ↓, decrease; ↑, increase. For references regarding the actions of n-3 fatty acids, see Sassen *et al.*[6] Reproduced with permission from Sassen *et al.*[6]

thromboxane (TX)A_3 is formed by cyclooxygenase from EPA at the expense of the strong agonist TXA_2, which is derived from arachidonic acid. Thus the lower ratio of TXA_2 to TXA_3 attenuates vasoconstriction and platelet aggregation, resulting in an increase in bleeding time.

In endothelial cells, n-3 fatty acids slightly reduce the production of prostaglandin (PG)I_2, but increase the production of the equally biologically active PGI_3, leading to a net vasodilatory effect, dependent on the TXA/PGI ratio. It has been shown that, compared with those from control animals, endothelial cells of vascular rings derived from animals fed with a diet enriched in n-3 fatty acids, release more endothelium-derived relaxing factor (EDRF) after a challenge with neurohumoral mediators, such as ADP, serotonin or bradykinin. Interference with the release mechanism of EDRF was excluded, as Ca^{2+} ionophores gave similar vasodilatory effects independent of n-3 fatty acid incorporation into the cell membrane.[7-9] One possible mechanism by which n-3 fatty acids could increase EDRF formation is by interfering with receptor-mediated signal transduction via phospholipase C.[10,11] This enzyme activates the phosphatidylinositol cycle, an important intracellular signalling process that mediates the transduction of extracellular stimuli, be they mechanical or neurohumoral, to the nucleus to affect cell growth and transcription processes. Hence, it is also likely that expression of endothelial adhesion molecules, and endothelial responses to mechanical stress and mitogenic responses of vascular smooth muscle cells, which are also biological functions that use the phosphatidylinositol cycle for intracellular signalling, are affected by n-3 fatty acids.

Other effects of n-3 fatty acids on platelets and endothelial cells are the inhibition of the production and release of growth factors, such as platelet-derived growth factor and fibroblast growth factor.[12] Consequently, n-3 fatty acids may, especially in the early phase of atherosclerosis, inhibit or retard the proliferation of smooth muscle cells and fibroblasts.

In monocytes, n-3 fatty acids reduce the production of cytokines (interleukin-1) and tissue factors, such as tumour necrosis factor and platelet aggregating factor, and thus alter the interaction between platelets and the vascular wall. In leukocytes, leukotriene production is affected via substrate competition between EPA and arachidonic acid for lipoxygenase, which results in reduced production of leukotriene (LT)B_4 and an increased level of LTB_5. Compared with LTB_4, LTB_5 is a relatively weak agonist; thus, dietary EPA can decrease chemotaxis and adhesion of monocytes and polymorphonuclear cells, modifying not only the inflammatory reponse, but also the interaction between these cells and the vascular wall. EPA may also retard intimal hyperplasia by these actions.

The effects of n-3 fatty acids on blood lipid and lipoprotein levels are predominantly characterized by a reduction in triglyceride levels. The dose of n-3 fatty acids critically determines the extent of triglyceride reduction. Furthermore, the pattern of effects on the plasma levels of triglycerides, very-low density lipoprotein (VLDL), low-density lipoprotein (LDL) and high-density lipoprotein (HDL) is also dose dependent. Moderate doses of n-3 fatty acids (1-3 g/day) produce a decrease in plasma triglycerides and VLDL in both normolipidaemic and hyperlipidaemic individuals.[13] With higher doses of n-3 fatty acids, the decrease in triglyceride levels becomes more pronounced, although it should be stressed that the effect is also more pronounced when the pretreatment levels of triglycerides are greater.

Postprandial hypertriglyceridaemia is attenuated by n-3 fatty acids, and this reduction in blood lipids may therefore also add to the beneficial effects of fish oil. The changes in plasma lipoprotein levels, however, are not as predictable as those of triglycerides. While most investigators have reported a decrease in VLDL levels, changes in levels of LDL have been inconsistent (Table I).

The effect of n-3 fatty acids on plasma HDL-cholesterol is highly dependent upon the dose used. Very high doses (>10 g/day) have been reported to cause a decrease, while doses of 5-10 g/day have been found to increase HDL levels.[13] The changes in plasma lipoprotein concentrations, however, may not necessarily reflect the potential anti-atherogenic effects of n-3 fatty acids on lipoproteins. The physical properties and composition of the lipoprotein particle may also be altered by n-3 fatty acids. Changes in apoprotein content, together with n-3 fatty acid-induced modification of cellular receptor function or lipoprotein-metabolizing enzymes and lipid transfer proteins may alter lipoprotein metabolism in a manner favourable to the prevention of atherosclerosis.[5,6]

There are several reports, however, that n-3 fatty acids may exert not only beneficial actions, but also some detrimental effects in the process of atherosclerosis. We have shown that incorporation of dietary n-3 fatty acids increased the susceptibility of heart membranes to free radicals after short periods of ischaemia.[14] Other investigators have observed that replacement of dietary polyunsaturated fatty acids with monounsaturated fatty acids reduced the susceptibility of LDL to oxidation, following *in vitro* incubation with copper sulphate.[15,16] It has also been shown that after oxidative modification, LDL particles are preferentially taken up by tissue macrophages *in vitro*.[17,18] It is therefore believed that the increased susceptibility of LDL to oxidative modification is implicated in the development and progression of atherosclerosis, as accumulation of the oxidative modified LDL particles in macrophages and smooth muscle cells may result in the formation of foam cells. Whitman *et al.*[19] recently showed, however, that the *in vitro* results of LDL oxidation may not reflect the situation *in vivo*. Incorporation of dietary n-3 fatty acids into LDL particles was found to increase their vulnerability to oxidative modification *in vitro*, but there was no increase in the percentage surface areas covered by atherosclerotic lesions in the various vessels studied. It is quite feasible that *in vivo*, circulating antioxidants and pro- and antioxidants present in the diet modify the effect of local antioxidant status in the vessel wall and surroundings, and thereby affect the progress of atherosclerotic processes. Hypertension and diabetes are other risk factors for the development of atherosclerotic lesions. Most of the evidence that fatty acids may play a role in blood pressure regulation comes from studies in humans. Such studies are complicated, however, by difficulties in assessing accurately the dietary fat intake, seasonal variations in both fat intake and blood pressure and such confounding factors as alcohol consumption, physical activity, age, gender and total food intake.

Beilin[20] has reviewed the evidence of the potential of fatty acids to lower blood pressure, and concluded that n-3 fatty acids have a mild antihypertensive effect, which can be most clearly demonstrated in patients with untreated hypertension and in the elderly. The effect of n-3 fatty acids may be mediated by their actions on platelet- and endothelium-derived mediators in the resistance vessels.

Data on the effects of n-3 fatty acids in patients with non-insulin-dependent diabetes mellitus are equivocal, and further research is needed to establish whether n-3 fatty acids have a beneficial effect on glucose homeostasis. A potential mechanism could be modulation of the function of the pancreatic islets by eicosanoids, altered membrane fluidity and a change in the balance between lipid and glucose oxidation.[21]

Relationship Between n-3 Fatty Acids and Atherosclerosis

The aforementioned biochemical effects of moderate to high doses of n-3 fatty acids are the basis for their biological effects, such as interference with inflammatory and coagulation processes, blood-vascular wall interactions, cell growth factors, cell signalling, free radical scavenging, lipoprotein metabolism and lipid infiltration of the vessel wall, which are all potentially beneficial. Although it is generally accepted that fish oil can interact with the processes involved in atherosclerosis, its contribution to the development, progression and regression of atherosclerotic lesions is still a point of discussion.

Most of the evidence has been collected from animal studies, but comparing the results from different studies is complicated because of the use of various animal models (e.g. different species, and different interventions to accelerate atherogenic processes) and diets (e.g. supplementation or replacement of n-6 fatty acids with n-3 fatty acids, duration of n-3 fatty acid feeding, cholesterol content, addition of bile acids). Also, different parameters may be studied to evaluate atherosclerosis, and genetic variability may be present in the population studied (e.g. hyper- and hyporesponders within a species with respect to cholesterol feeding).[6] Thus, to appreciate the effects of n-3 fatty acids on atherosclerosis it is not only necessary to investigate each possible mechanism and interaction, but the studies should be performed in relevant models. In order to ensure a valid and clinically useful outcome, a consensus should be reached on which animal model best resembles the human situation. As in man, atherosclerosis in such a model should not only develop spontaneously with early lesions or fatty streaks in the juvenile, progressing to advanced lesions when older, with complications such as fibrosis, calcification, ulceration and thrombosis, but should also involve the intima of the vessel wall.

Primates develop diet-induced lesions that closely resemble human atherosclerotic lesions, both anatomically and morphologically. However, animal rights activists and strict legislation make it difficult to use monkeys in experiments. Dogs and, more commonly, rabbits have been used extensively in atherosclerosis studies. Their biggest disadvantage is that neither of them develop atherosclerosis spontaneously. In rabbits, high-cholesterol feeding is necessary to induce atherosclerosis, but this also leads to excessive cholesterol (ester) accumulation in tissues. In contrast to man, where lesions are located in the abdominal aorta and epicardial coronary arteries, the main anatomical sites of lesions in rabbits are the aortic arch and the arterioles in the myocardium.[22] The content of the lesions also differ, in that they consist mainly of fat, and complicated lesions are rarely encountered. Atherosclerotic lesions are not easily obtained in dogs. In addition to feeding a high-cholesterol diet, damage to the endothelial surface or even the thyroid gland is required to obtain atherosclerosis and despite a similar arterial distribution of lesions, the injury primarily involves the media. In pigs, spontaneous development of atherosclerosis occurs and, besides being similar to that in man, it also starts at an early age (6 months).[23]

However, as atherosclerosis in the pig is also a very slow process, it takes several years before mature atherosclerotic lesions can be observed. So in most studies, induction of atherosclerosis is accelerated using diets with a high fat and/or cholesterol content and added bile acids, which in combination with endothelial injury can produce severe lesions. Also, the high costs of strictly controlled diets and housing of large animals under experimental conditions have been the major reasons why most large-animal studies have been of short duration and why the size of the experimental groups has been relatively small. That the latter may easily lead to erroneous (both positive and negative) conclusions has been amply demonstrated by Rich *et al.*[24]

In addition to the above problems of using the most appropriate animal model and experimental design, there appears to be no real consistency in the effect of n-3 fatty acids on atherosclerosis. In a recent review, we scrutinized the outcome of studies investigating the effect of n-3 fatty acids on atherogenesis in hypercholesterolaemic animals.[6] Although 10 out of the 21 studies showed a beneficial outcome and only four showed an unfavourable effect, the authors were critical about these results and argued that perhaps several studies yielding negative results were not submitted for publication, thereby possibly creating a bias towards positive results.

Effects of n-3 Fatty Acids in Studies from Our Laboratory

Our first studies were not aimed primarily at the effects of n-3 fatty acids on the progression and regression of atherosclerosis, but on the modification of plasma and cell membrane lipids and systemic haemodynamics, cardiac function, arrhythmias and ischaemia-reperfusion injury by these fatty acids.[22,25] These parameters were monitored in piglets from the Landrace x Yorkshire breed, which, shortly after weaning, were fed a basal diet to which 9% (w/w) of either lard fat or fish oil was added.

The group given fish oil showed a marked increase in the amount of n-3 fatty acids incorporated into cell membranes of platelets and cardiac cells and reductions in plasma triglycerides and both total and HDL-cholesterol levels. These changes did not lead to changes in systemic haemodynamics, arrhythmias and the cardiac response to ischaemia. However, after short periods of ischaemia, the hyperaemia in the animals given fish oil was increased, probably due to an increased vasodilatory response of the coronary vascular bed, which coincided with a decrease in the TXA_2:PGI_2 ratio. In the same model, the postprandial responses of plasma lipids and glucose were significantly altered compared with the group given lard fat.[26] Consistent with other reports, postprandial plasma triglycerides and free fatty acids were decreased by feeding pigs with fish oil. This is largely due to a decrease in VLDL production rather than an increased lipolysis by lipoprotein lipase and hepatic lipase.[27,28]

In a parallel series of experiments, we used a different supplement to the basal diet. Instead of 9% (w/w) fish oil, a mixture of 4.5% fish oil and 4.5% lard fat was added, which would be a more realistic dose of fish oil in man.[29,30] The duration of the study was increased to 16 weeks, but the responses of plasma triglycerides, total cholesterol and HDL-cholesterol at 8 and 16 weeks were identical to those obtained with the lower dose of n-3 fatty acids. The same was true for the postprandial responses at 16 weeks. These findings suggest that at doses between 4.5% (w/w) and 9% (w/w) there is no dose-dependent effect of fish oil on lipid levels in the normolipidaemic pig model. Although these studies were not designed to investigate atherosclerosis, the results indicate that n-3 fatty acids may exert an effect on the process of atherosclerosis. It is, however, interesting to note that not all changes were in the same direction. The decreased TXA_2:PGI_2 ratio suggests vasodilation and a reduction in thrombogenesis and thereby a reduction in cardiovascular risk factors. It has been proposed that lowering of postprandial lipid levels by n-3 fatty acids reduces the exposure time of the vessels and thereby the risk of atherosclerosis.[31] The same reasoning is also valid for the lower total cholesterol and triglyceride plasma levels. In contrast, HDL-cholesterol and the ratio of HDL to total cholesterol, which are believed to be inversely related to atherosclerosis, were reduced, suggesting an increased risk of atherosclerosis.

In subsequent studies, we investigated the effect of n-3 fatty acids on atherosclerosis variables in both normolipidaemic and hypercholesterolaemic Landrace x Yorkshire pigs. In normolipidaemic animals, development of atherosclerotic lesions was enhanced by implanting a Teflon constrictor with a fixed diameter of 2 mm around the left anterior descending coronary artery (LADCA).[32] Prior to surgery the animals were fed diets to which either 9% or 4.5% (w/w) lard fat and 4.5% (w/w) fish oil were added for a period of 2 months. The diet regimen extended for another 2 months before luminal encroachment was assessed as a measure of atherosclerosis. This study showed a favourable effect, as luminal encroachment at the site of the constrictor was reduced from 62±7% in the group fed lard fat to 11±4% in the group fed fish oil.[32] Furthermore an improvement was observed in the endocardial/epicardial blood flow ratio in the LADCA-perfused myocardial region of the group fed fish oil, and hence regional myocardial contractile function was found to be better preserved than in the group fed lard fat. This may indicate a better vasodilatory reserve of the endocardial layer due to n-3 fatty acids, which agrees with our earlier finding of a decreased TXA_2:PGI_2 ratio after multiple sequences of occlusion and reperfusion. Both phenomena are consistent with the reduced ADP-induced aggregation of platelets found in this study.

Regression of atherosclerosis in animal models has been shown in several species.[22,33-36] In a recent review on regression of atherosclerosis Schwartz *et al.* proposed four possible targets for intervention; plaque initiation, plaque progression, plaque stabilization and reduction in plaque size and removal of plaque constituents. Plaque initiation (formation of new lesions) and plaque stabilization, which involves thromboresistance and thromboregulation of the atherosclerotic plaque, have been shown to be affected by n-3 fatty acids (Table I). However, little is known about the effects of n-3 fatty acids on plaque progression (Table II) and reduction in plaque size. In subsequent studies, we therefore not only focused on the effects of n-3 fatty acids on progression, but also on regression (reduction in atheroclerotic lesions) of atherosclerosis. Similar to the model used by Weiner *et al.*,[37] a high cholesterol diet and abrasion of the endothelial surface were used to accelerate the development of lesions. In a first series of experiments, atherosclerosis was induced with a diet containing 2% cholesterol and 7% lard fat for 4 months, together with endothelial denudation of the LADCA and abdominal aorta in the second week.[38] At the end of the induction period, plasma levels of cholesterol had doubled (2 mmol/l at baseline), while the cholesterol plus cholesterol ester content of the denuded aorta was 45% higher than in the non-denuded aorta. Similarly, there was a nearly tenfold increase in luminal encroachment in the denuded coronary artery (1.3±0.3 % in the non-denuded coronary artery; Fig. 1). After the induction period, a low-cholesterol diet supplemented with 4.5% (w/w) or 9% (w/w) fish oil or lard fat was administered for 3 months to induce regression of atherosclerosis. In both fish-oil groups, plasma cholesterol levels returned to baseline and were significantly reduced compared with the group fed with only lard

Table II. Effects of n-3 fatty acids on experimental atherogenesis in pigs.

Author	Induction of atherosclerosis	Time (months)	Dose of EPA and/or DHA	I/S	Blood vessels	Assessment of atherosclerosis	Effect of fish oil
Hill *et al.*[44]	Hyper-cholesterolaemia + bile acids	24	6% total n-3 (weight % in diet)	I[a]	Aorta	LE[b]	=
						% lesions[b]	=
						Aortic lipids	FC=; EC=
					Coronary artery	LE[b]	=
			3% total n-3 (weight % in diet)	I[c]	Aorta	LE[b]	↓
						% lesions[b]	↓
						Aortic lipids	FC=; EC=
					Coronary artery	LE[b]	↓
Hill *et al.*[45]	Hyper-cholesterolaemia + bile acids	12	3% total n-3 (weight % in diet)	I	Aorta	LE[b]	=
						% lesions[b]	=
						Aortic lipids	FC=; EC=
					Coronary artery	LE[b]	=
Weiner *et al.*[37]	Hyper-cholesterolaemia + bile acids + abrasion	8	30 ml cod liver oil/day/animal	S	Coronary artery	LE	↓
Kim *et al.*[46]	Hyperlipidaemia	4	(330 EPA + 330 DHA)[d] – (100 EPA + 100 DHA)[e] (mg/kg/day)	S	Aorta	LE	↓
					Coronary artery	LE	↓
Hartog *et al.*[32]	Normo-cholesterolaemia + teflon constrictor	4	0.36% EPA + 0.23% DHA (weight % in diet)	I	Coronary artery	LE	↓
Sassen *et al.*[41]	Hyper-cholesterolaemia + bile acids + abrasion	8	(1040 EPA + 743 DHA)[d] – (242 EPA + 175 DHA)[e] (mg/kg/day)	I	Aorta	% lesion	=
						Aortic lipids	=
					Coronary artery	LE	=

Abbreviations: EPA=eicosapentaenoic acid (20:5, n-3), DHA=docosahexaenoic acid (20:6, n-3), I/S=isocaloric or supplementary administration of fish oil, LE=luminal encroachment, FC=free cholesterol, EC=esterified cholesterol, TC=total cholesterol. Effect of fish oil: =, unchanged; ↓, decrease; ↑, increase. % Lesions indicates the percentage of the surface of the vessel that is covered with intimal lesions. [a]=Tallow used as control diet, [b]=semiquantitative histological grading, [c]=coconut oil used as control diet, [d]=dose at the beginning of the dietary period, [e]=dose at the end of the dietary period. Adapted with permission from Sassen *et al.*[6]

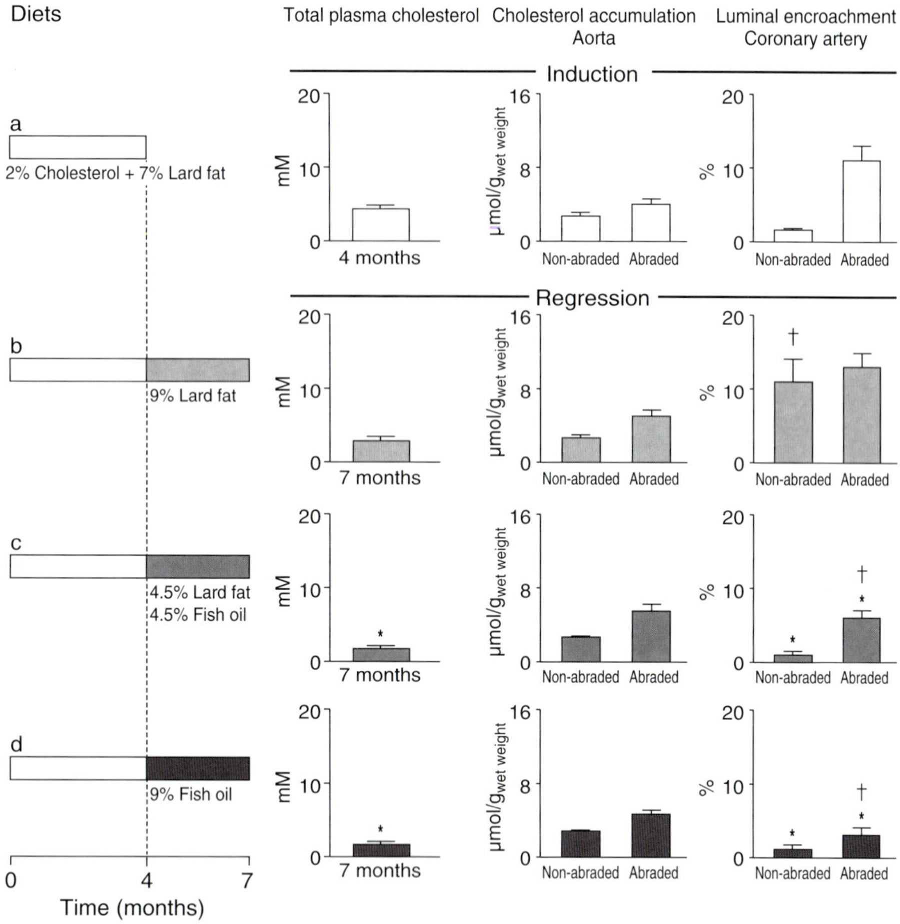

Fig. 1. Effect of n-3 fatty acids (c and d) on total plasma cholesterol, total cholesterol (cholesterol plus cholesterol ester) accumulation in the aorta, and luminal encroachment in the coronary artery in pigs, in which endothelial denudation was performed 2 weeks after the start of the diet. Panels on the left indicate the composition of the diets and the duration of the study. $^*p<0.05$ *vs* the corresponding value for the animals in group a. $^\dagger p<0.05$ *vs* the corresponding value for the animals in group b. Values are means±SEM.

fat. There was no effect on lipid accumulation in either the abraded or non-abraded aorta. In the abraded coronary artery, however, fish oil reduced, in a dose-dependent manner, the luminal encroachment and prevented progression of luminal encroachment in the non-abraded artery, compared with the findings in the group given lard fat. The latter finding corresponds with the observation by Clarkson *et al.*,[39] who found that elevated levels of plasma cholesterol correlated with progression of lesions. Plasma cholesterol levels and luminal encroachment after induction were considerably lower in our study than in those reported in the literature.[37,40] For instance, Weiner *et al.*[37] reported a luminal encroachment of 44% compared with only 11% in our study at the end of the induction period. This suggests less severe atherosclerotic lesions in our study, which consequently could have contributed to the positive results obtained in the regression period. The very high plasma cholesterol levels obtained by Weiner *et al.* (approximately 14 mmol/l compared with 4 mmol/l in our study) may underlie these differences.

We therefore performed a second series of experiments in which the development and regression of atherosclerosis was investigated in animals fed a basal diet for 8 months (instead of 4 months), to which 10% (w/w) lard fat, or 2% (w/w) cholesterol plus 8% lard fat, or 2% cholesterol plus 4% lard fat and 4% (w/w) fish oil were added, to induce atherosclerosis.[41] After 1 month, the LADCA and abdominal aortas were denuded and, in accordance with the study by Weiner *et al.*,[37] bile acids were added to the high-cholesterol groups to enhance the plasma cholesterol levels further. High plasma cholesterol levels, averaging 9 mmol/l, were obtained with this protocol. In the non-abraded aorta, fish oil prevented the accumulation of free cholesterol in the aortic wall, compared with the group fed cholesterol and lard fat, but had no effect on lipid content in the abraded segment of the aorta (Fig. 2). Staining the intimal surface of the aorta with Sudan IV, however, revealed no differences between the lard-fat and fish-oil groups. Luminal encroachment of both the abraded and non-abraded coronary arteries was not affected by fish oil during the induction of atherosclerosis, in contrast to the severe luminal encroachment reported by Weiner *et al.* (Fig. 2).[37]

The higher content of bile acids and saturated fat in the diets used by Weiner *et al.*, and hence the higher plasma cholesterol level, may account for these differences. Moreover, despite the longer duration of the induction period and addition of bile acids to the diet, there seems to be no difference in diet-induced atherosclerosis as assessed by total cholesterol (cholesterol plus cholesterol ester) accumulation in the aorta and luminal encroachment of the coronary artery between our two studies (Figs. 1 and 3).

Regression of atherosclerosis in our model was studied by removing the 2% cholesterol from the diet and substituting the 8% with 10% of lard fat and the 4% of lard fat and fish oil with 5% of each fat. After an induction period with cholesterol and lard fat, the animals were fed one of these diets for a period of 4 months (Fig. 3). In comparison with the group given lard fat, fish oil attenuated the progression of atherosclerosis, leading to less lipid accumulation in the damaged aortic wall and less luminal encroachment in the coronary arteries. However, in contrast to our previous study, there was no reduction in coronary luminal encroachment. These results are in agreement with those reported by Fincham *et al.*[42] (Table III). These investigators observed that, after an induction period of more than 1 year, fish oil was unable to induce regression of atherosclerosis in coronary arteries and the aorta of hypercholesterolaemic non-human primates. In addition to the study of Sassen *et al.*,[38] regression of atherosclerotic lesions has been observed by Zhu *et al.*,[43] who reported

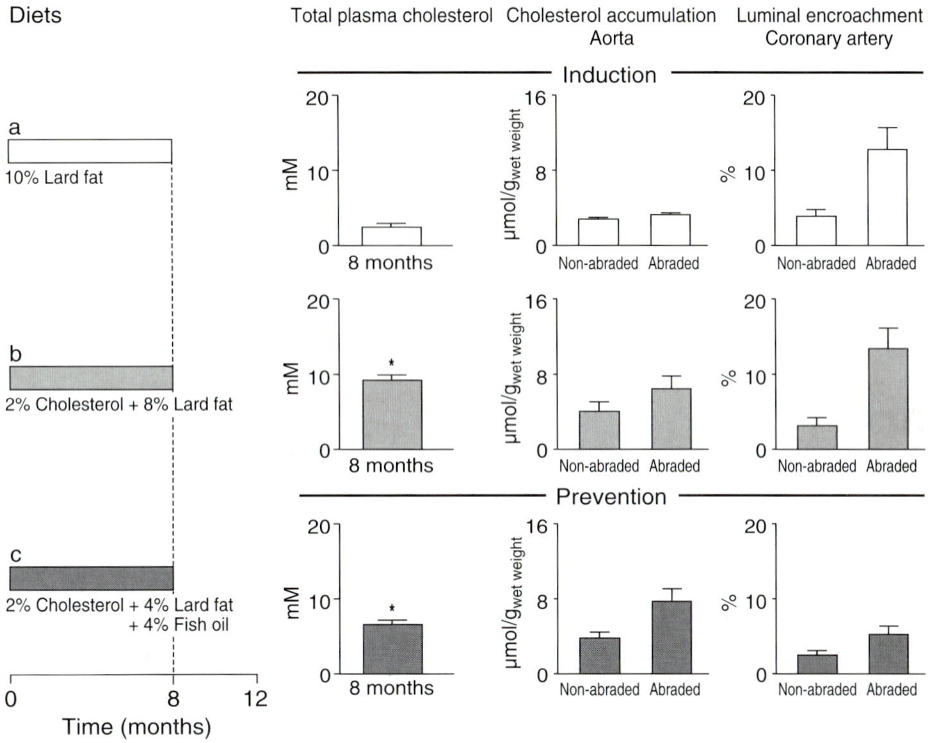

Fig. 2. Effect of n-3 fatty acids (c) on total plasma cholesterol, total cholesterol (cholesterol plus cholesterol ester) accumulation in the aorta, and luminal encroachment in the coronary artery in pigs, in which endothelial denudation was performed, and bile acids (0.5%, w/w) were added to the diet at 1 and 3 months, respectively, after the start of the diet. Panels on the left indicate the composition of the diets and the duration of the study. *$p<0.05$ *vs* the corresponding value for the animals in group a. Values are means±SEM.

a decrease in the percentage of aortic and pulmonary artery surface areas covered with atherosclerotic lesion after an induction period that lasted only 10 weeks.

The number of studies on the effect of fish oil on regression of atherosclerosis is small, but the results presented in Table III suggest that the duration of the induction period may be important, as only the studies with induction periods lasting less than 4 months showed positive results. The longer induction period possibly leads to a difference in structure and composition of the atherosclerotic lesions, which are more resilient to regression by fish oil.

Accelerating the process of atherosclerosis with high-cholesterol diets, bile acids and endothelial denudation render the foregoing studies open to criticism, as the induction process might affect the form and composition of the atherosclerotic lesions formed. The Landrace x Yorkshire pig probably represents a hyporesponder

Table III. Effect of n-3 fatty acids on the regression of atherosclerosis in animal models.

Author	Animal induction of atherosclerosis	Time (months) Ind.	Reg.	Dose of EPA and/or DHA (mg/kg/day)	I/S	Plasma lipids	Blood vessels	Assessment of athero-sclerosis	Effect of fish oil
Sassen *et al.*[38]	Pig (hyper-cholesterolaemia + abrasion)	4	3	188[a]-210[b] EPA 125[a]-140[b] DHA 380[a]-396[b] EPA 209[a]-220[b] DHA	I[a]	TC↓, Tg↓	Aorta Coronary artery	Lipids LE	PL=; TC=; Tg= ↓ (dose dependent)
Zhu *et al.*[43]	Rabbit (hyper-cholesterolaemia)	2.5	10	82[a]-73[b] EPA 55[a]-49[b] DHA	S	TC=, Tg=	Aorta Pulmonary artery	% lesion % lesions	↓ ↓
Fincham *et al.*[42]	Vervet monkey (hyper-cholesterolaemia)	24.5	20	30.1 EPA 9.7 DHA	I	TC=, Tg=	Aorta Cerebral artery Coronary artery	LE % lesions LE LE	= = = =
Sassen *et al.*[41]	Pig (hyper-cholesterolaemia + abrasion + bile acids)	8	4	309[a]-193[b] EPA 220[a]-137[b] DHA	I		Aorta - ascending (non-abraded) - abdominal (abraded) Coronary artery	% lesions Lipids Lipids LE	= PL=; EC↓; FC=; Tg= PL=; EC=; FC=; Tg= =

Abbreviations: Ind.=Induction, Reg.=Regression, EPA=eicosapentaenoic acid (20:5, n-3), DHA=docosahexaenoic acid (20:6, n-3), LE=luminal enchroachment, PL=phospholipids, FC=free cholesterol, EC=esterified cholesterol, TC=total cholesterol, Tg=triglycerides, I/S=isocaloric or supplementary administration of fish oil. % Lesions indicates the percentage of the surface of the vessel that is covered with intimal lesions. [a]=Dose at the beginning of the dietary period, [b]=dose at the end of the dietary period. Adapted with permission from Sassen *et al.*[6]

to cholesterol feeding and needs very long protocols to develop atherosclerosis spontaneously.

In contrast, Göttingen mini-pigs react more readily to a challenge with high cholesterol (Fig. 4). Together with their smaller stature and a lower rate of growth, which facilitates their handling, they are more suitable for studies on atherosclerosis. Because of these advantages, we have used Göttingen mini-pigs in our latest

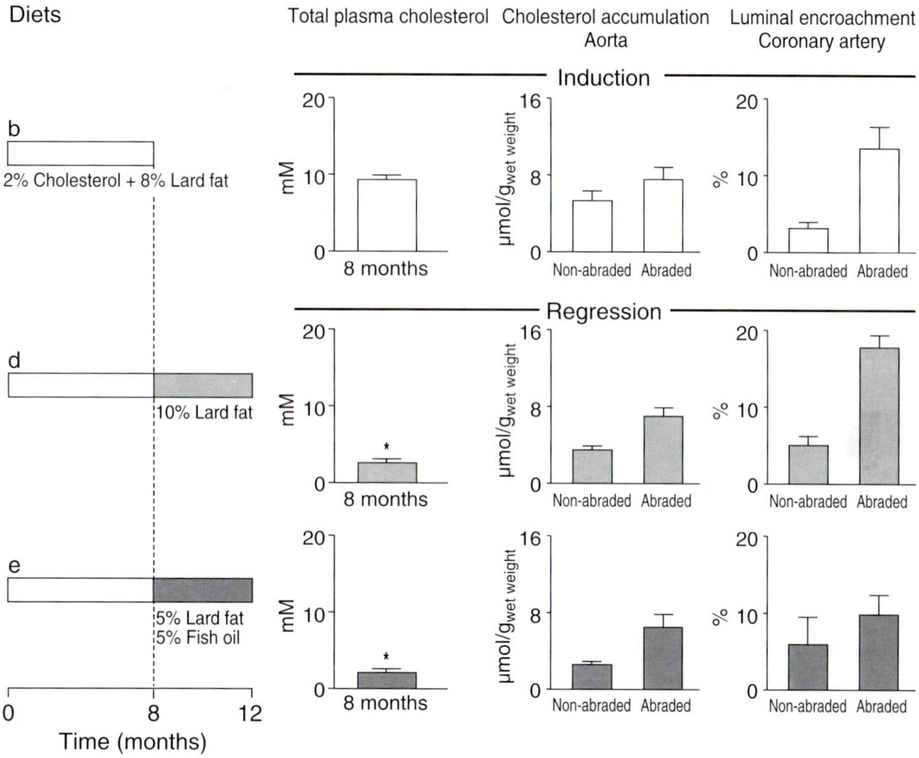

Fig. 3. Effect of n-3 fatty acids (d) on total plasma cholesterol and the regression of atherosclerosis as assessed by total cholesterol accumulation (cholesterol plus cholesterol ester) in the aorta, and luminal encroachment in the coronary artery in pigs, in which endothelial denudation was performed, and bile acids (0.5%, w/w) were added to the diet at, respectively, 1 and 3 months after the start of the diet. The 2% cholesterol was removed from the diet after 8 months of induction. The n-3 fatty acids had no significant effect on total cholesterol accumulation in the aorta and on luminal encroachment in the coronary artery. Panels on the left indicate the composition of the diets and the duration of the study. Values are means±SEM.

atherosclerosis study. In this study, diets containing 2% (w/w) cholesterol plus 9% (w/w) lard fat, 2% (w/w) cholesterol plus 4.5% (w/w) lard fat plus 4.5% (w/w) sunflower oil, or 2% (w/w) cholesterol plus 4.5% (w/w) lard fat plus 4.5% (w/w) fish oil increased total plasma cholesterol levels from about 3 mmol/l to about 14 mmol/l in 2 weeks, again without addition of bile acids. Furthermore, after 8 weeks, white-yellowish elevations on the inner surface of the abdominal aorta (fatty streak-like lesions) were observed. Compared with macroscopically normal tissue, the lesions contained more unesterified and esterified cholesterol. This model was used to study whether the protection afforded by fish oil is a direct effect of n-3 fatty acids or secondary to a fish oil-induced increase in the ratio of polyunsaturated to saturated fatty acid (P/S ratio). The dietary vitamin E regimen was chosen such that

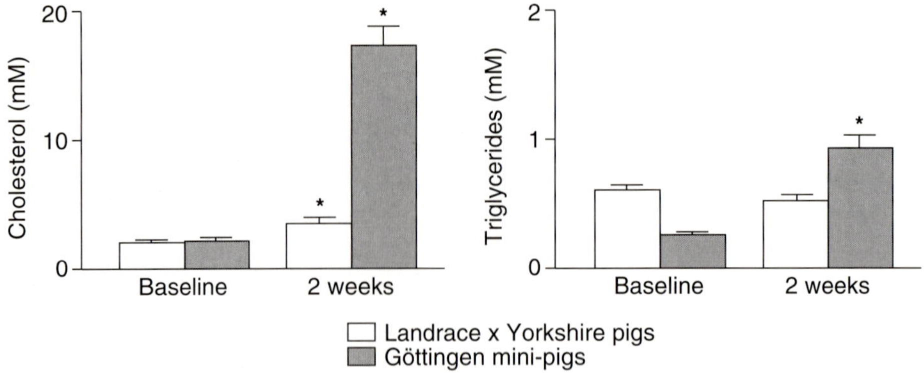

Fig. 4. Effects of 2% cholesterol feeding on plasma levels of cholesterol and triglycerides in Landrace x Yorkshire pigs and Göttingen mini-pigs. In contrast to the Landrace x Yorkshire pigs, the Göttingen mini-pigs responded with a marked increase in total plasma cholesterol. *p<0.05 *vs* baseline. Values are means±SEM.

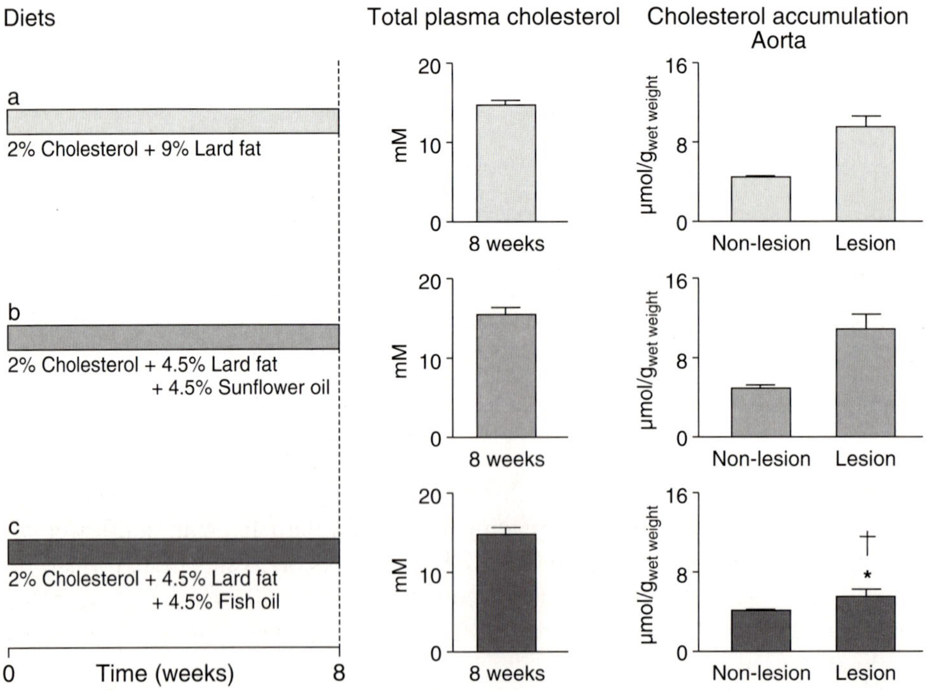

Fig. 5. Comparison of the effect of n-3 fatty acids (c) and n-6 fatty acids (d) on total plasma cholesterol and total cholesterol (cholesterol plus cholesterol ester) accumulation in the aorta in Göttingen mini-pigs, which were fed a high-cholesterol diet for 8 weeks. *p<0.05 *vs* the corresponding value for animals in group a. †p<0.05 *vs* the corresponding value for animals in group b. Values are means±SEM.

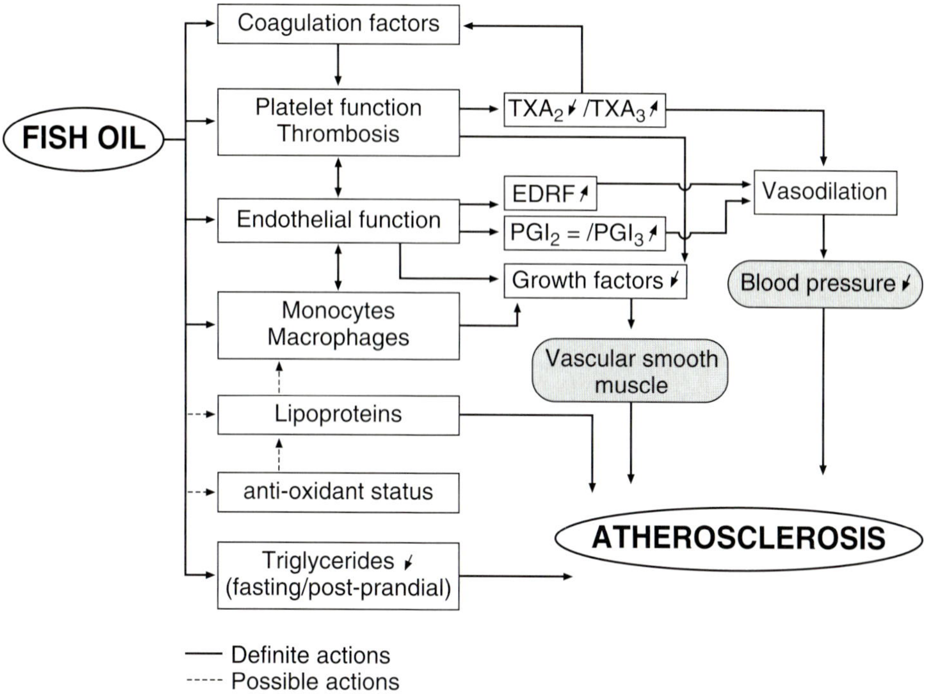

Fig. 6. The established and possible mechanisms of the effects of n-3 fatty acids on atherogenesis. TX=thromboxane, EDRF=endothelium-derived growth factor, PG=prostaglandin.

the levels of vitamin E in the various lipoproteins did not depend on the type of fatty acid or the P/S ratio in the diet. This experimental strategy is different from that used previously by ourselves and others, and was designed to exclude the possibility that the effects of dietary n-3 fatty acids could, at least in part, be ascribed to a changed oxidant status of the animal.

Vegetable oils rich in n-6 fatty acids are also reported to protect against ischaemic heart disease, probably due to a beneficial effect on plasma levels of lipoproteins and cholesterol. Replacing part of the lard fat with sunflower oil increased the P/S ratio from 0.49 to 1.50, but with fish oil as substitute for lard fat to only 0.83. Nevertheless, only the group fed with fish oil showed a favourable response of the fatty lesions in the aorta (total plasma cholesterol was not affected by the diets; Fig. 5).

Compared with both sunflower oil and lard fat, fish oil did not only reduce the number of animals in which lesions were observed, but also reduced the total cholesterol content in these lesions. It is therefore most likely that the prevention of cholesterol accumulation by fish oil is caused by a direct effect of n-3 fatty acids rather than by a higher P/S ratio. The direct effect of n-3 fatty acids on total cholesterol accumulation in the vessel wall may be attributed to the reduction in the VLDL-cholesterol level and cholesteryl ester-rich VLDL by n-3 fatty acids. Another objective was to study the influence of the three diets on the progression of intimal thickening in saphenous veno-arterial grafts. In these grafts, atherosclerosis develops in an accelerated fashion, similar to that in abraded vessels or vessels with a constrictor. It is thus quite feasible that fish oil also protects these vein-grafts against atherosclerosis. Our preliminary results indicated lower occlusion rates in the group given fish oil during the first 6 weeks after placement of the saphenous grafts in the carotid arteries. However, lipid accumulation in the graft was not affected, in contrast to the lipid accumulation in the undamaged abdominal aorta. This finding suggests that an intact endothelial layer and/or function may modify the effect of fish oil on the progression of atherosclerosis (Fig. 6).

Conclusions

From our studies we conclude that the presence of an intact endothelial layer, hypercholesterolaemia and the history of the lesion determine the ultimate effect of dietary n-3 fatty acid supplementation on the development and regression of atherosclerosis.

However, in these studies, other potentially atherogenic influences, such as hypertension, diabetes, ageing and smoking, were not taken into account. Because these parameters affect endothelial and platelet function, it is feasible that they could also modify the effect of n-3 fatty acids. Therefore, while in animal models with experimentally induced atherosclerosis, n-3 fatty acids are effective in preventing the formation of new lesions and in slowing the progression of established lesions, this does not necessarily imply that the same effects will be obtained in man, in which other risk factors may be present.

Acknowledgment

This study was supported by Netherlands Organization for Scientific Research (NWO) grant 900-562-111.

Summary

Populations consuming large amounts of fish (n-3 fatty acids) are reported to have a lower incidence of ischaemic heart disease, which is attributed to a reduction in atherosclerosis by n-3 fatty acids. The effects of n-3 fatty acids on the various biochemical variables are well documented. Yet it remains unclear how these effects of n-3 fatty acids affect the *in vivo* process of development, progression and regression of lesions. Studies in animal models on n-3 fatty acids and atherosclerosis showed, in contrast to the results from epidemiological studies, conflicting results, which may be attributed to the diversity in animal species used and experimental designs. In this paper we review the results from our own studies and relate them to those found in the literature. Our studies were performed in an experimental model in which pigs undergo dietary intervention with high cholesterol and either endothelial denudation or veno-arterial by-pass grafting for induction of atherosclerotic lesions. The effects of n-3 fatty acids on atherosclerosis were studied during the induction period and in a subsequent period after removal of cholesterol from the diet.

We conclude that n-3 fatty acids affect several, but not all parameters routinely used to assess the severity of atherosclerosis in experimental models, hence the reported effects of n-3 fatty acids on atherosclerosis are diverse. The duration of the induction period, and therefore the composition of the lesions, appears to be important in the few studies that reported on regression by intervention with n-3 fatty acids.

References

1. Dyerberg J., Bang H.O., Hjørne N.: Fatty acid composition of the plasma lipids in Greenland Eskimos. Am. J. Clin. Nutr. 1975; 28: 958-966
2. Kromhout D., Bosschieter E.B., Coulander C.L.: The inverse relation between fish consumption and 20-year mortality from coronary heart disease. N. Engl. J. Med. 1985; 312: 1205-1216
3. Simonsen T., Vartun A., Lyngmo V., Nordøy A.: Coronary heart disease, serum lipids, platelets, and dietary fish in two communities in nothern Norway. Acta. Med. Scand. 1987; 222: 237-245
4. Burr M.L., Fehily A.M., Gilbert J.F, Rogers S., Holliday R.M., Sweetnam P.M., Elwood P.C., Deadman N.M.: Effects of changes in fat, fish, and fibre intakes on death and myocardial reinfarction: diet and reinfarction trial (DART). Lancet 1989; ii: 757-761
5. Israel D.H., Gorlin R.: Fish oil in the prevention of atherosclerosis. J. Am. Coll. Cardiol. 1992; 19(1): 174-185
6. Sassen L.M.A., Lamers J.M.J., Verdouw P.D.: Fish oil and the prevention and regression of atherosclerosis. Cardiovasc. Drugs Ther. 1994; 8: 179-191
7. Shimokawa H., Vanhoutte P.M.: Dietary cod-liver oil improves endothelium dependent responses in hypercholesterolemic and atherosclerotic porcine coronary arteries. Circulation 1989; 78: 1421-1430
8. Vanhoutte P.M., Shimokawa H.: Endothelium-derived relaxing factor and coronary vasospasm. Circulation 1989; 80: 1-9
9. Vanhoutte P.M., Shimokawa H., Boulanger C.: Fish oil and platelet-blood vessel wall interaction. World Rev. Nutr. Diet 1991; 66; 233-244
10. Medini L., Colli S., Mosconi C., Tremoli E., Galli C.: Diets rich in n-9, n-6 and n-3 fatty acids differentially affect the generation of inositolphosphates and thromboxane by stimulated platelets, in the rabbit. Biochem. Pharmacol. 1990; 39: 129-133
11. Lamers J.M.J., Dekkers D.H.W., De Jong N., Meij J.T.A.: Modification of fatty acid composition of the phospholipids of cultured rat ventricular myocytes and the rate of phosphatidyl-4,5-bisphosphate hydrolysis. J. Mol. Cell Cardiol. 1992; 24: 605-618
12. Kinsella J.E.: Effects of polyunsaturated fatty acids on factors related to cardiovascular disease. Am. J. Cardiol. 1987; 60: 23G-32G
13. Harris W.S.: Fish oil and plasma lipid and lipoprotein metabolism in humans: a critical review. J. Lipid Res. 1989; 30: 785-807
14. Lamers J.M.J., Hartog J.M., Guarnieri C., Vaona I., Verdouw P.D., Koster J.F.: Lipid peroxidation in normoxic and ischaemic-reperfused hearts of fish oil and lard fat fed pigs. J. Mol. Cell Cardiol. 1988; 20: 605-615
15. Parthasarathy S., Khoo J.C., Miller E., Barnett J., Witztum J.I., Steinberg D.: Low density lipoprotein rich in oleic acid is protected against oxidative modification: implications for dietary prevention of atherosclerosis. Proc. Natl. Acad. Sci. USA. 1990; 87: 3894-3898

16. Reaven P., Parthasarathy S., Grasse B.J., Miller E., Almazan F., Mattson F.H., Khoo J.C., Steinberg D., Witztum J.L.: Feasibility of using an oleate-rich diet to reduce the susceptibility of low-density lipoprotein to oxidative modification in humans. Am. J. Clin. Nutr. 1991; 54: 701-706
17. Fogelman A.M., Shechter I., Seager J., Hokom M., Child JS., Edwards P.A. Malonaldehyde alteration of low density lipoproteins leads to cholesteryl ester accumulation in human monocyte-macrophages. Proc. Natl. Acad. Sci. USA. 1980; 77: 2214-2218
18. Goldstein J.L., HO Y.K., Basu S.K., Brown M.S.: Binding site on macrophages that mediates uptake and degradation of acetylated low density lipoprotein, producing massive cholesterol deposition. Proc. Natl. Acad. Sci. USA. 1979; 76: 333-337
19. Whitman S.C., Fish J.R., Rand M.L., Rogers K.A.: N-3 fatty acid incorporation into LDL particles renders them more susceptible to oxidation in vitro but not necessarily more atherogenic *in vivo.* Arterioscler. Thromb. 1994; 14: 1170-1176
20. Beilin L.J.: Dietary fats, fish, and blood pressure. Ann. N.Y. Acad. Sci. 1993; 683: 35-45
21. Vessby B.: Dietary supplementation with n-3 polyunsaturated fatty acids in Type 2 diabetes. Ann. N.Y. Acad. Sci. 1993; 683: 244-249
22. St. Clair R.W.: Atherosclerosis regression in animal models: Current concepts of cellular and biochemical mechanisms. Prog. Cardiovasc. Dis. 1983; 26: 109-132
23. Luginbühl H.: Spontaneous atherosclerosis in swine. In: Bustad L.K., McClellan R.O. (Eds.): *Swine in Biomedical Research.* Seattle; Frayn Printing Co., 1965: 347-363
24. Rich S., Miller J.F., Charous S., Davis H.R., Shanks P., Glagov S., Lands, W.E.M.: Development of atherosclerosis in genetically hyperlipidemic rabbits during chronic fish-oil ingestion. Arteriosclerosis 1989; 9: 189-194
25. Hartog J.M., Lamers J.M.J, Verdouw P.D.: The effects of dietary mackerel oil on plasma and cell membrane lipids, on hemodynamics and cardiac arrhythmias during recurrent acute ischemia in the pig. Basic Res. Cardiol. 1986; 81: 567-580
26. Hartog J.M., Lamers J.M.J., Montfoort A., Becker A.E., Klompe M., Morse H., Ten Cate F.J., Van der Werf L., Hülsmann W.C., Hugenholtz P.G., Verdouw P.D.: Comparison of mackerel-oil and lard-fat enriched diets on plasma lipids, cardiac membrane phospholipids, cardiovascular performance, and morphology in young pigs. Am. J. Clin. Nutr. 1987; 46: 258-266
27. Haug A., Hostmark A.T.: Lipoprotein lipases, lipoproteins and tissue lipids in rats fed fish oil or coconut oil. J. Nutr. 1987; 117: 1011-1017
28. Groot P.H.E, Scheek L.M., Dubelaar M.L., Verdouw P.D., Hartog J.M., Lamers J.M.J.: Effects of diets supplemented with lard fat or mackerel oil on plasma lipoprotein lipid concentrations and lipoprotein lipase activities in domestic swine. Atherosclerosis 1989; 77: 1-6
29. Hartog J.M., Lamers J.M.J, Achterberg P.W., Van Heuven-Nolsen D., Nijkamp F.P., Verdouw P.D.: The effects of dietary mackerel oil on the recovery of cardiac function after acute ischaemic events in the pig. Basic Res. Cardiol. 1987; 82: 223-234
30. Hartog J.M., Verdouw P.D., Klompe M., Lamers J.M.J.: Dietary mackerel oil in pigs: effect on plasma lipids, cardiac sarcolemmal phospholipids and cardiovascular parameters. J. Nutr. 1987; 117: 1371-1378
31. Illingworth D.R., Schmidt E.B.: The influence of dietary n-3 fatty acids on plasma lipids and lipoproteins. Ann. N. Y. Acad. Sci. 1993; 676: 60-69
32. Hartog J.M., Lamers J.M.J., Essed C.E., Schalkwijk W.P., Verdouw P.D.: Does platelet aggregation play a role in the reduction in localized intimal proliferation in normolipidemic pigs with fixed coronary artery stenosis fed dietary fish oil? Atherosclerosis 1989; 76: 79-88
33. Bevans M., Davidson J.D., Kendall F.E.: Regression of lesions in canine arteriosclerosis. Arch. Pathol. 1951; 51: 288-292

34. Daoud A.S., Jarmolych J., Augustyn J.M., Fritz K.E., Singh J.K., Lee K.T.: Regression of advanced swine atherosclerosis. Arch. Pathol. Lab. Med. 1976; 100: 372-379
35. Daoud A.S., Fritz K.E., Jarmolych J., Augustyn J.M., Lee K.T., Thomas W.A.: Regression of complicated atherosclerotic lesions in the abdominal aortas of swine. In: Manning G.W., Haust M.D. (Eds.): *Atherosclerosis: Metabolic, Morphologic, and Clinical Aspects*. New York; Plenum Press, 1977: 447-452
36. DePalma R.G., Bellon E.M., Klein L.R., Koletsky S., Insull W. Approaches to evaluating regression of experimental atherosclerosis. In: Manning G.W., Haust M.D. (Eds.): *Atherosclerosis: Metabolic, Morphologic, and Clinical Aspects*. New York; Plenum Press, 1977: 459-470
37. Weiner B.H., Ockene I.S., Levine P.H., Cuénoud H.F., Fisher M., Johnson B.F., Daoud A.S., Jarmolych J., Hosmer D., Johnson M.H., Natale A., Vaudreuil C., Hoogasian J.J.: Inhibition of atherosclerosis by cod-liver oil in a hyperlipidemic swine model. N. Engl. J. Med. 1986; 315: 841-846
38. Sassen L.M.A., Hartog J.M., Lamers J.M.J., Klompe M., Van Woerkens L.J., Verdouw P.D.: Mackerel oil and atherosclerosis in pigs. Eur. Heart J. 1989; 10: 838-846
39. Clarkson T.B., Bond M.G., Bullock B.C., McLaughlin K.J., Sawyer J.K.: A study of atherosclerosis in *Maccaca mulatta*. V. Changes in abdominal aorta and carotid and coronary arteries from animals with atherosclerosis induced for 38 months and then regressed for 24 or 48 months at plasma cholesterol concentrations of 300 or 200 mg/dl. Exp. Mol. Pathol. 1984; 41: 96-118
40. Fritz K.E., Augustyn J.M., Jarmolych J., Daoud A.S.: Sequential study of biochemical changes during regression of swine aortic atherosclerotic lesions. Arch. Pathol. Lab. Med. 1981; 105: 240-246
41. Sassen L.M.A., Lamers J.M.J., Sluiter W., Hartog J.M., Dekkers D.H.W., Hogendoorn A., Verdouw P.D.: Development and regression of atherosclerosis in swine: Effects of n-3 fatty acids, their incorporation into plasma and aortic plaque lipids and granulocyte function. Arterioscler. Thromb. 1993; 13: 651-660
42. Fincham J.E., Gouws E., Woodroof C.W., Van Wyk M.J., Kruger M., Smuts C.M., van Jaarsveld P.J., Taljaard J.J.F., Schall R., Strauss J.A., Benadé A.J.S.: Atherosclerosis. Chronic effects of fish oil and a therapeutic diet in nonhuman primates. Arterioscler. Thromb. 1991; 11: 719-732
43. Zhu B.Q., Sievers R.E., Isenberg W.M., Smith D.L., Parmley W.W.: Regression of atherosclerosis in cholesterol-fed rabbits: Effects of fish oil and verapamil. JACC 1990; 15(1): 231-237
44. Hill E.G., Lundberg W.O., Titus J.L.: Experimental atherosclerosis in swine I. A comparison of menhaden-oil supplements in tallow and coconut-oil diets. Mayo Clin. Proc. 1971; 46: 613-620
45. Hill E.G., Lundberg W.O., Titus J.L.: Experimental atherosclerosis in swine II. Effects of methionine and menhaden oil on an atherogenic diet containing tallow and cholesterol. Mayo Clin. Proc. 1971; 46: 621-625
46. Kim D.N., Ho H.T., Lawrence D.A., Schmee J., Thomas W.A.: Modification of lipoprotein patterns and retardation of atherogenesis by a fish oil supplement to a hyperlipidemic diet for swine. Atherosclerosis 1989; 76: 35-54

S.D. Kristensen, E.B. Schmidt, R. De Caterina, S. Endres
n-3 Fatty Acids: Prevention and Treatment in Vascular Disease
Bi & Gi Publishers, Verona - Springer Verlag, London, 1995

6. Atherosclerosis in Arctic Populations: Autopsy Studies

W.P. Newman III[1], J.P. Middaugh[2], H.S. Pedersen[3], G. Mulvad[3], E. Jul[4]

1. *Department of Pathology, Louisiana State University Medical Center, New Orleans, Louisiana, USA*
2. *Department of Health and Social Services, Division of Public Health, State of Alaska, Anchorage, Alaska*
3. *Queen Ingrid's Hospital, Nuuk, Greenland*
4. *Ilulíssat Hospital, Ilulíssat, Greenland*

Introduction

Low mortality from coronary heart disease (CHD) in Arctic natives has been attributed to a high intake of n-3 fatty acids in the traditional diet of the region.[1-3] This reduced CHD mortality has been interpreted by many investigators as synonymous with decreased mural atherosclerotic lesions when compared to populations with greater CHD mortality.[4] An opposite view has attributed the low incidence of deaths from CHD among Eskimos to their high mortality in youth before reaching middle age, when CHD mortality begins to peak.[5] Eskimo populations are reported to have relatively low levels of cholesterol, triglyceride, low-density lipoprotein and very low-density lipoprotein, and relatively high levels of high-density lipoprotein cholesterol.[1,2,6] These differences have been attributed primarily to diet rather than to genetic differences. In addition, the diet of Eskimos, typically high in n-3 fatty acids, is associated with decreased platelet aggregation and longer bleeding times.[7]

The prevalence and extent of atherosclerotic lesions in the coronary arteries and aorta have not been established by objective, standardized methods in either Alaska or Greenland. Through the participation of colleagues from these regions, the opportunity arose to collect autopsy specimens from Arctic residents with a high dietary intake of n-3 polyunsaturated fatty acids (PUFA).

These specimens were then used to evaluate the extent of arterial lesions and to analyse adipose tissue for its triglyceride fatty acid content. Results from the first 204 cases from Alaska have been published previously.[8] In this communication, a brief summary of the results from both these Arctic populations is presented.

Subjects and Methods

The population of Alaska in 1990 (550,043) consisted of about 84% non-natives and 16% natives. Non-native Alaskans included white, black, Hispanic, Asian/ Pacific Islander, and other groups; native Alaskans included Eskimo, American Indian and Aleuts. Aortas, coronary arteries and adipose tissue were collected from 130 (23%) of 454 native Alaskans and from 115 (9%) of 1155 non-native Alaskans who underwent forensic autopsy between February 1989 and December 1993. Of the native Alaskans, 66% died from violent causes (accidents, suicides, homicides), as did 65% of the non-native Alaskans. Autopsy samples were also collected from 103 Greenland natives. The mean ages at death of the non-native and native Alaskans, and Greenland natives were 39.9, 37.1 and 58.6 years, respectively.

The aorta was removed at autopsy by excision 2 cm proximal to the ligamentum arteriosum and 2 cm distal to the iliac bifurcation; it was then bisected longitudinally on the ventral surface midway between the openings of the intercostal and lumbar arteries.

The left half was fixed in 10% neutral buffered formalin. The right and the left anterior descending coronary arteries were dissected from the heart, opened and fixed in the same way as the aorta. The left circumflex artery and the right half of the aorta were stored frozen for subsequent chemical analyses. Adipose tissue was collected from the perirenal area, placed in prenumbered vials and stored frozen for chemical analysis. The fixed and frozen samples were periodically shipped to Louisiana State University Medical Center (LSUMC). The fixed arteries were stained with Sudan IV[9] and packaged in plastic bags labelled with the case identification number.

Three pathologists at the LSUMC, who had no information about the exact source of the samples, independently graded atherosclerotic lesions in the aorta and in the two coronary arteries. The procedure provided estimates of the proportion of the intimal surface associated with fatty streaks, fibrous plaques, calcified plaques and complicated lesions. The sum of the areas affected by the last three types of lesions, together termed 'raised lesions', is an estimate of the extent of intima involved with the more advanced lesions. This grading procedure has proved to be practical and reliable for population comparisons and for the study of risk factors associated with atherosclerotic lesions.[10]

Cross-sections of the macroscopically most severely raised (advanced) lesions were embedded in plastic and stained with toluidine blue and basic fuchsin for analysis of lesion components in 1 μm thick sections. They were also embedded in paraffin for fibrinogen immunohistochemistry and more definitive identification of thrombotic components.

The fatty acid composition of the adipose tissue samples was determined by gas-liquid chromatography as reported previously.[11]

Results

The results of the total sample are presented. The extent of both aortic and coronary intima involvement with raised lesions increased strikingly with age in both the natives and non-natives in the total sample. This progression of atherosclerotic lesions is illustrated for the aortas of native and non-native Alaskans up to the age of 54 years in Figure 1. Results for the older individuals from Alaska are not shown, as there were too few cases for reliable estimates. Similarly, the number of cases from Greenland in the age range 15-54 years was limited because of the older population that was autopsied.

The age- and sex-adjusted mean percentages of intimal surface involved with atherosclerotic lesions in the aorta and in the two coronary arteries are shown in Figure 2.

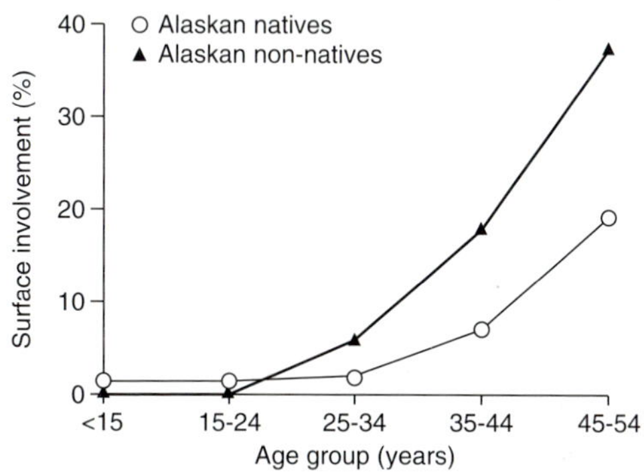

Fig. 1. Relationship between age and mean percentage of intimal surface of aorta involved with raised lesions in autopsied native and non-native Alaskans.

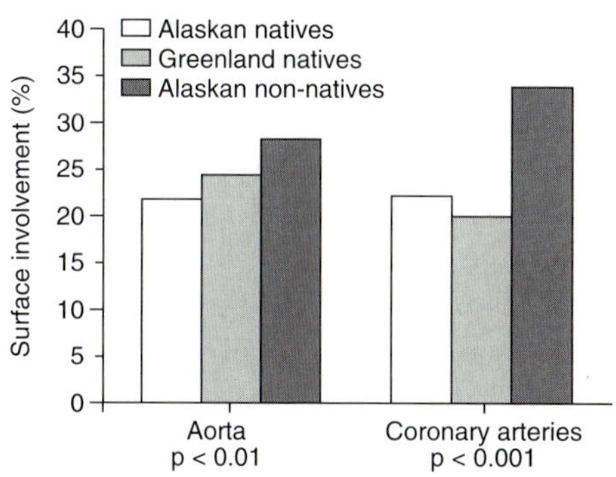

Fig. 2. Age- and sex-adjusted percentage of intimal surface of aorta and coronary arteries involved with raised lesions in different ethnic groups.

Table I. Macroscopic differences in haemorrhage and/or thrombi in the right coronary artery and the left anterior descending artery in male and female native Alaskans.

	Alaskan Males				Alaskan Females			
	Native		Non-native		Native		Non-native	
Haemorrhage								
RC	90	5.6	87	12.6	37	0.0	27	0.0
LAD	89	2.2	86	7.0	36	0.0	27	3.7
Thrombus								
RC	90	0.0	87	3.4	37	0.0	27	0.0
LAD	89	0.0	86	1.2	36	0.0	27	0.0

Abbreviations: RC=right coronary artery, LAD=left anterior descending artery.

Natives from Alaska and Greenland had a significantly lower mean percentage of intimal surface involved with raised lesions in both the aortas and coronary arteries than non-native Alaskans.

After the initial independent grading, the two coronary arteries were re-examined for consensus as to the presence of plaque haemorrhage or thrombus in the coded vessels.

The results are given in Table I for the native and non-native Alaskans. (Consensus grading for plaque haemorrhage and thrombus has not been completed for the Greenland vessels.) Plaque haemorrhage was detected more commonly in the coronary arteries from non-native than from native male Alaskans, and the only thrombi detected were in the non-native males. Plaque complications were very uncommon in females in this study.

The results of the microscopic differences in the aorta have been published,[12] and are summarized below. Advanced lesions from the aortas of 41 native Alaskans (mean age 44.2 years) and 65 non-native Alaskans (mean age 43.3 years) were studied. The mean thickness of the lesions was 1.30 mm in natives and 1.83 mm in non-natives. Of the advanced lesions from natives, 61% had a lipid core, whereas 78% of the lesions sampled from non-natives had a lipid core. Thrombotic deposits were found on the advanced lesions in samples from 20% of the natives and in 38% of the samples from non-natives. In addition, 22% of the plaques from natives and 29% of those from non-natives had old thrombotic remnants within the lesions.

Age- and sex-adjusted mean levels of triglyceride fatty acids in adipose tissue from this autopsy population are summarized in Table II.

Table II. Age- and sex-adjusted mean levels of selected long-chain fatty acids in the adipose tissue of different ethnic groups.

Fatty acid	Alaskan natives (n=124)	Greenland natives (n=83)	Alaskan non-natives (n=99)	p value
18:3	0.52	0.50	0.54	0.5452
20:5	0.11	0.22	0.05	0.0001
22:5	0.35	0.53	0.23	0.0001
22.6	0.30	0.62	0.12	0.0001
18:2	12.25	7.81	13.02	0.0001
20:2	1.47	1.51	1.37	0.2812
20:3	0.23	0.16	0.24	0.0013
20:4	0.17	0.15	0.20	0.0014

The mean levels of long-chain n-3 fatty acids (20:5, 22:5 and 22:6) were highest in Greenland natives and lowest in non-native Alaskans. In contrast, mean levels of long-chain n-6 fatty acids, especially 20:4, were higher in non-native Alaskans.

Discussion

Mortality statistics from Greenland and Alaska indicate low rates of CHD among Eskimos living in these areas.[1,3] Most of the reported studies of Eskimos originate from epidemiological reviews of death certificate data or risk factor evaluations in living populations;[13-18] we were unable to find evidence of objective systematic evaluation of the prevalence and extent of atherosclerotic lesions in the coronary arteries or aortas for these native Arctic populations.

The low incidence of myocardial infarction in Greenland has been attributed to a delayed atherosclerotic process because of low levels of cholesterol, triglyceride, low-density lipoprotein and very low-density lipoprotein in Eskimos.[1,2,6] Eskimos also have relatively high levels of high-density lipoprotein cholesterol, and this lipid pattern appears to be related to diet.[6] The diet of Eskimos, typically high in n-3 fatty acids, is associated with decreased platelet aggregation and longer bleeding times.[7,19] Differences in coagulation factors raise the possibility that Eskimos have less mural thrombi superimposed on atherosclerotic plaques.

In the present study, the extent of raised atherosclerotic lesions increased with age, but the increase was slower in natives from Alaska and Greenland than in non-native Alaskans. The differences in extent of atherosclerosis among the three populations studied were significant after adjusting for age and sex in both the aorta and the coronary arteries. There were also microscopic differences in the thickness and composition of advanced lesions in the aorta, and fewer thrombotic components were detected in the lesions from natives than from non-natives. It is known that the diets of these Arctic populations, and especially those of Greenland residents, are high in n-3 fatty acids. As expected, the present study of fatty acids in adipose tissue also revealed higher levels of n-3 fatty acids in Arctic natives than in non-native Alaskan residents.

Evidence is mounting suggesting that elements of the haemostatic system may have an active role in the progression of atherosclerosis.[20-22] Fibrin and fibrin degradation products have been found in atherosclerotic lesions.[23,24] Also, it has been suggested that the potential protective effect on CHD may be due to the inhibitory effects of n-3 fatty acids on platelets.[4,22] We still know little about the critical question as to whether there is an actual observable effect of PUFA on developing atherosclerotic lesions.

We have shown that there are differences in lesion prevalence and extent, that there are differences in n-3 fatty acids in adipose tissue and that there are differences in the microscopic characteristics of the lesions among the study populations. These findings point to the need for research directed toward the identification of determinants of the reduced incidence of atherosclerosis in Arctic natives. Results from such investigations should provide insights for further characterizing the aetiology of atherosclerosis and CHD.

The effects of the unique diet of Arctic natives, which is high in n-3 fatty acids, are particularly worthy of further investigation. The study of diet and atherosclerosis in Arctic natives may provide a basis for more effective measures for retarding the progression of atherosclerosis, and thereby contributing to the prevention of early disability and death from CHD.

Summary

Reports suggest that a high dietary intake of n-3 fatty acids by Arctic natives contributes to differences in mortality from coronary heart disease. We have studied advanced (raised) atherosclerotic lesions in aortas and coronary arteries from 130 Alaskan natives, 115 Alaskan non-natives, and 103 Greenland natives, dying from all causes. The percentage of raised lesions, adjusted for age and sex, was lower in aortas ($p<0.01$) and coronary arteries ($p<0.001$) from both Alaskan natives and Greenland natives than in the blood vessels from Alaskan non-natives.

Histological analysis of advanced lesions in the aortas from the Alaskan non-natives revealed a higher number of thrombotic deposits on, or incorporated within, lesions than seen in the advanced lesions of Alaskan natives. Only small levels of long-chain fatty acids (n-3 and n-6) are stored in adipose tissue. However, in the populations studied, native men from Alaska had a higher level of n-3 fatty acids, and a lower level of n-6 fatty acids in adipose tissue than non-native men. These data suggest that the lower mortality rates from coronary heart disease reported result from less mural atherosclerotic lesions and fewer complications within these lesions, and that these differences may be attributed, in part, to diet.

References

1. Bang H.O., Dyerberg J., Nielsen A.B.: Plasma lipid and lipoprotein pattern in Greenlandic West Coast Eskimos. Lancet 1971; i: 1143-1146
2. Bang H.O., Dyerberg J.: Lipid metabolism and ischemic heart disease in Greenland eskimos. Adv. Nutr. Res. 1980; 3:.1-22
3. Bjerregaard P., Dyerberg J.: Mortality from ischemic heart disease and cerebro-vascular disease in Greenland. Int. J. Epidemiol. 1988; 17: 514-519
4. Dyerberg J., Bang, H.O.: Dietary fat and thrombosis. Lancet 1978; i: 152
5. McGill H.C. Jr: The relationship of dietary cholesterol to serum cholesterol concentration and to atherosclerosis in man. Am. J. Clin. Nutr. 1979; 32: 2664-2702
6. Bang H.O., Dyerberg J.: Plasma lipids and lipoproteins in Greenlandic West Coast Eskimos. Acta Med. Scand. 1972; 192: 85-94
7. Dyerberg J., Bang H.O.: Haemostatic function and platelet polyunsaturated fatty acids in Eskimos. Lancet 1979; i: 433-435
8. Newman W.P., Middaugh J.P., Prost M.T., Rogers D.R.: Atherosclerosis in Alaska natives and non-natives. Lancet 1993, 341: 1056-1057
9. Guzman M.A., McMahan C.A., McGill, H.C. Jr, Strong J.P., Tejada C., Restrepo C., Eggen D.A. Robertson W.B., Solberg L.A.: Selected methodologic aspects of International Atherosclerosis Project. Lab. Invest. 1968; 18: 479-497
10. Guzman M.A., McMahan C.A., Strong J.P.: Unaided visual estimation of atherosclerotic lesions: biologic variability compared with grading variability. Lab. Invest. 1974; 31: 398-402
11. Malcom G.T., Bhattacharyya A., Velez-Duran M., Guzman M.A., Oalmann M.C., Strong J.P.: Fatty acid composition of adipose tissue in humans: differences between subcutaneous sites. Am. J. Clin. Nutr. 1989; 50: 288-291
12. Yin J., Stary H.C.: Differences in thrombosis and composition of advanced atherosclerotic lesions between Natives and non-Natives of Alaska. FASEB J. 1994; 8(4): A268 (Abstract)
13. Young, T.K., Moffatt, M.E.K., O'Neil, J.D.: Cardiovascular diseases in a Canadian Arctic population. Am. J. Public Health 1993; 83: 881-887
14. Bartelsen A.: Gronlandsk medicinsk statistik og nosografi. Medd. Gronland 1935; 117: 1-83
15. Rabinowitch I.M.: Clinical and other observations on Canadian Eskimos in the Eastern Arctic. Can. Med. Assoc. J. 1936; 34: 487-501
16. Gottman A.W.: A report of 103 autopsies on Alaskan natives. AMA Arch. Pathol. 1960; 70: 117-124
17. Arthaud J.B.: Cause of death in 339 Alaskan natives as determined by autopsy. AMA Arch. Pathol. 1970; 90: 433-438
18. Middaugh J.P.: Cardiovascular deaths among Alaskan natives, 1980-86. Am. J. Public Health 1990; 80: 282-285
19. Dyerberg J., Bang H.O., Stoffersen E.: Eicosapentaenoic acid and prevention of thrombosis and atherosclerosis? Lancet 1978; 1: 117-119
20. Bini A., Fenoglio J.J.Jr., Sobel J., Feigel M., Kaplan K.L.: Immunochemical characterization of fibrinogen, fibrin I, and fibrin II in human thrombi and atherosclerotic lesions. Blood 1987; 69: 1038
21. Shekhonin B.V., Tararak E.M., Samokhin G.P., Mitkevich O.V., Mazurov A.V., Vinogradov D., Vlasik T.N., Kalantarov G.F., Koteliansky V.E.: Visualization of apo B, fibrinogen/fibrin, and fibronectin in the intima of normal aorta and large arteries and during atherosclerosis. Atherosclerosis 1990; 10: 263

22. Goodnight S.H.: The effects of n-3 fatty acids on atherosclerosis and vascular response to injury. Arch. Pathol. Lab. Med. 1993; 117: 102
23. Bini, A., Fenoglio J.J.Jr., Mesa-Tejada R., Kudryk B., Kaplan K.L.: Identification and distribution of fibrinogen, fibrin, and fibrinogen degradation products in atherosclerosis. Use of monoclonal antibodies. Arteriosclerosis 1989; 9: 109
24. Smith E.B., Kee G.A., Grant A., Stirk C.: Fate of fibrinogen in human arterial intima. Arteriosclerosis 1990; 10: 263

S.D. Kristensen, E.B. Schmidt, R. De Caterina, S. Endres
n-3 Fatty Acids: Prevention and Treatment in Vascular Disease
Bi & Gi Publishers, Verona - Springer Verlag, London, 1995

7. Evidence for Antiatherothrombotic Effects of n-3 Fatty Acids: Graft Patency after Coronary Bypass Surgery

H. Arnesen, J. Eritsland

Ullevål University Hospital, Oslo, Norway

Coronary artery bypass grafting is widely used in the treatment of patients with extensive coronary artery disease. The short- and long-term results depend on the persistence of graft patency.

The incidence of graft occlusions during the first postoperative year is reported to be up to 30% for venous grafts and up to 10% for internal mammary artery (IMA) grafts.

Graft occlusions occurring during the first postoperative weeks are mainly thrombotic, whereas later occlusions occur as a result of increasing intimal hyperplasia, with or without a superimposed thrombosis.

Antithrombotics, such as aspirin and warfarin, have been shown to partially reduce the number of occlusions.

Dietary supplementation with n-3 fatty acids (FA) has been shown to reduce the risk of atherothrombotic disease in humans and to retard experimental atherosclerosis in animals.

The Shunt Occlusion Trial (SHOT) was a randomized, prospectively controlled study, designed to assess the effect of dietary supplementation with n-3 FA on the occlusion rate during the first year of coronary artery bypass grafts. A total of 610 patients undergoing coronary artery bypass surgery were randomized to receive a fish-oil concentrate (Omacor®, Pronova, Norway; 4 g/day), containing 3.4 g of n-3 FA [ratio of eicosapentaenoic acid (EPA) to docosahexaenoic acid (DHA)=2:1] or not (controls), in addition to either aspirin (300 mg/day) or warfarin (target range, international normalized ratio 4.2-2.5).

Dietary records revealed no differences between the groups and no changes in dietary habits occurred during the observation period besides supplementation with n-3 FA.

The FA concentration in serum phospholipids was measured at the start of the study and after 9 months. Levels of total n-3 FA, EPA and DHA increased by 44%, 140% and 14%, respectively, in patients receiving fish oil, whereas levels did not change in the control group. Furthermore, the level of serum triglycerides decreased by 20% in the patients treated with fish oil.

Fourteen deaths occurred during the observation period, but these were evenly distributed between the study groups. Angiography was performed in 581 patients (97.5% of the survivors) after 1 year. The occlusion rates of distal venous anastomoses were 27.4% in the n-3 FA-treated group *versus* 32.9% in the controls (odds ratio (OR) 0.77; 95% confidence interval (CI) 0.60-0.99; p=0.034). Sixty-six patients deviated from the assigned treatment for more than 28 days. The corresponding occlusion rates, calculated on an 'on treatment basis', were 26.3% and 33.5%, respectively (OR 0.71; 95% CI 0.54-0.93; p=0.009).

The number of patients with one or more vein graft occlusions was 42.9% in the n-3 FA group and 51.1% in the controls (OR 0.72; 95% CI 0.51-1.01; p=0.05). Calculated on an 'on treatment basis', the figures were 40.9% and 51.8%, respectively (OR 0.64; 95% CI 0.45-0.93; p=0.014). No significant differences were detected in the frequencies of IMA graft occlusions between the group treated with n-3 FA and the controls. Furthermore, no differences in IMA or venous graft occlusions were detected between the aspirin- and warfarin-treated groups.

Finally, when the occlusion rates of venous grafts were compared with the change in serum fatty acid concentrations measured during the study period, a linear relationship between reduced occlusion rates and increased concentrations of n-3 FA was demonstrated. Thus, patients in the upper quartile of relative changes in serum phospholipid n-3 FA concentrations had an OR of 0.49 (95% CI 0.29-0.83; p for trend=0.0037) for having one or more venous graft occlusions when compared with the lower quartile.

In conclusion, the results of the SHOT study demonstrate a reduced frequency of venous aorto-coronary artery graft occlusions after dietary supplementation with n-3 FA for 1 year. These results provide evidence for an antiatherothrombotic effect of n-3 FA in humans.

n-3 Fatty Acids
and
Ischaemic Heart Disease

S.D. Kristensen, E.B. Schmidt, R. De Caterina, S. Endres
n-3 Fatty Acids: Prevention and Treatment in Vascular Disease
Bi & Gi Publishers, Verona - Springer Verlag, London, 1995

8. Control of the Cardiac Rhythm by Dietary Choices

J.X. KANG[1], A. LEAF[1,2]

1. *Department of Medicine, Harvard Medical School, Massachusetts General Hospital, Charlestown, MA, USA*
2. *Department of Medicine, Brockton/West Roxbury VA Medical Center, West Roxbury, MA, USA*

Introduction

The possibility that dietary fatty acids might directly influence the basic function of the heart has aroused little interest, except for the well-publicized role of fatty acids in affecting blood cholesterol levels and thereby indirectly changing the course of coronary heart disease. The epidemiologic and dietary observations by Bang *et al.*[1] of the low mortality rate from coronary heart disease among Greenland Eskimos, despite a dietary fat intake similar to that in Denmark and the United States, has stimulated interest in fatty acids and heart disease. The focus of investigations into the possible preventive effects of n-3 fatty acids from fish oils has been the process of atherogenesis, continuing the pioneering work of the Danish investigators. Many studies have now been performed to examine the effects of fish oil fatty acids on plasma lipid levels, on atherogenesis in experimental animals and on the biochemical and physiological changes that are thought to influence the atherogenic process. Investigators have vied in their eagerness to either substantiate or negate the beneficial effects of n-3 fatty acids on atherogenesis and its major clinical manifestation, coronary heart disease. Many reports have demonstrated that polyunsaturated fatty acids (PUFA) have no significant effects on blood lipid profiles, except for a highly significant reduction in triglyceride levels, the clinical relevance of which is still undetermined. A significant reduction in total or low density lipoprotein (LDL) cholesterol levels in serum only occurs if supplementation with fish oils is coupled to a reduction in saturated fatty acids in the diet. High density lipoprotein (HDL) levels are likely to show only minimal increases. Experimental studies in several species have shown the dramatic prevention of atherosclerosis and coronary heart disease, but these have been countered by studies in other laboratories which have failed to show a beneficial effect of fish oils. These discrepancies are often glaring and remain largely unexplained. Perhaps most encouraging are the considerable number of biochemical and physiological effects of n-3 fatty acids which would seem to be antiatherogenic, such as the recent evidence that they suppress the production of endothelial adhesion proteins[2] and other factors (reviewed in Connor,[3] and Leaf[4]). More clinical trials using randomized, placebo-controlled, double-blinded procedures are needed to establish whether PUFA are indeed antiatherogenic in humans. Two successful, but apparently largely ignored clinical trials are described later in this review.

Antiarrhythmic Effects of n-3 Fatty Acids

While many investigators were investigating the potential antiatherogenic effects of n-3 fatty acids, McLennan *et al.* in Australia were testing possible antiarrhythmic actions of these fatty acids.[5-7] Experiments conducted in rats showed that tuna fish oil prevented fatal ventricular fibrillation following an experimental myocardial infarction caused by ligation of a coronary artery, with or without reflow. This antiarrhythmic effect was later demonstrated in marmosets.[7]

As the results from this group appeared so definite, we started to study the possible mechanism(s) of action of these fatty acids. A cultured neonatal rat cardiac myocyte preparation[8] was used as the assay for potential antiarrhythmic effects. This *in vitro* preparation facilitated the direct observation of the rate and amplitude of contractions of cultured cardiac cells beating rhythmically and synchronously on a microscope cover slip, while being perfused with medium to which any soluble reagents were added at a constant concentration. The cells plated on the cover slip grew into a syncytium and, therefore, the edge monitor measured the beating rate and amplitude of cells with coordinated activity. When the fatty acids eicosapentaenoic acid (EPA, C20:5 n-3) or docosahexaenoic acid (DHA, C22:6 n-3) were added to the perfusion fluid at a concentration of 5-10 mM, a gradual slowing of the beating rate occurred within 2-3 minutes, with no change in the amplitude of contractions. Addition of delipidated bovine serum albumin (BSA), which binds free fatty acids avidly, to the perfusion medium removed the EPA or DHA from the cells and the original beating rate returned. When arrhythmogenic factors, such as elevated Ca^{2+}, toxic levels of ouabain, or β-adrenergic agonists, were added to the perfusion medium, tachyarrhythmias occurred in the myocytes, often accompanied by asynchronous beating. Addition of low concentrations of EPA to the perfusion medium prevented or stopped the tachyarrhythmias (Fig. 1) induced by elevated Ca^{2+} or oubain.[9] After addition of high concentrations of Ca^{2+}

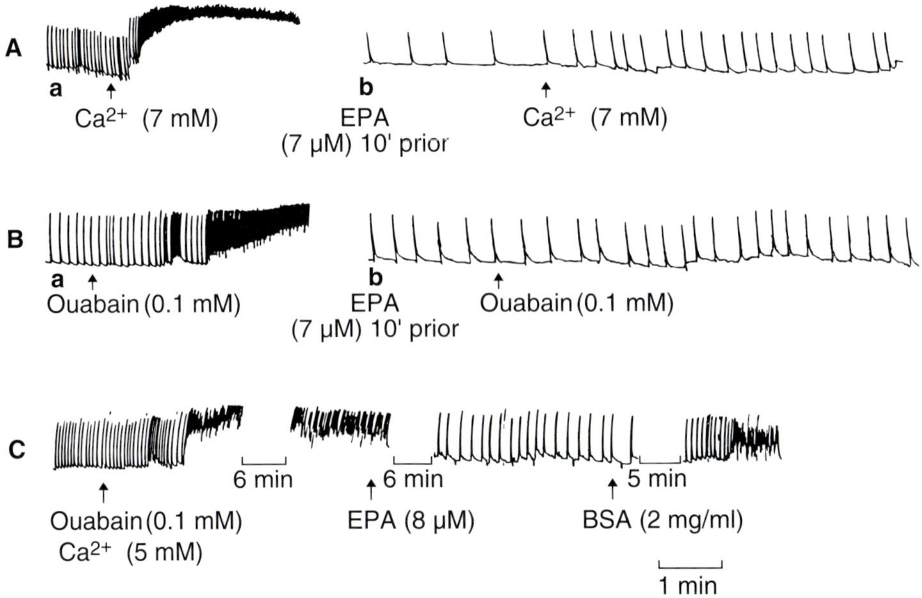

Fig. 1. Tracings showing prevention and termination of arrhythmias by eicosapentaenoic acid (EPA). (a) and (b) Perfusion of rat cardiac myocytes with a solution containing Ca^{2+} (7 mM) (Aa) or ouabain (0.1 mM) (Bb) induced contracture and fibrillation of the myocytes. Washing the cells with medium containing Ca^{2+} (1.1 mM) for 5-8 minutes returned the rhythm to the control beating rate. Cells were then perfused with a medium containing EPA (7 mm). After 5-8 minutes, when the beating rate was slowed, addition of Ca^{2+} (7 mM) (Ab) or ouabain (0.1 mM) (Bb) failed to induce contracture of fibrillation in the same cells. The slow beating rate returned to the control rate after addition of delipidated BSA (2 mg/ml), which has a high binding affinity for free fatty acids, to the perfusate (not shown). (C) After induction of contracture with fibrillation by toxic concentrations of Ca^{2+} (5 mM) and ouabain (0.1 mM), addition of EPA (8 mM) terminated the fibrillations and contractures and led to slow normal contractions. Subsequent addition of BSA (2 mg/ml) extracted EPA from the myocytes and, in the continued presence of high concentrations of Ca^{2+} and ouabain, re-established the contractures and fibrillations.

(5 mM) and ouabain (0.1 mM) to the perfusion fluid, a violent tachyarrhythmia occurred. Addition of EPA (5 mM) stopped the arrhythmia after a short time, but when the free EPA was withdrawn from the myocytes using delipidated BSA, the arrhythmia returned.

Two important conclusions can be made from this simple experiment: first, free fatty acid has antiarrhythmic activity, and second, it is not the incorporation of the fatty acids into membrane phospholipids that affords protection, but rather it is the free fatty acid partitioned into the phospholipids of the cell membranes or reversibly bound to membrane proteins that prevents the arrhythmias. Addition of ethyl esters or triglycerides of EPA and/or DHA to the perfusion medium afforded no protection against the tachyarrhythmias, indicating that the free carboxyl group is essential for the antiarrhythmic effect.

Furthermore, the finding that delipidated BSA, which extracts only free fatty acids from myocytes, reversed the protective effects of EPA and DHA, indicates that their antiarrhythmic action does not involve covalent linkages to phospholipids or other molecules in the cell membranes.

This last conclusion was surprising, as the results of feeding experiments, during which fatty acids are incorporated into phospholipids, has created the expectation that PUFA exert their physiological effects through changes in the properties of membrane phospholipids. Alternatively, it could be that n-3 fatty acids in phospholipids are simply the storage form from which the active free fatty acid can be liberated by phospholipases.

Antiarrhythmic Effects of n-6 Fatty Acids

Other long-chain PUFA have been studied in the *in vitro* assay system described above. Results indicate that the antiarrhythmic action is not restricted only to EPA and DHA, but is a property of all long-chain PUFA with two or more unsaturated carbon-carbon bonds. Thus, α-linolenic acid, linoleic acid, and arachidonic acid (AA, C20:4 n-6) are all antiarrhythmic. However, monounsaturated oleic acid and saturated fatty acids lack this protective property. The fact that n-6 fatty acids share this protective action with n-3 fatty acids is consistent with the considerable reduction in experimental myocardial infarctions observed by McLennan *et al.*[5] in rats fed safflower oil.

However, AA appears to be a special case. Of 48 experiments conducted with AA, only one-third showed a characteristic antiarrhythmic action in the rat myocyte system. In the remaining two-thirds, AA either failed to show any antiarrhythmic effects or was indeed arrhythmogenic by itself. However, the arrhythmogenic effect was abolished by addition of inhibitors of cyclooxygenase and lipoxygenase with the AA.

This indicates that the arrhythmogenic action of AA was caused by eicosanoids formed from the AA and was not the direct effect of the AA itself on the myocytes. This interpretation was greatly strengthened by the finding that eicosatetraenoic acid (ETYA), the 20-carbon fatty acid analog of AA, with four acetylenic triple carbon-carbon bonds rather than double bonds, was always antiarrhythmic. ETYA has long been used to block the action of oxidative enzymes that produce potent eicosanoids from AA.

The finding that arachidonic acid may produce or contribute to the development of serious ventricular arrhythmias through the production of its arrhythmogenic eicosanoids, indicates that n-3 fatty acids, rather than n-6 fatty acids, are the preferred class of fatty acids to consider for potential clinical antiarrhythmic application.

Mechanisms for the Antiarrhythmic Effects of Fatty Acids

β-Adrenergic agonists are well-documented arrhythmogenic agents which are known to contribute to lethal ventricular arrhythmias associated with myocardial ischaemia. Isoproterenol (1-3 μM), a β-adrenergic agonist, produced persistent tachyarrhythmias in the cultured neonatal rat cardiac myocyte assay system.[10] EPA or DHA (5-10 mM) prevented or stopped these arrhythmias.[10] It is known that the β-adrenergic agonist binds to its β-adrenoreceptor on the cell membranes of cardiac myocytes, which activates a Gs protein. This in turn activates adenylylcyclase to increase production of cyclic-AMP (c-AMP). c-AMP activates protein kinase-A, which phosphorylates ion channels in the cell membrane, causing the alteration in ion channel conductances that are responsible for the arrhythmia. Addition of dibutyryl-c-AMP (250 μM) produced a tachyarrhythmia similar to that caused by isoproterenol; this arrhythmia was also prevented or stopped by EPA or DHA. This result indicates that the preventive action(s) of n-3 fatty acids are exerted, not by blocking a step in intracellular second messenger systems, but by the electrical excitation system itself or by coupling of the electrical to the mechanical events in cardiac cell contractions.

In light of this hypothesis, in collaboration with Dr Yong-Fu Xiao, we examined the electrophysiology of the electrical cycle of cardiac cells that controls the rhythmicity of cardiac contractions. Briefly, this study showed that the electrical current needed to initiate an action potential increased by about 50% when n-3 fatty acids were present in the perfusion medium.[11] This effect was due to a modest hyperpolarization of the diastolic membrane potential together with a more positive threshold potential to gate the sodium current, which creates the up-stroke of the action potential. In addition, however, the presence of PUFA markedly prolonged the refractory period of the myocyte by about 150%. This effect was associated with marked prolongation of phase 4 depolarization. Together, these changes would contribute to a decrease in the excitability of cardiac cells, making them less prone to respond to stray or aberrant electrical impulses that might occur during ischaemia or reflow. These effects would account for the predictable slowing of the beating rate of the isolated cardiac myocytes in the presence of PUFA. They also indicate that multiple ion channels are likely to be affected by the presence of PUFA in the membranes. A great deal more research is needed to determine further the mechanism of the antiarrhythmic action of PUFA.

Relevance to Ischaemia-Induced Arrhythmias

The relevance of these results to ischaemia-induced ventricular arrhythmias (sudden cardiac death) was investigated in experiments conducted with Dr George E. Billman (Ohio State University, Columbus, OH). A canine model of myocardial

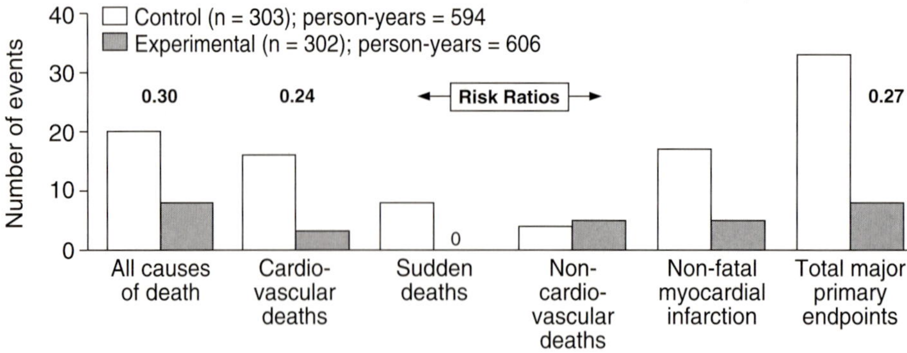

Fig. 2. Summary of the clinical trial investigating a Mediterranean α-linolenic-acid-rich diet in the secondary prevention of coronary heart disease.[14] A total of 605 men who had recently suffered a heart attack were randomized equally into control and experimental groups. The control group was instructed to follow a prudent post-infarction diet, while the experimental group was given more stringent dietary instructions, which included omitting red meats and dairy fat and eating more vegetables, fruit, legumes and bread. The use of olive oil and a soft margarine made of canola oil, which contains some 11% α-linolenic acid, was allowed. The figure summarizes the main results of this study after a mean of 27 months' follow-up. Of relevance to the present topic was the suppression of sudden death among the experimental cohort. (Reproduced with the permission of de Logeril *et al.*[14]).

infarction in a prepared, conscious, exercising dog was used.[12] Following compression of the left circumflex coronary artery, the dog would almost invariably develop an acute and lethal ventricular fibrillation, which could be defibrillated. Intravenous administration of EPA and DHA just prior to compression of the left circumflex artery, however, prevented the fatal arrhythmias in 11 of 14 dogs tested. Compression of the left circumflex coronary artery induced ventricular fibrillation in all five animals tested without the n-3 fatty acid infusion. We are therefore reassured that the results from the isolated, cultured, neonatal cardiac myocytes are relevant to ischaemia-induced, lethal ventricular arrhythmias.

It remains to be established whether these results are relevant to human sudden cardiac death. Two human studies have been conducted in which n-3 fatty acids were administered in secondary prevention trials.[13,14] In both studies, striking reductions in all-cause and cardiac mortality were found in the experimental group, who received n-3 fatty acids. Prevention of cardiac sudden death contributed to the beneficial outcome.

Figure 2 shows a summary of the more recent clinical trial.[14] There was a reduction of about 70% in all causes of death, which was accounted for by the reduction in cardiovascular deaths. Of note is the prevention of 'sudden deaths' in the experimental group receiving dietary α-linolenic acid. The survival curves for both studies, which demonstrated separation of mortality for the experimental *versus* the control groups, commencing very early with implementation of the experimental diets, are not shown. This is quite different from the 2 years, approximately, that are required for the separation of survival curves between experimental and control cohorts in cholesterol-lowering trials.

Although these are dietary studies in which many factors invariably change in addition to the intake of the n-3 fatty acids, it is not unreasonable to conclude from the feeding studies of Charnock and McLennan[5-7] and from our studies, that the antiarrhythmic actions of PUFA play an important role.

In the USA alone, sudden cardiac death accounts for most of the 300,000 deaths each year from acute myocardial infarctions, which occur in the first few hours following heart attacks, representing about 60% of coronary heart disease mortality. Further studies should reveal whether the findings summarized here have any relevance to this major public health problem in western, industrialized countries.

Acknowledgements

Studies reported from this Laboratory were supported in part by a National Institute of Health research grant, RO1-DK 38165.

Summary

Most studies on the cardiovascular effects of n-3 polyunsaturated fatty acids have focused on their potential antiatherogenic effects. We have examined the antiarrhythmic effects of these fatty acids. Neonatal rat cardiac myocytes in culture beat spontaneously with a regular rhythm. Severe tachyarrhythmias are induced in these cells by agents known to be arrhythmogenic in humans. Examples of such agents include elevated serum calcium concentrations, overdoses of cardiac glycosides, β-adrenergic agonists, lysophosphatidyl choline and acylcarnitine. Eicosapentaenoic (EPA) and docosahexaenoic acid (DHA) (5 μM) prevent or stop the tachyarrhthmias and fibrillation caused by these agents. This antiarrhythmic action is associated with a slowing of the beating rate of isolated cardiac myocytes. Patch clamp electrophysiological studies have revealed that EPA and DHA markedly reduce the automaticity/excitability of isolated myocytes by increasing the diastolic hyperpolarization of the membrane potential and by raising the threshold for gating fast sodium channels. Perhaps even more important is the prolongation by EPA and DHA of the refractory state of the myocytes, particularly slowing of phase 4 depolarization. The effects of these fatty acids have been tested in a conscious, unanesthetized, exercising dog, surgically prepared to develop fatal ventricular arrhythmias, with compression of the left circumflex coronary artery, while running on a treadmill. Intravenous infusion of n-3 fatty acids just prior to the ischaemic insult prevented the occurrence of these fatal arrhythmias in 11 of 14 dogs tested ($p<0.001$). The potential use of these fatty acids in the prevention of the high incidence of sudden death following acute myocardial infarctions or other ischaemic stress in humans is being pursued.

References

1. Bang H.O., Dyerberg J., Horne N.: The composition of food consumed by Greenland Eskimos. Acta Med. Scand. 1976; 200: 69-73
2. DeCaterina R., Cybulski M.I., Clinton S.K., Gimbrone M.A., Libby P.: The omega-3 fatty acid docosahexaenoate reduces cytokine-induced expression of proatherogenic and proinflammatory proteins in human endothelial cells. Arterioscler. Thromb. 1994; 14: 1829-1836
3. Connor W.E.: Omega-3 fatty acids and heart disease. In: Kritchevsky D., Carroll K.K. (Eds.): *Nutrition and Disease Update: Heart Disease*. Champaigne, Illinois; American Oil Chemists' Society Press 1994: 7-42
4. Leaf A.: Health claims: omega-3 fatty acids and cardiovascular disease. Nutr. Rev. 1993; 50: 150-154
5. McLennan P.L., Abeywardena M.Y., Charnock J.S.: Influence of dietary lipids on arrhythmias and infarction after coronary artery ligation in rats. Can. J. Physiol. Pharmacol. 1985; 63: 1411-1417
6. McLennan P.L., Abeywardena M.Y., Charnock J.S.: Dietary fish oil prevents ventricular fibrillation following coronary artery occlusion and reperfusion. Am. Heart. J. 1988; 16: 709-717
7. McLennan P.L., Bridle T.M., Abeywardena M.Y., Charnock J.S.: Dietary lipid modulation of ventricular fibrillation threshold in the marmoset monkey. Am. Heart. J. 1992; 123: 1555-1561
8. Hallaq H., Sellmayer A., Smith T.W., Leaf A.: Protective effect of eicosapentaenoic acid on ouabain toxicity in neonatal rat cardiac myocytes. Proc. Natl. Acad. Sci. USA 1990; 87: 7834-7838
9. Kang J.X., Leaf A.: Effects of long-chain polyunsaturated fatty acids on the contraction of neonatal rat cardiac myocytes. Proc. Natl. Acad. Sci. USA 1994; 91: 9886-9890
10. Kang J.X., Leaf A.: Prevention and termination of β-adrenergic agonist-induced arrhythmias by free polyunsaturated fatty acids in neonatal rat cardiac myocytes. Biophys. Biochem. Res. Commun. 1995; 208: 629-636
11. Kang J.X., Xiao Y-F., Leaf A.: Free long-chain polyunsaturated fatty acids reduce membrane electrical excitability in neonatal rat cardiac myocytes. Proc. Natl. Acad. Sci. USA 1995; 92: 3997-4001
12. Billman G.E., Hallaq H., Leaf A.: Prevention of ischaemia-induced ventricular fibrillation by omega-3 fatty acids. Proc. Natl. Acad. Sci. USA 1994; 91: 4427-4430
13. Burr M.L., Fehily A.M., Gilbert J.F., Rogers S., Holliday RM., Sweetnam PE., Elwood P.C., Deadman N.M.: Effects of changes in fat, fish and fiber intakes on death and myocardial reinfarction: diet and reinfarction trial (DART). Lancet 1989; 334: 757-761
14. de Logeril M., Renaud S., Mamelle N., Salen P., Martin F-L., Monjaud I., Guidollet J., Touboul P., Delayue J.: Mediterranean alpha-linolenic acid-rich diet in secondary prevention of coronary heart disease. Lancet 1994; 343: 1454-1459

S.D. Kristensen, E.B. Schmidt, R. De Caterina, S. Endres
n-3 Fatty Acids: Prevention and Treatment in Vascular Disease
Bi & Gi Publishers, Verona - Springer Verlag, London, 1995

9. n-3 Fatty Acids and Experimental Arrhythmogenesis

R.A. RIEMERSMA

Cardiovascular Research Unit, University of Edinburgh, UK

Introduction

Ischaemic heart disease (IHD) is the major cause of death in the Western world. It has been known for some time that dietary factors play a role in this disease. Platelet eicosapentaenoic acid (EPA), which reflects consumption of fish oil, is a risk factor for angina pectoris in Scottish men, and is independent of classical risk factors, such as serum and high density lipoprotein (HDL) cholesterol, blood pressure and smoking.[1] Several studies have shown that in countries where fish consumption is low, individuals who regularly consume moderate amounts of fish have a lower incidence of coronary heart disease (CHD) than those who do not.[2,3] The underlying mechanism of this phenomenon is often assumed to be related to reduced platelet aggregation and/or a tendency for thrombosis. However, mortality from CHD, but not the total number of ischaemic events, is reduced in patients with an acute myocardial infarction, who have been advised to consume fatty fish regularly.[4] These findings have led to the suggestion that fatty acids from fish oil may inhibit the development of serious arrhythmias, but not the precipitating ischaemic events that lead to such disorders.[5]

Experimental Models

Ventricular fibrillation (VF) is commonest during the reversible, ischaemic phase of an acute heart attack and may also be the principal cause of sudden cardiac death. Animal experiments have shown that many factors promote the development of this arrhythmia. These are not yet fully understood, but include infarct size and location, imbalanced sympathetic/parasympathetic activity and low tissue K^+. Nutritional factors may also be important; in particular, diets rich in linoleic acid, which is one of the polyunsaturated fatty acids (PUFA) common in plant oils, protect against ischaemia-induced VF in animals.[6,7] The position of the methyl terminal carbon-carbon double bond of PUFA in fish oil differs from that in plant oils. PUFA from these two sources are not interconvertible in humans and therefore act as two distinct families, referred to as n-3 FA and n-6 FA in fish and plant oil, respectively.

There is no consensus about the mechanism that underlies the antiarrhythmic effect of n-6 FA, but, as linoleic acid is the precursor to arachidonic acid and its eicosanoid derivatives, it is assumed to be mediated by prostaglandins.[8,9] However, as diets rich in linoleic acid are low in saturated fatty acids, it remains to be established whether saturated fatty acids are pro-arrhythmogenic or whether polyunsaturates are anti-arrhythmogenic.

Arrhythmias are common during clinical and experimental acute myocardial ischaemia. However, they may also be readily induced by the intramyocardial application of drugs, such as aconitine, ouabain and isoprenaline to a well-perfused heart without coronary lesions. The relevance of such models of arrhythmia is questionable. Equally questionable are models of sudden cardiac death, in which large quantities of isoprenaline or arachidonic acid are injected intraperitoneally or intravenously. In these cases, the mode of death is assumed to be arrhythmic, but the electrical activity of the heart is rarely monitored. It has been shown that fish oil fatty acids may affect the activity of ion channels in beating neonatal cardiomyocytes. For the purpose of this brief review, the results obtained from drug-related models will be omitted and for information on the effects of fish-oil fatty acids on ion channels, the reader is referred to the article by J.X. Kang and A. Leaf in another chapter in this book (pp. 89-96). Reviewed instead will be whether n-3 FA can exert similar beneficial anti-arrhythmogenic effects to their n-6 counterparts.

A milestone was reached with the Lambeth Conventions. For the first time, detailed recommendations for the design and conduct of experimental studies of acute myocardial ischaemia and infarction were given.[10] Definitions for serious ventricular arrhythmias were agreed upon, and the need to use contemporary controls and to exclude the effect of confounding influences on results was emphasized. This may now seem obvious and unnecessary, but until these recommendations were made, many criteria of good experimental practice had been ignored. It was also recognised that inadequate group sizes had been a problem in studies of arrhythmia using hard, but categorical endpoints, such as incidence of ventricular tachycardia (VT) or VF.[10] Large groups are considered necessary in order to achieve statistically significant results.

Early Studies

Dietary supplementation with large amounts of fish oil (about 25% of calories for 7-9 weeks) increased the concentration of EPA in platelet phospholipids of pigs and dogs from less than 1% of fatty acids to 10-12%. This increase occurred at the expense of arachidonic acid. The arrhythmia results of these studies were inconclusive because of the inadequately low number of animals studied.[11,12] This was not a problem in studies conducted by McLennan *et al.* using rats.[13] Rats (n=17-35/group) were fed a high-fat diet, enriched with saturated fatty acids (polyunsaturated (P) to saturated (S) fatty acid ratio=0.2), n-3 polyunsaturated fat from tuna fish oil (P/S=1.3) for 6-20 months. Acute myocardial ischaemia was induced by ligation of a coronary artery in the open chest, anaesthetized animal. The incidence of VT and of VF during ischaemia and after reperfusion was determined. The results were compared with those obtained following supplementation with a diet enriched with n-6 FA (P/S=3.9) and a low fat reference diet (P/S=1.3). During acute ischaemia, the incidence of VT and VF in the reference group were 93% and 46%, respectively, and in the saturated fatty acid group, the incidence was 97% and 68%, respectively. After long-term administration of tuna fish oil, the incidence of VT and VF was 41% and 6%, respectively, while the corresponding figures for animals fed a diet rich in PUFA were 68% and 21%. The diet rich in saturated fatty acids did not affect reperfusion arrhythmias, but the diet high in fish oil reduced the incidence of VT during reperfusion from 94% to 59% and the incidence of VF from 50% to 12% (both $p<0.05$ *versus* the reference diet group). However, a comparison with the reference diet group is not valid because the two diets were not calorifically balanced, and animals eating a high-fat (*i.e.* high-energy) diet will consume proportionally less other nutrients and salts to satisfy their energy requirements. Dietary potassium influenced the incidence of ischaemic VF in this model (E. Winslow, Organon, Newhouse, Scotland, personal communication). Nevertheless, the results did not vary if the reference group was excluded from the statistical analysis and it can therefore be concluded that a diet high in n-3 FA reduced both VT and VF. (The diet high in n-6 FA did not affect the incidence of reperfusion arrhythmias). A much larger number of animals per group is required to examine whether the apparent difference between n-3 and n-6 FA is statistically significant.

Large Dose Studies

Subsequent studies from McLennan, Charnock and colleagues from CSIRO in Adelaide have demonstrated a significant reduction in the incidence of VF after dietary supplementation with large amounts of tuna fish oil (23.5% of energy intake) in comparison with a diet high in saturated fat.[14,15] Factors influencing the effectiveness of these PUFA diets were also examined. Protective effects were documented in old animals and in animals fed saturated fat for a long time. This can be explained by the higher incidence of VF in older animals, which makes it easier to show a given statistical reduction in the incidence of VF. The animals studied did not develop coronary vascular lesions and the reversible, protective effect could not be attributed to an anti-atherogenic effect. The fatty acid composition of myocardial phospholipids was altered under these conditions and the relative amount of arachidonic acid was reduced, whereas that of EPA and docosahexaenoic acid (DHA) was increased. This protective effect is not limited to tuna fish oil and was recently documented with another EPA-rich oil (ShakleeEPA, Shaklee Corp, USA). After 12 weeks of treatment with ShakleeEPA, the incidence of VF during a 15 minute period of acute myocardial ischaemia was reduced from 57% to 0% ($p<0.05$) and from 29% to 0% during the subsequent reperfusion period, although the latter reduction was not significant.[16]

This study highlights the problems involved in combined ischaemia-reperfusion studies. The heart could be reperfused only in 50% of the animals fed a diet high in saturated fat and therefore these animals were to some degree, preselected. The hearts of all the animals receiving fish oil were reperfused. As ischaemic arrhythmias were infrequent during the first 5 minutes of myocardial ischaemia, the effect of fish oil on reperfusion arrhythmias was also examined after 5 minutes of acute ischaemia. Fish oil reduced reperfusion VF from 50% to 10% ($p<0.05$). In animals fed a diet rich in linoleic acid, the incidence in reperfusion VF declined from 50% to 25%. The difference between the n-3 and n-6 FA diets was not significant because of the small number of animals used. It is probably easier to document such a difference using non-categoric endpoints.

Fish Oil and Susceptibility to Arrhythmias

Electrical stimulation of the heart helps to identify patients or animals who are vulnerable to sudden cardiac death clinically or experimentally. In these electrophysiological protocols, extra stimuli, at an intensity above the diastolic excitation threshold, are given during the refractory period of the heart at increasing currents until VF occurs. These programmed stimulations can be carried out before and during acute myocardial ischaemia. The effect of large amounts of ShakleeEPA or tuna fish oil in the diet (6.2% or 19% of energy for 16 weeks and 30 months, respectively) on the threshold current necessary to induce VF has been examined in anaesthetized marmoset monkeys.[17,18] Tuna fish oil increased the VF threshold (VFT) in animals susceptible to this procedure, although VF could not be induced in one-third of these animals under normoxic, well-perfused conditions.

A similar increase in VFT was seen in animals fed sunflower seed oil, which is rich in n-6 FA. Ischaemia induced a small, but significant, reduction in the VFT, irrespective of the diet ($p<0.01$) and higher currents were necessary to induce VF in monkeys fed n-3 or n-6 FA than in those fed a diet high in saturated fat ($p<0.05$).

The effects of ShakleeEPA differed from those of tuna fish oil mentioned above. During normoxia, a much higher VFT was obtained in animals fed ShakleeEPA than in those on a diet of tuna fish oil. A comparison was again made against sunflower seed oil and the VFT was almost identical to that observed in the previous experiment with this oil. Again, VFT fell during ischaemia and a higher VFT was detected in monkeys fed n-3 FA compared with those receiving n-6 FA ($p<0.05$). In these two studies, differences in the area of the myocardium made ischaemic were excluded.

The reason for the differences between sunflower seed oil, tuna fish oil and ShakleeEPA oil is not clear. The authors suggested that the difference may be due to differing amounts of saturated fat in the n-3 and n-6 FA diets. However, as shown in Table I, this is not the case.

Surprisingly, the VFT measured in animals receiving the two sunflower seed oil diets were similar, despite a marked increase in the relative amount of saturated fat and the decrease in n-6 FA in the second experiment compared with the first experiment. In both experiments, the VFT was reduced. The inconsistency between the two experiments calls into question the simple conclusion that there is an intrinsic difference in the efficacy of n-3 and n-6 FA.

Quality of Fish Oil

The quality of fish oil varies considerably. Some oils contain high anisidine values (>30), reflecting the presence of aldehydic degradation products from lipid peroxidation. We have examined whether the anti-arrhythmic effect of fish oil depends on the quality of the oil. A highly purified fish oil (CPL fish oil, Lipid Teknik, Stockholm) at a dose from which 7% of dietary energy was derived from fat, and the same oil oxidized to an anisidine value of 50, was fed to rats for 8 weeks

Table I. The fatty acid (FA) composition of two experimental diets.

	Experiment 1		**Experiment 2**	
	Tuna fish oil	**Sunflower seed oil**	**Shaklee EPA**	**Sunflower seed oil**
Saturates	29.3	23.3	46.9	48.4
n-6 FA	10.8	53.5	9.7	18.6
n-3 FA	22.8	-	12.4	2.3

Fatty acid composition is expressed as % of fatty acids.[18,19]

and the incidence of ischaemia (first 20 minutes) and reperfusion arrhythmias determined. Both diets were compared with a diet typical of Scottish men, with a P/S ratio of 0.3. All three semi-synthetic diets contained sufficient linoleic acid to prevent essential fatty acid deficiency. Cages were changed daily and remnants of spilled foods were removed to prevent lipid peroxidation, particularly of the fish oil diets.

There was a marked reduction in the ischaemic VF in animals receiving the two fish oil diets. The incidence of VF was 59% in the control group and 25% and 30% in the groups receiving pure fish oil and 'oxidized' fish oil, respectively ($p<0.001$ and $p<0.025$ compared with control group). No difference was observed in the fatty acid composition of myocardial phospholipids from animals fed the two fish oil diets. The relative content of EPA and DHA increased by more than 7000% and 230%, respectively, and the level of arachidonic acid fell by 45% (all $p<0.01$) when compared with the fatty acid composition of the hearts from the control group.

Oxidation of highly purified oils is not identical to the purification of oxidized oils. Therefore, a second experiment was conducted in which groups of animals were fed a commercial crude fish oil before and after purification. The incidence of VF during acute myocardial ischaemia was 28% in rats fed crude fish oil compared with 34% in those receiving purified fish oil (not significant).

These studies cannot reveal whether the reduction in VF is due to the n-3 FA or merely reflects the displacement of the putative pro-arrhythmogenic long-chain saturated fatty acids. More importantly, the relevance of all these high fish oil diets to man is questionable because of the quantity of fish oil given.

Low-Dose Fish Oil

The use of low-dose fish oil is attractive for several reasons. Firstly, fish oil can be given orally, by gavage in animal studies, thereby eliminating the problem of lipid peroxidation of the food. Secondly, a small supplement will not affect the basic diet and therefore all other dietary factors should be identical in all groups. However, the most important reason is perhaps that the beneficial effects documented in epidemiological studies have been observed with relatively small amounts of fish oil.

The effect of small amounts of fish oil (equivalent to 0.1%, 0.2% and 0.4% energy from fat) on myocardial phospholipid fatty acid composition was examined.[19] To do this, the actual volume of pure fish oil required was 0.021-0.096 ml/day/rat, making the administration of such small amounts of fish oil inaccurate. Therefore, a small amount of olive oil was retained from the basic diet and used to dilute the fish oil. In this way, 0.5-0.7 ml/day could be given. Control animals received olive oil. Administration of fish oil for 8 weeks (0.4% of energy) increased the amount of EPA in myocardial phospholipids from 6.6 ± 2.8 to 28 ± 17 mg/g wet weight ($p<0.001$), but the increase in DHA was less marked (1488 ± 84 to 1802 ± 199

μg/g wet weight, $p<0.05$). Fish oil reduced the amount of arachidonic acid from 3882 ± 914 to 3012±426 μg/g wet weight ($p<0.05$). At a lower dose of 0.2% total energy, the increase in EPA was significant but the increase in DHA was not (not shown). Administration of fish oil (0.4% energy) for 8 weeks did not affect heart rate, coronary occlusion-induced reduction in flow, lactate production or release of lactate dehydrogenase. There was a reduction in the incidence of VF from 60% to 45%, but this did not reach the usual criteria of statistical significance.

Long-term supplementation with fish oil (6 months) did not reduce the incidence of VF in this isolated, perfused rat heart model (control, 40% *versus* fish oil, 39%, not significant). Neither of the fish oil experiments showed a reduction in the high incidence of VF during ischaemic reperfusion (>95%). It is worth emphasizing that under these dietary feeding conditions the intake of saturated fatty acids was unaltered and linoleic acid intake did not differ. Indeed, the fatty acid composition of adipose tissue did not differ between the control and fish oil groups (not shown).

Mechanisms

Together, these results demonstrate that there is a consensus that large amounts of fish oil reduce the incidence of serious ventricular arrhythmias during acute experimental myocardial ischaemia. The fact that this is observed both *in vivo* and *in vitro*, and is accompanied by an increase in the threshold required to induce VF by programmed electrical stimulation, even in the absence of acute ischaemia, suggests that fish oil alters the intrinsic electrical stability of the heart. In contrast, there is no agreement about the effect of fish oil on reperfusion arrhythmias. The experiments conducted *in vivo* suggest that fish oil may be protective under these circumstances, but the high incidence of VF in the isolated, perfused rat heart was resistant to any dietary manipulation. The underlying mechanism in the *in vivo* model is difficult to establish as no coronary venous blood samples can be obtained. The effect of fish oil *ex vivo* suggests an alteration in the balance between the anti-arrhythmogenic effects of prostacyclin and the pro-arrhythmogenic effects of thromboxane. However, it remains to be established whether such changes occur during acute myocardial ischaemia. Flurbiprofen (10^{-5} M) did not block the anti-arrhythmic effect of n-6 FA in the isolated perfused rat heart, despite a near total reduction in the production of the metabolite of prostacyclin, 6-oxo-prostaglandin $F_{1\alpha}$. Leaf and colleagues and Gudbjarnason and colleagues are examining the effect of fish oil fatty acids on ion channels and adrenergic receptor expression (see review by J.X. Kang and A. Leaf in this book, pp. 89-96).

To date, the use of high dietary fish oil has always been accompanied by a corresponding reduction in dietary saturated fat intake. Dietary supplementation with n-6 FA, such as linoleic acid, is also accompanied by a reduction in saturated fat, and much confusion exists about the relative efficacy of n-3 and n-6 FA, as most studies have insufficient statistical power to test whether the difference in the incidence of VF is significant. No such statistical problems are expected to occur with numerically expressed data such as VFT. Unfortunately, in this study, the VFT data did not show a consistent difference between n-3 and n-6 FA.[17,18]

Relevance to Humans

High fat doses used in these studies are probably irrelevant to humans and are perhaps unnecessary for changing the fatty acid composition of myocardial phospholipids, as low doses of fish oil had similar and significant effects. This low dose corresponds to 1-2 ml fish oil/day in humans. However, the incidence of VF during acute myocardial ischaemia was not altered by low-dose fish oil, whether given for 8 weeks or for 6 months. These studies were not confounded by reciprocal changes in dietary levels of saturated fat or linoleic acid, nor by a change in the severity of myocardial ischaemia from fish oil.

Patients who suffer from serious ventricular arrhythmias during acute myocardial infarction have similar levels of n-3 FA in platelet membranes as those with no history of arrhythmias.[20] The only change in fatty acid composition in those requiring treatment for serious ventricular arrhythmias was an increase in the level of saturated fatty acids in adipose tissue. The only way to resolve the issue of whether fish oil fatty acids protect against serious ventricular arrhythmias in high-risk patients with acute myocardial ischaemia or infarction, is to conduct a proper double-blind intervention trial. One preliminary study in 38 cardiology patients has shown a non-significant reduction in the incidence of arrhythmias.[21] It is clear that further studies are needed to answer this important question.

Acknowledgements

I am indebted to Carol Sargent and Mrs Jean Samuel, who helped me to conduct the Edinburgh studies. These studies were supported by a grant from the British Heart Foundation and the highly purified fats and oils were a generous gift from Lipid Teknik, Stockholm.

Summary

There is increasing evidence that dietary fatty acid composition affects the mortality rate from coronary heart disease (CHD) in humans. Early studies focused on the cholesterol-raising effect of saturated fatty acids. However, recent evidence suggests that a diet low in essential fatty acids (n-3 or n-6) may predispose to CHD, independently of classical risk factors. Sudden cardiac death, due to ventricular fibrillation (VF) during acute myocardial ischaemia, is common. As fish oils have been shown to prevent cardiac deaths, but not total numbers of ischaemic events in patients with acute myocardial infarction, it has been suggested that n-3 fatty acids may be antiarrhythmic.

The effects of n-3 fatty acids on myocardial phospholipids and serious ventricular arrhythmias has been examined during acute myocardial ischaemia in the rat, dog, pig, and marmoset monkey. Early studies used inadequate numbers of animals and lacked the statistical power to detect an antiarrhythmic effect. Diets containing large amounts of fish oil (10% of energy for 8-16 weeks) significantly reduced the incidence of ischaemia-induced VF *in vivo* and *in vitro*, and increased the relative levels of n-3 eicosapentaenoic and docosahexaenoic acid in myocardial phospholipids. However, ischaemic-reperfusion arrhythmias were not reduced by this dose of fish oil in the isolated perfused rat heart, although a reduction was observed *in vivo*. The relevance of such doses of fish oil to humans is questionable. Fish oil (0.4% of energy) administered in both short- (8 weeks) and long-term (6 months) experiments did not protect against ischaemia-induced VF in the isolated perfused rat heart, although typical changes in fatty acid composition were observed. Saturated fatty acid intake was not changed by fish oils at low doses.

Thus, there is a consensus that large amounts of fish oil are antiarrhythmic during acute experimental ischaemia. The mechanism by which fish oils exert these effects is being investigated by several groups. The question of whether the effects of n-3 fatty acids differ from those of n-6 fatty acids remains controversial. However, since diets in which 10% of energy is derived from fish oil are low in saturated fatty acids, it is possible that their replacement by n-3 (or n-6) fatty acids is responsible for protection against ischaemic arrhythmias. Furthermore, the saturated fatty acid content of adipose tissue is related to arrhythmias in patients with myocardial infarction.

References

1. Wood D.A., Riemersma R.A., Butler S., Thomson, M., Macintyre C., Elton R.A., Oliver M.F.: Linoleic acid and eicosapentaenoic acid in adipose tissue and platelets and risk of coronary heart disease. Lancet 1987; i: 177-183
2. Kromhout D., Bosschieter E.B., Coulander C. de L.: The inverse relation between fish consumption and 20-year mortality from coronary heart disease. N. Engl. J. Med., 1985; 312: 1205-1209
3. Shekelle R.B., Missell L.V., Paul O., Shryock A.M., Stamler J.: Fish consumption and the mortality from coronary heart disease. N. Engl. J. Med. 1985; 313: 820
4. Burr M.L., Fehily A.M., Gilbert J.F., Rogers, S., Holliday, R.M., Sweetnam, P.M., Deadman N.M.: Effects of changes in fat, fish and fibre intakes on death and myocardial infarction: Diet and reinfarction trial (DART). Lancet 1989; ii: 757-761
5. Riemersma R.A., Sargent C.A., Abraham R.A., Wright R.L., Oliver M.F.: Fish and the heart. Lancet 1989; ii: 1450
6. McLennan P.L., Abeywardena M.Y., Charnock J.S.: Influence of dietary lipids on arrhythmias and infarction after coronary artery ligation in rats. Can. J. Physiol. Pharmacol. 1985; 63: 1411-1417
7. Riemersma R.A., Sargent C.A., Saman S., Rebergen S.A., Abraham R.: Dietary fatty acids and ischaemic arrhythmias. Lancet 1988; ii: 285-286
8. Abeywardena M.Y., McLennan P.L., Charnock J.S.: Differential effects of dietary fish oil on myocardial PGI_2 & TXA_2 production. Am. J. Physiol. 1991; 260: H379-385
9. Leprán I., Nemecz G.Y., Koltai M., Szekeres L.: Effect of linoleic acid rich diet on the acute phase of coronary occlusion in conscious rats: influence of indomethacin and aspirin. J. Cardiovasc. Pharmacol. 1981; 3: 847-853
10. Walker M.J.A., Curtis M.J., Hearse D.J., Campbell R.W.F., Janse M.J., Yellon D.M., Cobbe S.M., Coker S.J., Harness J.B., Higgins A.J.: The Lambeth Conventions: guidelines for the study of arrhythmias in ischaemia, infarction, and reperfusion. Cardiovasc. Res. 1988; 22: 447-455

11. Culp B.R., Lands W.E.M., Lucchesi B.R., Pitt B., Romson J.: The effect of dietary supplementation of fish oil on experimental myocardial infarction. Prostaglandins 1980; 20: 1021-1031
12. Hartog J.M., Lamers J.M., Verdouw P.D.: The effects of dietary mackerel oil on plasma and cell membrane lipids, on hemodynamics and cardiac arrhythmias during recurrent acute ischaemia in the pig. Basic Res. Cardiol. 1986; 81: 567-580
13. McLennan P.L., Abeywardena M.Y., Charnock J.S.: The influence of dietary fat in an animal model of sudden cardiac death. Austr. N.Z. J. Med. 1987; 17 (Suppl. 2): 597
14. McLennan P.L., Abeywardena M.Y., Charnock J.S.: The influence of age and dietary fat in an animal model of sudden cardiac death. Austr. N.Z. J. Med. 1989; 19: 1-5
15. McLennan P.L., Abeywardena M.Y., Charnock J.S.: Reversal of the arrhythmogenic effects of long-term saturated fatty acid intake by dietary n-3 and n-6 polyunsaturated fatty acids. Am. J. Clin. Nutr. 1990; 51: 53-58
16. McLennan P.L.: Relative effects of dietary saturated, monounsaturated, and polyunsaturated fatty acids on cardiac arrhythmias in rats. Am. J. Clin. Nutr. 1993; 57: 207-212
17. McLennan P.L., Bridle T.M., Abeywardena M.Y., Charnock J.S.: Dietary lipid modulation of ventricular fibrillation in the marmoset monkey. Am. Heart. J. 1992; 123: 1555-1561
18. McLennan P.L., Bridle T.M., Abeywardena M.Y., Charnock J.S.: Comparative efficacy of n-3 and n-6 polyunsaturated fatty acids in modulating ventricular fibrillation threshold in marmoset monkeys. Am. J. Clin. Nutr. 1993; 58: 666-669
19. Sargent C.A.: Dietary n-3 polyunsaturated fatty acids and ischaemic arrhythmias. In: Sargent C.A. (PhD Thesis). *Dietary Fat and Ischaemic Arrhythmias*. Edinburgh; University of Edinburgh, 1990; 7: 165-180
20. Abraham R., Riemersma R.A., Wood D., Elton R., Oliver M.F.: Adipose tissue fatty acid composition and the risk of serious ventricular arrhythmias in acute myocardial infarction. Am. J. Cardiol. 1989; 63: 269-272
21. Christensen J.H., Gustenhoff P., Ejlersen E., Jessen J., Rasmussen K., Dyerberg J., Schmidt E.B.: The effect of polyunsaturated fatty acids on cardiac ventricular arrhythmias - a pilot study. In: De Caterina R., Endres S., Kristensen S.D., Schmidt E.B. (Eds.): *n-3 Fatty Acids and Vascular Disease*.Verona; Bi & Gi Publishers, 1993; 16: 151-157

S.D. Kristensen, E.B. Schmidt, R. De Caterina, S. Endres
n-3 Fatty Acids: Prevention and Treatment in Vascular Disease
Bi & Gi Publishers, Verona - Springer Verlag, London, 1995

10. n-3 Fatty Acids and Ventricular Arrhythmias in Post-Myocardial Infarction Patients with a Low Ejection Fraction

J.H. Christensen[1], P. Gustenhoff[2], E. Korup[2], J. Aarøe[2], E. Toft[2], J. Møller[2], K. Rasmussen[2], J. Dyerberg[3], E.B. Schmidt[1]

1. *Department of Endocrinology, Aalborg Hospital, Denmark*
2. *Department of Cardiology, Aalborg Hospital, Denmark*
3. *Medi-Lab a.s., Copenhagen, Denmark*

Introduction

There is evidence for an antiarrhythmic effect of n-3 fatty acids (FA), mainly generated from the experimental work of Charnock, McLennan and colleagues in Australia.[1-6] This group has shown that FA protect against ischaemia- and reperfusion-induced ventricular tachyarrhythmias in rats and monkeys, with n-3 FA being superior to n-6 FA. This protective effect of n-3 FA is apparently not caused by their antiatherosclerotic effects.[7]

In the Diet and Reinfarction Trial (DART), it was found that patients with a first myocardial infarction (MI) who were advised to eat fatty fish at least twice a week (or a comparable amount of a fish-oil concentrate) had a 29% overall reduction in 2-year mortality compared with patients not given this advice.[8] Approximately 2000 patients were included in the study. The causes of death were not recorded, but post-MI patients are known to be at high risk of sudden cardiac death, believed to be caused by ventricular fibrillation. On the basis of the observed antiarrhythmic effect of n-3 FA in experimental animals, the authors suggested that the reduction in mortality in patients given n-3 FA could be due to a reduction in the incidence of ventricular fibrillation. This intriguing hypothesis, however, needs confirmation from well-designed clinical trials.

The aim of the present study was to investigate the effect of a dietary supplement of n-3 FA on ventricular arrhythmias in patients who had previously suffered an MI and who had a low ejection fraction.

Patients and Methods

The study was performed at the out-patients' clinic of the Department of Cardiology, Aalborg Hospital. Patients were eligible if they had been discharged from the Department after an MI between November 1991 and August 1993. Furthermore, inclusion required that echocardiography, performed within the first week after the MI and prior to treatment with an angiotensin-converting enzyme inhibitor, showed a ventricular ejection fraction below 0.40.

Patients with the following conditions were excluded: over 75 years of age, an implanted pacemaker, sustained tachyarrhythmias, and other serious non-cardiac diseases. A total of 81 patients were asked to participate in the double-blind, placebo-controlled study; 55 of these gave their informed consent and were randomized to receive either 5.2 g n-3 FA daily (4.3 g eicosapentaenoic acid (EPA) and docosahexaenoic acid (DHA), equivalent to eight capsules of Pikasol®, Pronova Biocare A/S, Norway) or olive oil rich in monounsaturated fatty acids. The supplements were given daily for 12 weeks. Dietary habits and medication were kept constant during the trial.

Prior to randomization, a 24-hour Holter recording was obtained from each patient, and this was repeated at the end of the study. The tapes from the Holter recordings were analysed on a Reynolds Pathfinder IV system. During the trial, one patient from the control group died, two patients did not complete the study for personal reasons, and three patients were excluded (one developed a ventricular aneurism, one developed atrial flutter and one was excluded because of technical problems with the Holter recording). The study protocol was approved by the Ethics Committee of Northern Jutland.

Table I gives the clinical characteristics of the remaining 49 patients, and shows that the experimental and placebo groups were comparable. The two groups were also similar with respect to the time that had elapsed from MI to inclusion in the study (mean time, 21 months). The cardiovascular medications of the patients are shown in Table II. The Mann-Whitneys rank-sum test was used for statistical analysis between the groups, and Wilcoxon's signed rank test was used for comparison within groups. A p value below 0.05 (two-tailed) was considered significant.

Results

Three episodes of non-sustained ventricular tachycardia were found at baseline in the n-3 FA study group (in three patients), while two episodes were found after

Table I. Characterization of the patients given n-3 fatty acids (FA) or placebo (control). Values are exact numbers or means±SD.

Characteristics	n-3 FA	Control
Number	26	23
Age (years)	65±5	62±8
Q-wave infarction (n)	21	17
Location of infarction		
Anterior (n)	16	12
Inferior (n)	7	6
Other (n)	3	5
Smoker (n)	9	9
Hypertension (n)	4	2

supplementation with n-3 FA. One episode was observed in the same patient before and at the end of the study in the placebo group. Statistical comparison was not meaningful because of the low number of events.

The mean number of ventricular extrasystoles/24 hours (VE/24 hours) decreased from 1347 at baseline to 281 after supplementation in the n-3 FA group, and from 558 to 308 in the control group. However, the numbers ranged from 3 to 22525 in the former and from 1 to 7580 in the latter. Therefore, in order to minimize the variance and to allow conventional medical statistics, the natural logarithm of VE/24 hour was calculated. The results are given in Table III.

The natural logarithm of VE/24 hours was also calculated separately in high-risk patients with Q-wave infarctions and in high-risk patients with anterior infarctions.

Table II. Number of patients in the n-3 fatty acid (FA) and placebo (control) groups receiving cardiovascular medication.

Cardiovascular medication	n-3 FA	Control
Aspirin	26	21
Diuretics	12	11
Digoxin	3	5
Beta-blocker	3	2
Calcium-blocker	8	7
Other antiarrhythmic drugs	1	1

Table III. The natural logarithms of the number of ventricular extrasystoles (VE)/24 hours in patients before and after administration of n-3 fatty acids (FA) or placebo. Values are means±SD, with the range given in parentheses.

Log$_e$ VE/24 hours			
n-3 FA		Placebo	
Before	After	Before	After
4.7±2.3 (1.1-10.0)	4.5±1.8 (0-7.8)	4.3±2.2 (0-8.9)	4.0±1.9 (0-7.9)

The results are shown in Table IV. Overall, there was no statistically significant differences within or between the two groups.

Discussion

Patients with a previous MI are known to be at risk of sudden cardiac death from malignant ventricular tachyarrhythmias. Suppression of spontaneous arrhythmias occurring after an MI may reduce sudden cardiac death, although results from clinical trials with antiarrhythmic drugs have been disappointing.[9-13] Post-MI patients with low ejection fractions are likely to have large myocardial scars. They are therefore more likely to develop sustained ventricular arrhythmias, if the heart is exposed to episodes of repetitive VE.

Table IV. The natural logarithm of the number of ventricular extrasystoles (VE)/24 hours in patients with anterior or Q-wave infarctions before and after administration of n-3 fatty acids (FA) or placebo. Values are means±SD, with the range given in parentheses.

	Log$_e$ VE/24 hours			
	n-3 FA		Placebo	
Infarction type	Before	After	Before	After
Q-wave	4.8±2.2 (1.1-10.0)	4.3±1.9 (0-7.8)	4.1±2.0 (1.1-8.9)	3.7±1.5 (2.0-7.9)
Anterior	4.0±2.3 (1.1-10.0)	3.9±1.8 (0-7.2)	4.0±2.3 (0-8.9)	3.3±1.6 (0-7.3)

We chose to monitor ventricular arrhythmias in a well-defined group of patients, in whom a low ejection fraction and number of VE were independent mortality risk factors.[13-15] Not unexpectedly, only a few episodes of non-sustained ventricular tachycardia were found in this relatively small group of 49 patients, who had survived an MI and were receiving various cardiovascular medications. Thus, the major end-point in the present study was the number of VE before and after supplementation with n-3 FA.

Results showed that n-3 FA did not reduce the number of VE in this high-risk group of patients. Neither did n-3 FA have any effect in subgroups of patients who had suffered from a transmural MI (Q-wave) or from large anterior MIs.

Considering the results of the Cardiac Arrhythmia Suppression Trial (CAST),[10] it may be questioned whether suppression of VE in a post-MI population is relevant. The CAST study recruited some 2309 patients who were comparable to those described in the present study. Before the patients were enrolled in the final part of the CAST study, it was required that they had a reduction in VE of more than 80%, achieved by the use of one of three drugs (encainide, flecainide or moricizine). Approximately 1700 patients fulfilled this criterion and were randomly assigned to receive one of the three drugs under investigation or placebo. The study was stopped, because death from arrhythmias (and other causes) was more than three times more common (relative risk=3.6) in patients treated with encainide or flecainide than in the controls.[10] These results indicate that suppression of VE by means of an antiarrhythmic drug (with a possible proarrhythmic effect) in post-MI patients does not prolong survival. The DART study,[8] however, showed that mortality was reduced in post-MI patients given n-3 FA; thus, in the present study the effect of n-3 FA on VE was examined.

Only two studies demonstrating the effect of n-3 FA on arrhythmias in humans have previously been published. In a non-blinded, non-controlled, crossover study from Iceland[16], 18 men with a recent MI were divided into two groups. One group received cod liver oil supplementation for 6 weeks, while the other group received no diet supplement. Crossover was performed after the first 6 weeks, and the trial continued for another 6 weeks. Any carry-over effect or 'wash-out' was disregarded. Holter recordings were obtained over 48 hours at baseline, at the time of crossover and at the end of the study. Although no effect was seen on VE, the study was thus flawed in that it was non-blinded, non-controlled and comprised only a small number of patients.

In a more recent study, we randomized patients with documented ventricular tachyarrhythmias to 5.2 g n-3 FA daily or placebo (corn oil) for 16 weeks in a double-blind design.[17,18] We found a trend towards a reduction in VE in the patients receiving n-3 FA, but a lack of statistical significance, which could be due to a type 2 error (small sample size, n=19). It may also be questioned whether corn oil, given to the controls, was inert, as n-6 FA have been shown to have some antiarrhythmic effect in animals.[1-6] This problem was solved in the present study, where the controls were given olive oil, which apparently has no antiarrhythmic effect.[19]

There are several mechanisms by which n-3 FA may reduce cardiac vulnerability to ventricular arrhythmias. The incorporation of EPA and DHA at the expense of arachidonic acid into myocardial membranes after fish-oil supplementation may stabilize the myocardial membrane, making it more resistant to proarrhythmogenic stimuli.[20-22] Also, the balance between locally formed eicosanoids, such as thromboxane A_2 and prostaglandin I_2, may be involved in arrhythmogenesis.[23-25] This balance was changed in a favourable way in marmoset monkeys fed n-3 FA-supplemented diets compared with marmosets fed diets rich in saturated fat.[26]

It has been reported that n-3 FA may act like calcium channel blockers in rat myocytes, thus decreasing the risk of arrhythmias.[21,27] Interestingly, this effect on calcium channels may be independent of the incorporation of EPA and DHA into the myocardial membranes, as a recent study reported an antiarrhythmic effect shortly after intravenous infusion of n-3 FA.[28]

In conclusion, the present study showed no effect of n-3 FA supplementation for 12 weeks on ventricular arrhythmias in post-MI patients. Although of great theoretical interest, it is unlikely that the effects of n-3 FA on ventricular fibrillation in humans can be tested. It is more likely that future studies in this intriguing area will use more sensitive methods, such as monitoring heart rate variability, which is known to be a powerful predictor of mortality in post-MI patients.[29] Furthermore, in order to strengthen statistical power, the number of high-risk patients included in such studies needs to be increased.

Summary

There is evidence for an antiarrhythmic effect of n-3 fatty acids (FA) in animals, and such an effect is further supported by results from *in vitro* studies. The aim of the present study was to investigate the effect of dietary n-3 FA on ventricular arrhythmias in patients with a previous myocardial infarction. Fifty-five patients were randomized to receive either 5.2 g of n-3 FA daily (4.3 g of eicosapentaenoic acid + docosahexaenoic acid) for 12 weeks or olive oil in a double-blind, placebo-controlled study. Prior to randomization a 24-hour Holter recording was obtained, and this was repeated at the end of the study. The tapes from the Holter recordings were analysed on a Reynolds Pathfinder IV system. The mean number of ventricular extrasystoles/24 hours decreased from 1347 at baseline to 281 after supplementation in the n-3 group, and from 558 to 308 in the controls, but this difference was not statistically significant. Future studies in this intriguing area should take advantage of more sensitive methods such as the monitoring of heart rate variability, and the number of high-risk patients included in such trials may need to be increased.

References

1. McLennan P.L., Abeywardena M.Y., Charnock J.S.: The influence of age and dietary fat in an animal model of sudden cardiac death. Aust. N.Z. J. Med. 1989; 19: 1-5
2. McLennan P.L., Abeywardena M.Y., Charnock J.S.: Dietary fish oil prevents ventricular fibrillation following coronary artery occlusion and reperfusion. Am. Heart J. 1988; 116; 709-717
3. McLennan P.L., Abeywardena M.Y., Charnock J.S.: Reversal of the arrhythmogenic effects of long-term saturated fatty acid intake by dietary n-3 and n-6 polyunsaturated fatty acids. Am. J. Clin. Nutr. 1990; 51: 53-58
4. McLennan P.L., Bridle T.M., Abeywardena M.Y., Charnock J.S.: Dietary lipid modulation of ventricular fibrillation threshold in the marmoset monkey. Am. Heart J. 1992; 123: 1555-1561
5. Siebert B.D., McLennan P.L., Woodhouse J.A., Charnock J.S.: Cardiac arrhythmias in rats in response to dietary n-3 fatty acids from red meat, fish oil and canola oil. Nutr. Res. 1993; 13: 1407-1418
6. Charnock J.S.: Lipids and cardiac arrhythmias. Prog. Lipid Res. 1994; 4: 355-385
7. Turner J., McLennan P.L., Abeywardena M.Y., Charnock J.S.: Absence of coronary or aortic atherosclerosis in rats having dietary lipid modified vulnerability to cardiac arrhythmias. Atherosclerosis 1990; 82: 105-112
8. Burr M.L., Fehily A.M., Gilbert J.F., Rogers S., Holliday R.M., Sweetnam P.M., Elwood P.C., Deadman N.M.: Effects of changes in fat, fish, and fibre intakes on death and myocardial reinfarction: Diet and reinfarction trial (DART). Lancet 1989; ii: 757-761
9. Amlie J.P.: New trends in the diagnosis and treatment of cardiac arrhythmias (Editorial). J. Intern. Med. 1993; 233: 429-431
10. CAST (Cardiac Arrhythmia Suppression Trial). Preliminary report. Effect of encainide and flecainide on mortality in a randomized trial of arrhythmia suppression after myocardial infarction. N. Engl. J. Med. 1989; 321: 406-412
11. Krikler D.M., Curry P.V.K.: Torsade de pointes, an atypical ventricular tachycardia. Br. Heart J. 1976; 38: 117-120
12. Myerburg R.J., Kessler M.K., Castallsnos A.: Sudden cardiac death: epidemiology, transient risk, and intervention assessment. Ann. Intern. Med. 1993; 119: 1187-1197
13. Myerburg R.J., Kessler M.K., Chakko S., Cox M.M., Fernandez P., Interian A., Castellanos A.: Future evaluation of antiarrhythmic therapy. Am. Heart J. 1994; 127: 1111-1118
14. Bigger J.T., Fleiss J.L., Kleiger R., Miller J.P., Rolnitzky L.M., the Multicenter Post-Infarction Research Group: The relationships among ventricular arrhythmias, left ventricular dysfunction, and mortality in the 2 years after myocardial infarction. Circulation 1984; 69: 250-258
15. Bigger J.T.: Antiarrhythmic therapy: an overview after myocardial infarction. Am. J. Cardiol. 1984; 53: 8B-16B
16. Hardarson T., Kristinsson A., Skuladottir G., Asvaldsdottir H., Snorrason S.P.: Cod liver oil does not reduce ventricular extrasystoles after myocardial infarction. J. Intern. Med. 1989; 226: 33-37
17. Christensen J.H., Gustenhoff P., Ejlersen E., Jessen T., Korup E., Rasmussen K., Dyerberg J., Schmidt E.B.: n-3 fatty acids and ventricular extrasystoles in patients with ventricular tachyarrhythmias. Nutr. Res. 1995; 15: 1-8
18. Christensen J.H., Gustenhoff P., Ejlersen E., Jessen T., Rasmussen K., Dyerberg J., Schmidt E.B.: The effect of n-3 polyunsaturated fatty acids on cardiac ventricular arrhythmias - a pilot study. In: De Caterina R., Endres S., Kristensen S.D., Schmidt E.B. (Eds) *n-3 Fatty Acids and Vascular Disease.* Verona; Bi & Gi Publishers, 1993: 151-157
19. McLennan P.L.: Relative effects of dietary saturated, monounsaturated, and polyunsaturated fatty acids on cardiac arrhythmias in rats. Am. J. Clin. Nutr. 1993; 57: 207-212

20. Patten G.S., Rinaldi J.A., McMurchie E.J.: Effects of dietary eicosapentaenoate (20:5: n-3) on cardiac beta-adrenergic receptor activity in the marmoset monkey. Biochem. Biophys. Res. Comm. 1989; 2: 686-693
21. Hallaq H., Sellmayer A., Smith T.W., Leaf A.: Protective effects of eicosapentaenoic acid on ouabain toxicity in neonatal rat cardiac myocytes. Proc. Natl. Acad. Sci. USA 1990; 87: 7843-7838
22. McMurchie E.J., Burnard S.L., Rinaldi J.A., Patten G.S., Neumann M., Gibson R.A.: Cardiac membrane lipid composition and adenylate cyclase activity following dietary eicosapentaenoic acid supplementation in the marmoset monkey. J. Nutr. Biochem. 1992; 3: 13-22
23. Lepran I., Nemecz G.Y., Koltai M., Szekeres L.: Effect of a linoleic acid-rich diet on the acute phase of coronary occlusion in conscious rats: influence of indomethacin and aspirin. J. Cardiovasc. Pharmacol. 1981; 3: 847-853
24. Coker S.J., Parratt J.R.: Prostacyclin – antiarrhythmic or arrhythmogenic? Comparison of the effect of intravenous and intracoronary prostacyclin and ZK36374 during coronary artery occlusion and reperfusion in anaesthetised greyhounds. J. Cardiovasc. Pharmacol. 1983; 5: 557-567
25. Nowak J., Murray J.J., Fitzgerald G.A.: Eicosanoids and sudden cardiac death. Adv. Prostaglandin Thromboxane Leukotriene Res. 1987; 17: 20-24
26. Abeywardena M.Y., McLennan P.L., Charnock J.S.: Differential effects of dietary fish oil on myocardial prostaglandin I_2 and thromboxane A_2 production. Am. J. Physiol. 1991; 260: 375-385
27. Hallaq H., Smith T.W., Leaf M.: Modulation of dihydropyridine sensitive calcium channels in heart cells by fish oil fatty acids. Proc. Natl. Acad. Sci. USA 1992; 89: 1760-1764
28. Billman G.E., Hallaq H., Leaf A.: Prevention of ischemia-induced ventricular fibrillation by omega-3 fatty acids. Proc. Natl. Acad. Sci. USA 1994; 91: 4427-4430
29. Stein P.K., Bosner M.S., Kleiger R.E., Conger B.M.: Heart rate variability: A measure of cardiac autonomic tone. Am. Heart J. 1994; 127: 1376-1381

S.D. Kristensen, E.B. Schmidt, R. De Caterina, S. Endres
n-3 Fatty Acids: Prevention and Treatment in Vascular Disease
Bi & Gi Publishers, Verona - Springer Verlag, London, 1995

11. The Effect of n-3 Fatty Acids on the Development of Restenosis after Percutaneous Transluminal Coronary Angioplasty

S.D. Kristensen

University Department of Cardiology, Skejby Hospital, Aarhus, Denmark

Introduction

In 1977, Gruentzig and co-workers performed the first human percutaneous transluminal coronary angioplasty (PTCA). Both the technique and the equipment have since been greatly modified and improved and, today, PTCA is widely used and well documented in the treatment of coronary heart disease. Other mechanical, catheter-based approaches, such as intracoronary stent implantation, atherectomy, and rotational and laser angioplasty have been developed and have proved useful in selected cases.

The major clinical problem associated with these interventional techniques is the development of coronary restenosis. This occurs in approximately one-third of the dilated vessels within the first weeks or months after PTCA. The fact that PTCA is now often used in the treatment of two- and even three-vessel disease, underlines the necessity for research into the pathogenesis and prevention of restenosis after PTCA.

Although the cause of restenosis is unknown, it is believed to be multifactorial. When PTCA is performed successfully, the vessel is stretched at the site of dilatation, and the plaque is fissured and disrupted, resulting in exposure of the coronary arterial wall to blood flowing in the vessel lumen. In some cases, elastic recoil of the vessel may be an important event in the occurrence of restenosis. Other contributory factors may include adhesion and activation of platelets and leukocytes at the site of plaque disruption, the consequent synthesis and release of cytokines and growth factors with proliferative properties, and the generation of thrombin and formation of a local thrombus, which may become incorporated into the disrupted plaque. Although proliferation of smooth muscle, and to some extent of fibrous tissue, is believed to be a key event in the development of restenosis, a role for lipids and lipoproteins, comparable to that in atherogenesis, cannot be ruled out.

Several trials have tested the potential value of various drugs in the prevention of restenosis. The factors changed or modulated by these drugs are listed in Table I. Unfortunately, most of these trials have been unsuccessful. An advantage of n-3 fatty acids is, however, that they modulate several of the factors listed in Table I, highlighting the question of whether a multifactorial problem can be solved by an intervention that may act on multiple factors. This review will summarize briefly some of the actions of n-3 fatty acids and will then discuss the randomized trials conducted to examine the use of n-3 fatty acids in the prevention of restenosis after PTCA.

Important Actions of n-3 Fatty Acids

Endothelium

In patients with ischaemic heart disease, dietary intake of n-3 fatty acids prior to bypass surgery has been shown to increase the synthesis of prostacyclin from the saphenous vein, atrial tissue or the aorta.[1] In some studies, n-3 fatty acids have been shown to increase the urinary excretion of prostacyclin metabolites,[2,3] whereas other reports have demonstrated unchanged or decreasing values.[4] Synthesis of endothelial-derived relaxing factor, now known to be nitric oxide, is stimulated in animals fed n-3 fatty acids.[5,6] Prostacyclin and nitric oxide are both platelet inhibitors and vasodilators. Studies conducted *in vitro* using endothelial cells in culture have shown that n-3 fatty acids inhibit the synthesis of platelet-derived growth factor (PDGF) like protein[7], and recently, the n-3 fatty acid, docosahexaenoic acid, was shown to reduce the cytokine-induced expression of leukocyte adhesion molecules.[8] Thus, n-3 fatty acids may exert important anti-thrombotic vasodilatory and antiproliferative properties in the coronary artery, which may be important in the development of restenosis.

Table I. Various cellular and biochemical systems or compounds that may play a role in the development of restenosis after percutaneous transluminal coronary angioplasty (PTCA).

• Endothelium	• Lipids and lipoproteins
• Platelets	• Smooth muscle cells
• Leukocytes	• Connective tissue
• Coagulation and fibrinolysis	• Vascular tone

Platelets

Dietary intake of n-3 fatty acids in healthy individuals or in patients with ischaemic heart disease can moderately prolong the bleeding time and inhibit platelet aggregation (for review see Kristensen *et al.*[9]). This is probably due mainly to the inhibition of thromboxane synthesis.[9] However, reports showing that the intake of n-3 fatty acids also prolongs the bleeding time in patients treated with aspirin[10,11] suggest that n-3 fatty acids may also have platelet-inhibiting properties that are not mediated by cyclooxygenases. In addition, n-3 fatty acids have been shown to inhibit the adhesion of platelets to collagen and to cause the fibrinogen-independent inhibition of platelet aggregation.[12]

The importance of platelets in the development of restenosis after PTCA has been underlined recently by the results of the EPIC study.[13,14] In high risk patients undergoing PTCA, treatment with a strong inhibitor of platelet aggregation (glycoprotein IIb/IIIa antagonist) not only decreased the number of acute vascular events,[13] but also significantly decreased the incidence of restenosis.[14]

Leukocytes

Leukocyte adhesion, activation and secretion of cytokines are believed to play a role in atherogenesis and are also likely to be important in the development of restenosis after PTCA. Several *in vitro* experiments, animal studies, and studies in healthy individuals and patients with ischaemic heart disease have shown that n-3 fatty acids inhibit the adhesion and migration of leukocytes, probably in part by inhibiting the production of bioactive leukotrienes,[15] and also suppress the production of cytokines,[16] including PDGF.[17]

Lipids and lipoproteins

The role of lipids in the development of restenosis is not well established. However, there is now no doubt that lipids are important in atherogenesis, and lowering of low density lipoprotein (LDL)-cholesterol has recently been shown to decrease mortality in patients with ischaemic heart disease.[18] The effect of dietary supplementation with n-3 fatty acids on lipids and lipoprotein metabolism has been studied extensively.[19,20] In short, n-3 fatty acid supplementation lowers triglycerides, whereas the effect on LDL- and high density lipoprotein (HDL)-cholesterol is, in most cases, neutral.

Smooth muscle cells

Proliferation of smooth muscle cells is a hallmark of restenosis. n-3 fatty acids may decrease the synthesis of PDGF by the endothelium[7] and by leukocytes[17] and perhaps also by platelets. The effect of n-3 fatty acids on experimental atherosclerosis has, in some studies, been beneficial and the interesting results of these studies have been reviewed elsewhere[21] and in another chapter of this book by Soei *et al.* (pp 55-75).

Vascular tone and blood pressure

The inhibition of thromboxane synthesis and the stimulation of the production of nitric oxide and perhaps also of prostacyclin, elicited by n-3 supplementation, may lead to local or general diminished vascular tone. n-3 fatty acids may also reduce vasoconstriction induced by adrenaline.[22] In patients with mild hypertension, dietary supplementation with n-3 fatty acids causes a small, but significant, reduction in blood pressure.[23,24]

n-3 Fatty Acids in the Prevention of Restenosis after PTCA

Definition and evaluation of restenosis

Over the years, the definition of restenosis and the recommended methods for evaluating the effect of drugs or other therapies that may influence the incidence of restenosis after PTCA have changed. The use of a clinical definition based on recurrence of symptoms and, for example, the demonstration of ischaemia by exercise ECG, is now considered obsolete. Angiographic evaluation of the dilated stenosis 6 months after the PTCA is now mandatory. The use of computerized quantitative coronary angiography is strongly recommended in order to reduce observer bias and to increase reproducibility. However, even with the use of quantitative coronary angiography, different definitions of restenosis have been used.[25]

Clinical trials with n-3 fatty acids

Eleven studies have been published in English to date on the effect of n-3 fatty acids in the prevention of restenosis (Table II).[26-36]

Design

In all studies, allocation to a treatment- or control-group was randomized, but only five of the studies were double-blind.[28,30,32,34,36]

The placebo used was vegetable oil or olive oil,[30,32,34] administered in capsules identical to those containing n-3 fatty acids. Complete blinding, particularly of the patients, may be difficult, as a fishy after-taste is often experienced after intake of capsules of n-3 fatty acids. A potential method for overcoming this problem is to add a flavour, such as peppermint, to the capsules[34,37] or to add a very small amount of n-3 fatty acids to the placebo capsules.[36] Another problem is that placebo oils may not be totally inert, and may in fact affect various cellular systems that influence the development of restenosis. Therefore, it may be difficult to conduct a perfect double-blind trial using n-3 fatty acids. Some of the actions of n-3 fatty acids are clearly dependent on their incorporation into the phospholipids of platelet and other cell membranes. As this incorporation may take up to 1 week,[38] it seems logical to start treatment with n-3 fatty acids at least 1 week prior to PTCA, in order to achieve an optimal effect on restenosis. This was carried out in only three of the studies.[27,32,36] In three other studies,[30,33,35] treatment with n-3 fatty acids was initiated 1-7 days before PTCA, whereas in the remaining studies, treatment with n-3 fatty acids was started after PTCA.[26,28,29,31,34]

In some trials, patients were urged to take a large number of capsules each day. It may be important, therefore, to assess patient compliance, ideally by measurement of the incorporation of n-3 fatty acids into cell membranes. This was conducted in only four of the trials.[27,28,34,36]

End-points

In seven trials, the end-point used was an angiographic assessment of restenosis.[27,28,31,32,34-36] However, in only three of the studies[32,35,36] was quantitative coronary angiography performed in all patients. In the study by Bairati *et al.*,[32] the angiography data were evaluated using four different definitions of restenosis for each patient, illustrating the fact that several different international standards have been used and recommended. In four of the trials, only a clinical assessment of the effect of n-3 fatty acids on restenosis was used.[26,29,30,33]

Dose

The dose of n-3 fatty acid used per day varied from 2.7 g to 8 g in the 11 studies (Table II). This range of doses has been used in hundreds of studies conducted to test the effect of n-3 fatty acids on various biochemical and cellular functions in healthy individuals and in patients with cardiovascular disease. Although the effect of n-3 fatty acids on lipids and platelet function may show a direct dose-response relationship,[39] it is quite evident from Table II that the dose and effect of n-3 fatty acids are not directly related. It is interesting to note that in the study by Bairati *et al.*,[32] a relationship was seen between even a very low habitual dietary intake of fish and the inhibition of restenosis.

Similarly, in the Diet and Reinfarction Trial (DART),[40] a fairly low daily consumption of n-3 fatty acids (dietary intake of fatty fish at least twice a week) decreased mortality after a first acute myocardial infarction. Thus, the question of

Table II. Results from eleven randomized controlled trials conducted to examine the effect of fish oil on the rate of restenosis following percutaneous transluminal coronary angioplasty (PTCA).

	Restenoses /patients				
	Fish oil (%)	Placebo (%)	Signif-icance	n-3 FA/ day (g)	Treatment started before PTCA
Slack *et al.*[26]	8/50 (16)	21/63 (33)	+	2.7	No
Dehmer *et al.*[27]	8/43 (19)	18/39 (46)	+	5.4	Yes (7 days)
Grigg *et al.*[28]	15/54 (28)	19/60 (32)	0	3.0	No
Milner *et al.*[29]	21/95 (22)	35/99 (35)	+	4.5	No
Reis *et al.*[30]	44/124 (35)	15/62 (24)	0	6.0	Yes (1-7 days)
Nye *et al.*[31]	5/36 (14)	18/71 (25)	+	3.6	No
Bairati *et al.*[32]	18/59 (31)	29/60 (48)	+	4.5	Yes (21 days)
Kaul *et al.*[33]	19/58 (33)	13/49 (27)	0	3.0	Yes (1-7 days)
Franzen *et al.*[34]	30/92 (33)	29/83 (35)	0	3.2	No
Bellamy *et al.*[35]	17/60 (28)	15/53 (28)	0	3.0	Yes (1-2 days)
Leaf *et al.*[36]	117/226 (52)	101/221 (46)	0	8.0	Yes (12-14 days)
Total	**302/897 (34)**	**313/860 (36)**			

Abbreviations: FA=fatty acids, + = statistically significant reduction in restenosis rate in the fish-oil group compared with the control group, 0=no statistically significant difference between the groups.

which dose of n-3 fatty acids should be tested in future studies in patients undergoing PTCA is currently impossible to answer.

Results

As indicated in Table II, a statistically significant reduction in the incidence of restenosis after PTCA has been reported to occur following administration of n-3 fatty acids in five of the 11 studies. No such effect was demonstrated in the six other studies.[28,30,33-36]

As stated above, the studies used different designs, doses and, most importantly, end-points. Furthermore, the number of patients has been fairly low in most of the studies. Therefore, it may be difficult to make a valid general conclusion.

A possible method for reaching such a conclusion is to pool the data from different trials in order to increase the number of patients and then to perform meta-analysis. Clearly, when the trial design is as nonhomogeneous as in the present situation, the validity of such an approach is highly debatable. Another important set-back of meta-analysis is that negative, unpublished trials are neglected. Despite this, serious attempts at meta-analysis have been published.[41-43]

O'Connor and co-workers[41] have reviewed all the data from the first seven trials[26-32] and have estimated the overall effect and 95% confidence interval for these studies. The typical odds ratio (treatment *versus* control) was 0.71 (95% confidence interval, 0.54-0.94, $p=0.016$). A strong and highly significant ($p<0.0001$) relationship was identified between the dose of n-3 fatty acids and gastrointestinal side-effects.[41] In a formal meta-analysis based on six of the trials, Goodnight *et al.*[42] reported an odds reduction of 26.7% (95% confidence interval, 2-45.2%, $p<0.05$). Finally, Roy[43] conducted a meta-analysis of three studies in which the definition of restenosis was based on an angiographic follow-up published up to 1992. The typical *odds ratio* reduction was 40% (95% confidence interval, 22-70%, $p<0.05$).

The conclusion drawn following the meta-analysis by O'Connor *et al.* in 1992 was that the data available was compatible with a small-to-moderate beneficial effect of n-3 fatty acids on restenosis, but that this result required confirmation in a randomized clinical trial large enough to distinguish between a clinically meaningful benefit and a null result.[41]

The results of such a trial have been published very recently.[36] The trial was a large, American, multicentre trial in which Alexander Leaf and colleagues randomized 551 patients undergoing elective PTCA to receive treatment with n-3 fatty acids (8 g) or corn oil (placebo, 8 g) for 6 months.[36] The end-point was evaluated using quantitative coronary angiography and the definition of restenosis was a >30% increase in narrowing at the stenosis site or a loss of at least half of the gain achieved at the time of PTCA and a final restenosis diameter of >50%. Treatment was started 12-14 days before the PTCA procedure, the two groups were well-matched and compliance, as judged by incorporation of n-3 fatty acids into red cell phospholipids, was good.

The number of side-effects was minor and did not differ between the two groups. After 6 months, 447 patients were available for assessment and the rate of restenosis was 52% for the group treated with n-3 fatty acids and 46% for the group treated with corn oil ($p=0.37$). This convincing trial, using a high dose of n-3 fatty acids, clearly provides no support for a role of n-3 fatty acids in the reduction of the rate of restenosis in patients undergoing PTCA.

The results of another large study are currently awaited. In this Canadian trial, a total of 800 patients undergoing PTCA will be randomized to receive n-3 fatty acids (4.5 g/day for 4 months) or placebo, and low molecular weight heparin or no heparin in a factorial design. The end-point will be restenosis, evaluated by quantitative coronary angiography.

Conclusion

Dietary supplementation with n-3 fatty acids may have a beneficial influence on several biochemical functions and cellular events that may play a role in the development of restenosis after coronary angioplasty. Of the 11 randomized trials conducted to examine the effects of n-3 fatty acids published to date, five showed a significant reduction in the incidence of restenosis after PTCA, whereas six studies were neutral. Only three studies used a quantitative angiographic assessment of restenosis, which is now considered mandatory. One of these three studies demonstrated a significant reduction in the incidence of restenosis in patients given n-3 fatty acids.[32] However, in the recent study by Leaf *et al.*,[36] no effect of n-3 fatty acids on the rate of restenosis was demonstrated. Although the results of another large study are awaited, there is currently no clear evidence that n-3 fatty acids have a favourable effect on the rate of restenosis in patients undergoing PTCA.

Summary

Restenosis is the major clinical problem in patients undergoing percutaneous transluminal coronary angioplasty (PTCA) and occurs in 25-50% of the patients. Dietary supplementation with n-3 fatty acids has been shown to modify cardiovascular risk factors in a beneficial way in these patients. These beneficial effects include an inhibition of thromboxane production and platelet reactivity, a vasodilatation mediated by an increased synthesis of endothelial-derived relaxing factor or other vasodilating substances, antiinflammatory properties induced by inhibition of synthesis of leukotrienes and cytokines, and a decrease in plasma triglycerides and in blood pressure. These positive effects and epidemiological evidence combined with interesting effects on atherogenesis in experimental models have encouraged researchers to evaluate the effects of n-3 fatty acids on the incidence of restenosis after PTCA. To date, 11 randomized trials have been published; five have shown a significant reduction in the incidence of restenosis after PTCA, whereas six studies have been neutral. Only three of the studies have used quantitative coronary angiographic assessment of restenosis, which now is considered mandatory. In one of these studies, the incidence of restenosis was reduced in the patients given n-3 fatty acids, but in a recent large, multicenter trial comprising 551 patients such an effect could not be confirmed. Although the results of another large study are awaited, there is at the present time no clear evidence that n-3 fatty acids have a favourable effect on restenosis rate in patients undergoing PTCA.

References

1. De Caterina R., Gianness D., Mazzone A., *et al.*: Vascular prostacyclin is increased in patients ingesting omega-3 polyunsaturated fatty acids before coronary artery bypass surgery. Circulation 1990; 82: 428-438
2. Fischer S., Weber P.C.: Prostaglandin I is formed in man after dietary eicosapenaenoic acid. Nature 1984; 307: 165-168
3. von Schacky C., Fischer S., Weber P.C.: Long-term effects of dietary marine omega-3 fatty acids upon plasma and cellular lipids, platelet function and eicosanoid formation in humans. J. Clin. Invest. 1985; 76: 1626-1631

4. FitzGerald G.A.: Eicosanoid dependent and independent effects of n-3 fatty acids on platelets and vascular function. In: De Caterina R., Kristensen S.D., Schmidt E.B. (Eds.) *Fish oil and Vascular Disease*. Verona, Bi & Gi Publishers, 1992: 97-102
5. Shimokawa H., Lam J.Y.T., Chesebro J.H., Bowie E.J.W., Vanhoutte P.M.: Effects of dietary supplementation with cod-liver oil on endothelium-dependent responses in porcine coronary arteries. Circulation 1987; 76: 898-905
6. Komori K., Shimokawa H., Vanhoutte P.M.: Endothelium-dependent relaxation in response to aggregating platelets in porcine femoral veins and its modulation by diet. Circulation 1989; 80: 401-409
7. Fox P., DiCorleto P.: Fish oils inhibit endothelial cell production of platelet-derived growth factor-like protein. Science 1988; 241: 453-456
8. De Caterina R., Cybulsky M.I., Clinton S.K., Gimbrone M.A. Jr., Libby P.: The omega-3 fatty acid docosahexaenoate reduces cytokine-induced expression of proatherogenic and proinflammatory proteins in human endothelial cells. Arterioscler. Thromb. 1994; 14: 1829-1836
9. Kristensen S.D., Schmidt E.B., Dyerberg J.: Dietary supplementation with n-3 polyunsaturated fatty acids and human platelet function: a review with particular implications for cardiovascular disease. J. Int. Med. 1989; 225 (Suppl 731): 141-150
10. Thorngren M., Gustafsen A.: Effects of 11-week increase in dietary eicosapentaenoic acid on bleeding time, lipids, and platelet aggregation. Lancet 1981; ii: 1190-1193
11. Harris W.S., Silveira S., Dujovne C.A.: The combined effects of n-3 fatty acids and aspirin on haemostatic parameters in man. Thromb. Res. 1990; 57: 517-526
12. Li X., Steiner M.: Fish oil: A potent inhibitor of platelet adhesiveness. Blood 1990; 76: 938-945
13. The EPIC Investigators. Use of a monoclonal antibody directed against the platelet glycoprotein IIb/IIIa receptor in high-risk coronary angioplasty. N. Engl. J. Med. 1994; 330: 956-961
14. Topol E.J., Califf R.M., Weisman H.F., *et al.*, on behalf of the EPIC Investigators.: Randomized trial of coronary intervention with antibody against platelet IIb/IIIa integrin for reduction of clinical restenosis: results at 6 months. Lancet 1994; 343: 881-886
15. Lehr H.A., Nolte D., Hubner C., Messmer K.: n-3 fatty acids and leucocyte adhesion. In: De Caterina R., Endres S., Kristensen S.D., Schmidt E.B. (Eds.) *n-3 Fatty Acids and Vascular Disease*. Verona; Bi & Gi Publishers; 1993: 39-47
16. Endres S., Eisenhut T., Sinha B.: n-3 fatty acids and cytokines. In: De Caterina R., Endres S., Kristensen S.D., Schmidt E.B. (Eds.) *n-3 Fatty Acids and Vascular Disease*. Verona; Bi & Gi Publishers, 1993: 31-38
17. Kaminsky W.E., Jendraschak E., Kiefl R., *et al.*: Dietary w-3 fatty acids lower levels of platelet-derived growth factor mRNA in human mononuclear cells. Blood 1993; 81: 1871-1879
18. Scandinavian Simvastatin Survival Study Group. Randomised trial of cholesterol lowering in 4444 patients with coronary heart disease: the Scandinavian Simvastatin Survival Study (4S). Lancet 1994; 344: 1383-1389
19. Harris W.S.: Fish oils and plasma lipid and lipoprotein metabolism in humans: a critical review. J. Lipid Res. 1989; 30: 785-807
20. Schmidt E.B., Kristensen S.D., De Caterina R., Illingworth D.R.: The effect of n-3 fatty acids on plasma lipids and lipoproteins and other cardiovascular risk factors in patients with hyperlipidemia. Atherosclerosis 1993; 103: 107-121
21. Sassen I.M.A., Lamers J.M.J., Verdouw P.D.: Fish oil and the prevention and regression of atherosclerosis. Cardiovasc. Drugs Ther. 1994; 8: 179-191
22. Lam J.Y.T., Badimon J.J., Ellefson R.D., Fuster V., Chesebro J.H.: Cod liver oil alters platelet-

arterial wall response to injury in pigs. Cir. Res. 1992; 71: 769-775

23. Knapp H.R., FitzGerald G.A.: The antihypertensive effects of fish oil: A controlled study of polyunsaturated fatty acids supplements in essential hypertension. N. Engl. J. Med. 1989; 320: 1037-1043
24. Bonaa K.H., Bjerve K.S., Straume B., Gram I.T., Thelle D.: Effect of eicosapentaenoic and docosahexaenoic acid on blood pressure in hypertension. N. Engl. J. Med. 1990; 322: 795-780
25. Califf R.M., Ohman M., Frid D.J., et al.: Restenosis: The clinical issues. In: Topol E.J., (Ed.) *Textbook of Interventional Cardiology*. Philadelphia; WB Saunders Company, 1990: 363-394
26. Slack J.D., Pinkerton C.A., VanTassel J., *et al.*: Can oral fish oil supplement minimize re-stenosis after percutaneous transluminal angioplasty? J. Am. Coll. Cardiol. 1987; 9: 64A (Abstract)
27. Dehmer G.J., Popma J.J., van den Berg E.K., *et al.*: Reduction in the rate of early restenosis after coronary angioplasty by a diet supplemented with n-3 fatty acids. N. Engl. J. Med. 1988; 319: 733-740
28. Grigg L.E., Kay T.W.H., Valentine P.A., *et al.*: Determinants of restenosis and lack of effect of dietary supplementation with eicosapentaenoic acid on the incidence of coronary restenosis after angioplasty. J. Am. Coll. Cardiol. 1989; 13: 665-672
29. Milner M.R., Gallino R.A., Leffingwell A., *et al.*: Usefulness of fish oil supplements in preventing clinical evidence of restenosis after percutaneous transluminal angioplasty. Am. J. Cardiol. 1989; 64: 294-299
30. Reis G.J., Boucher T.M., Sipperly M.E., *et al.*: Randomized trial of fish oil for prevention of restenosis after coronary angioplasty. Lancet 1989; ii: 177-181
31. Nye E.R., Ilsley C.D.J., Ablett M.B., Sutherland W., Robertson M.C.: Effect of eicosapentaenoic acid on restenosis rate, clinical course and blood lipids in patients after percutaneous transluminal angioplasty. Aust. N.Z. J. Med. 1990; 20: 549-552
32. Bairati I., Roy L., Meyer F.: Double-blind randomized controlled trial of fish oil supplements in prevention of the recurrence of stenosis after coronary angioplasty. Circulation 1992; 85: 950-956
33. Kaul U., Sanghvi S., Bahl V.K., Dev V., Wasir H.S.: Fish oil supplements for prevention of restenosis after coronary angioplasty. Int. J. Cardiol. 1992; 35: 87-93
34. Franzen D., Schannwell M., Oette K., Hopp H.W.: A prospective, randomized, and double-blind trial on the effect of fish oil on the incidence of restenosis following PTCA. Cathet. Cardiovasc. Diagn. 1993; 28: 301-310
35. Bellamy C.M., Schofield P.M., Faragher E.B., Ramsdale D.R.: Can supplementation with omega-3 polyunsatured fatty acids reduce coronary angioplasty restenosis rate? Eur. Heart J. 1992; 3: 1626-1631
36. Leaf A., Jorgensen M.B., Jacobs A.K., *et al.*: Do fish oils prevent restenosis after coronary angioplasty? Circulation 1994; 90: 2248-2257
37. Kristensen S.D., Schmidt E.B., Andersen H.R., Dyerberg J.: Fish oil in *angina pectoris.* Atherosclerosis 1987; 64: 13-19
38. Knapp H.R., Reilly I.A., Allessadrini P., *et al.*: *In vivo* indexes of platelet and vascular function during fish-oil administration in patients with atherosclerosis. N. Engl. J. Med. 1986; 314: 937-942
39. Schmidt E.B., Varming K., Ernst E., Madsen P., Dyerberg J.: Dose-response studies on the effect of n-3 polyunsaturated fatty acids on lipids and haemostasis. Thromb. Haemost. 1990; 63: 1-5
40. Burr M.L., Fehily A.M., Gilbert J.F., *et al.*: Effects of changes in fat, fish and fibre intake on death and myocardial infarction: diet and reinfarction trial (DART). Lancet 1989; ii: 757-761
41. O'Connor G.T., Malenka D.J., Olmstead E.M., Johnson P.S., Hennekens C.H.: A meta-analysis of randomized trials of fish oil in prevention of restenosis following coronary angioplasty. Am. J. Prev. Med. 1992; 8: 186-192
42. Goodnight S.H., Cairns J.A., Fisher M., FitzGerald G.A.: Assessment of the therapeutic use of n-3 fatty acids in vascular disease and thrombosis. Chest 1992; 102: 374S-384S
43. Roy L.: Fish oil in the prevention of recurrence of stenosis after coronary angioplasty. In: De Caterina R., Endres S., Kristensen S.D., Schmidt E.B., (Eds.) *n-3 Fatty Acids and Vascular Disease*. Verona; Bi & Gi Publishers, 1993: 143-149

S.D. Kristensen, E.B. Schmidt, R. De Caterina, S. Endres
n-3 Fatty Acids: Prevention and Treatment in Vascular Disease
Bi & Gi Publishers, Verona - Springer Verlag, London, 1995

12. n-3 Fatty Acids and Sudden Cardiac Death

T. Saldeen[1,2], R. Luostarinen[1], J.L. Mehta[2]

1. Department of Forensic Medicine, University of Uppsala, Sweden
2. Department of Medicine, University of Florida, Gainesville, Florida, USA

Introduction

Sudden cardiac death (SCD) is the most common cause of death in Western countries. Most instances of SCD are related to total or subtotal occlusion of an atherosclerotic coronary artery and consequent lethal cardiac dysrhythmia. Over the last 50-100 years, the number of these deaths has increased and during the same time period, there has been a change in the consumption of different fatty acids (FA).[1] The consumption of saturated and n-6 FA has increased, while the consumption of n-3 FA has decreased. These changes in FA intake may be one explanation for the increase in the incidence of SCD. In order to examine the possibility that n-3 FA may protect against SCD, we have performed autopsies and conducted clinical and animal studies. This paper is a review of these investigations.

FA Composition of Coronary Arteries in SCD

A FA pattern with low levels of polyunsaturated and a high level of saturated FA in plasma phospholipids may be an important risk factor for ischaemic heart disease (IHD).[2] Whether there is a correlation between the FA pattern in coronary arteries and SCD is unknown. An analysis was therefore made of the FA composition of the total phospholipid fraction of human coronary arteries in cases of SCD.[3] Coronary arteries from victims of SCD were compared with controls, most of whom were traffic accident victims. SCD was defined as an unexpected and instant death from

IHD outside hospital; in 50% of the cases, death was the first sign of IHD. All three major coronary arteries (left anterior descending, left circumflex and right coronary) were collected from all autopsy cases of SCD and from all traffic accident victims aged 35-55 years over a 1-year period. Data from 30 victims of SCD (aged 40±5 years, mean±SD) and 29 road traffic accident victims (mean age 45±5 years) were obtained. Most victims were men, with five women in each group.

Blood vessels were removed from the heart at autopsy, washed thoroughly with cold saline and stored in tightly sealed plastic bags at -70°C. For analysis, vessels were thawed, and the intima and media were carefully separated. The final samples contained the whole intima and most of the media, as confirmed by histology. Coronary arteries from victims of SCD and controls were handled in parallel through each stage of the study procedure, from thawing to analysis of FA composition.

All three coronary arteries were classified into four groups according to the severity of atherosclerosis (fatty streaks with or without fibrous plaques) as follows: grade 0=no atherosclerosis; grade 1=slight atherosclerosis; grade 2=moderate atherosclerosis; and grade 3=severe and extensive atherosclerosis. The mean atherosclerosis score of all three arteries was 1.73±0.75 in SCD victims and 0.68±0.66 in the controls ($p<0.001$). The heart weight was 450±130 g (range 80-830 g) in SCD victims and 350±70 g (range 190-470 g) in control subjects ($p<0.001$).

The FA composition of the phospholipid fraction in the intima and media of coronary arteries from victims of SCD and controls is shown in Figures 1 and 2.

The coronary arteries from victims of SCD contained a significantly higher percentage of palmitic acid (16:0) and linoleic acid (18:2 n-6) compared with the

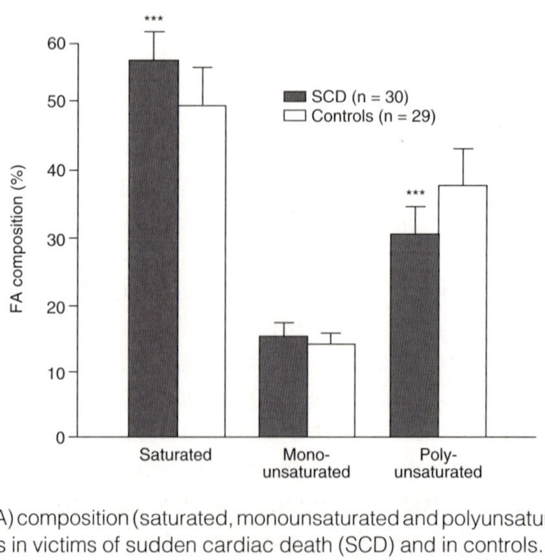

Fig. 1. Fatty acid (FA) composition (saturated, monounsaturated and polyunsaturated) in phospholipids of coronary arteries in victims of sudden cardiac death (SCD) and in controls. Values are mean±SD. ***Indicates a significant difference between victims of SCD and controls ($p<0.001$).

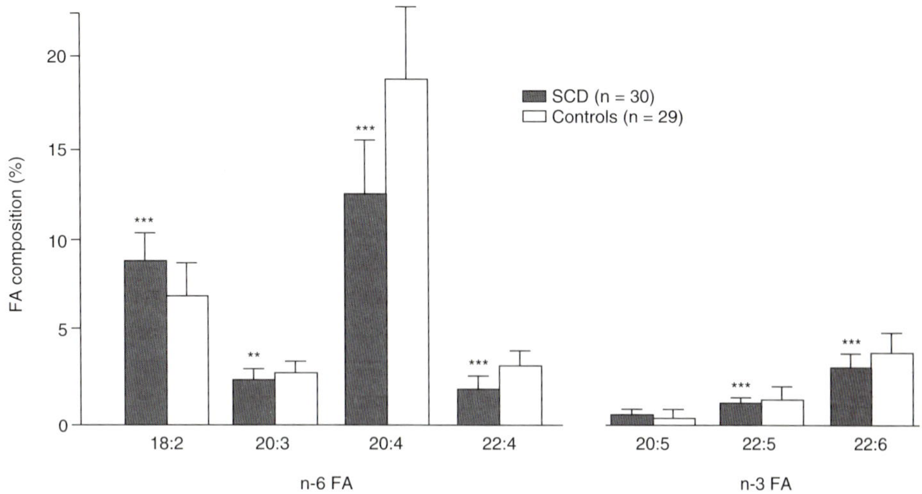

Fig. 2. Fatty acid composition (n-6 and n-3 FA) in phospholipids of coronary arteries in victims of SCD and in controls. ** and *** Indicates a significant difference between victims of SCD and controls ($p<0.01$ and $p<0.001$, respectively).

arteries from controls. In contrast, the percentage of arachidonic acid (20:4) and other major polyunsaturated fatty acids (PUFA) was significantly lower in SCD victims compared with control subjects. Strong positive correlations were detected between the extent of atherosclerosis and the percentage of saturated FA ($r=0.718$, $p<0.001$) and linoleic acid ($r=0.478$, $p<0.01$), respectively, in coronary arteries in the entire group, whereas a negative correlation was detected between the grade of atherosclerosis and the percentage of PUFA ($r=0.733$, $p<0.001$).

In summary, this study showed increased saturated FA, in particular palmitic acid (16:0), no change in monosaturated FA, and a reduction in PUFA, with the exception of linoleic acid, which was markedly increased, in the coronary arteries of victims of SCD compared with control subjects. Both n-6 FA [dihomo γ-linolenic acid (20:3), arachidonic acid (20:4) and adrenic acid (22:4)] and n-3 FA [docosapentaenoic acid (DPA; 22:5) and docosahexaenoic acid (DHA; 22:6)] were lower in the coronary arteries of victims of SCD than in controls. These results suggest that a reduction in n-3 FA and an increase in saturated FA may be of importance in the pathogenesis of SCD. The results also suggest an impairment in the metabolism of linoleic acid, possibly due to a decrease in delta-6-desaturase activity, in the coronary artery wall of SCD victims. Alternatively, increased oxidation of the long chain PUFA in atherosclerosis could also be a reason for the difference.

It has been shown that dietary n-3 FA are incorporated into advanced human atherosclerotic plaques.[4] A recent study in pigs showed a reduction in atherosclerosis following supplementation of an atherogenic diet with fish oil.[5] We have also found that the atheromatous regions of coronary arteries produced much greater amounts of the vasoconstrictor thromboxane (TX)A_2 than normal regions (Fig. 3).[6] This increased synthesis of TXA_2 may be due, at least in part, to an increased release of arachidonic acid from the phospholipid pool of the vessel wall cell membranes.[7] Hence, there could be yet another explanation for the diminished level of arachidonic acid in the phospholipid fraction in victims of SCD, i.e. increased release of arachidonic acid. Another reason for the increased production of TXA_2 in the coronary artery wall may be increased generation of thrombin in atherosclerosis. Thrombin has been shown to increase the production of TXA_2 in the vessel wall.[8] TXA_2 produced in the vessel wall may induce not only vasoconstriction and arrhythmias, but also facilitate smooth muscle proliferation. It may be argued that TXA_2 production in the vascular wall is very small compared with the amount produced by platelets. However, the half-life of TXA_2 in the circulation is extremely short (a few seconds), and local production of this prostanoid in the vessel wall may be more important than its production by intravascular platelets.

The major cyclooxygenase enzyme in platelets appears to be COX-1 (constitutive), while the major cyclooxygenase in the atherosclerotic vessel wall is COX-2 (inducible). COX-2 is much less sensitive to indomethacin and other classic cyclooxygenase inhibitors than COX-1. Linoleic acid, which is markedly increased in coronary arteries of victims of SCD, is a selective substrate for COX-2.[9] This phenomenon may have important implications because the classic COX inhibitors may not be able to influence TXA_2 synthesis in the coronary arteries. The altered FA pattern observed may occur exclusively in the arterial wall, as linoleic acid and other PUFA in the cardiac muscle phospholipids were similar in SCD victims and controls.

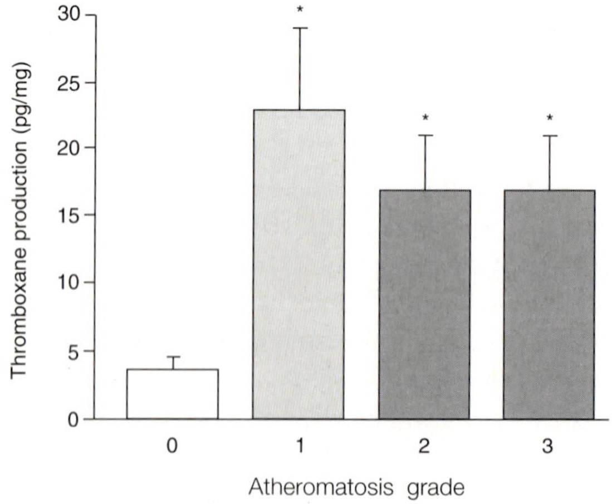

Fig. 3. Production of thromboxane A_2 *in vitro* in normal (grade 0) and atheromatous regions of human coronary arteries from 23 autopsy cases. * Indicates significant difference from normal regions of the arteries ($p<0.05$).

Dietary Supplementation with n-3 FA and Cardiac Risk Factors

In order to study the role of n-3 FA in the pathogenesis of SCD further, we determined the effect of a stabilized fluid fish oil concentrate, which is insensitive to oxidation, on risk factors for IHD. Notably, fish oil preparations used previously were often unstable, had limited amounts of antioxidants, and consequently caused lipid peroxidation.[10-14] As fatty fish and fish oils have been shown to exert beneficial effects on the incidence of SCD,[15] it was important to use a fish oil preparation as similar as possible to that obtained from fish, with minimal purification and chemical modification. For practical reasons, we used a fairly high dose of fish oil over a short period of time, believing that this strategy would be equivalent to a smaller dose administered over a longer period of time. Fluid fish oil was used rather than encapsulated, as fish oil in this form can be used as a substitute for other types of fat.[16]

The fish oil preparation used in our studies was stabilized by natural antioxidants including a mixture of E vitamins, and it contained about 38% n-3 FA (18% eicosapentaenoic acid (EPA) and 12% DHA). In clinical studies,[17-29] this fish oil preparation was found to exert dose-dependent potentially salutary effects on several cardiac risk factors, such as triglycerides, total cholesterol, high density lipoprotein (HDL) and fibrinogen levels. Blood pressure also fell, as did plasma lipoprotein (a) levels. Concomitantly, neutrophil function, measured as chemotactic response to the bacterial peptide f-MLP, fell and superoxide dismutase (SOD) activity was enhanced. With this fish oil preparation, there was no evidence of a decrease in vitamin E levels or an increase in malondialdehyde, as is observed with conventional fish oil preparations.[18]

Effect of Dietary Fish Oil on Myocardial Dysfunction and Arrhythmias

Dietary supplementation with fish oil has been shown to decrease mortality after myocardial infarction in some studies. This reduction in mortality is most likely due to a reduction in arrhythmias. We hypothesized that fish oil may reduce arrhythmias following ischaemia and reperfusion. To examine this phenomenon, studies were carried out in Sprague-Dawley rats, which were fed a diet supplemented with fish oil for 5 days.[30] Fish oil was added to the standard nonpurified diet, containing 46% carbohydrates, 20% protein and 5% fat; the final fat content was 17%. The fish oil preparation used was ESKIMO-3 (Cardinova, Uppsala, Sweden) and contained 25% saturated FA, 25% monosaturated FA and 38% n-3 FA. This fish oil contains low levels of peroxide (<1 meq/kg) and anisidine (<7) and these levels did not increase after exposure of the oil to air at room temperature for several months. Other groups of rats from the same batch were fed a nonpurified diet enriched with butter (to achieve a total fat content of 17%) or a standard diet as a control. Both control and fish-oil-rich nonpurified foods were refrigerated to prevent oxidation and the rats were fed fresh food every day. Rats were anaesthetized with pentobarbital, administered intraperitoneally. Blood was collected via the carotid artery. Hearts were excised rapidly and placed in cold Krebs-Henseleit buffer. Within 1 minute, the hearts were transferred to a perfusion apparatus and perfused via the aorta with oxygenated (95% O_2 + 5% CO_2) Krebs-Henseleit buffer at 37°C (pH 7.4), according a modified Langendorff procedure.[30] The hearts were allowed to beat spontaneously and were perfused with a constant flow of Krebs-Henseleit buffer (4.5-5.0 ml/minute). Mean coronary perfusion pressure was measured via a catheter placed just proximal to the coronary arteries and connected to a pressure transducer. To measure the force of cardiac contraction, a metal hook was attached to the apex of the heart and connected to a tension transducer via a custom-designed lever. The preload prior to any intervention was kept at 2.0 g. Both the force of cardiac contraction and the coronary perfusion pressure were recorded continuously. Heart rate was calculated from a fast-speed recording of cardiac contraction signal. After 20 minutes of stabilization, hearts were subjected to 15 minutes of ischaemia (perfusion stopped), followed by 10 minutes of reperfusion. Coronary effluent was collected before ischaemia and several times during reperfusion, and was placed in ice for subsequent measurement of creatine kinase. Another aliquot was stored for measurement of TXB_2 after completion of the experiment. Hearts were stored at -70°C before measurements of phospholipids.

The myocardial content of long-chain unsaturated FA was 26.7±0.3 g/100 g phospholipid in the control hearts and 40.6±0.4 g/100 g phospholipid in hearts from rats fed fish oil ($p<0.01$). The myocardial content of n-3 FA in hearts from rats fed fish oil was higher than in the hearts from control rats (26.6±0.2/100 g *versus* 12.7±2 g/100 g phospholipid, $p<0.01$). The level of n-6 essential FA in hearts from rats fed fish oil was lower than in the hearts from control rats (19.2±0.1/100 g *versus* 32.3±0.2 g/100 g phospholipid, $p<0.01$). The phospholipid composition of plasma showed similar changes to those in the myocardial tissues.

In control rats, platelet aggregation in response to ADP (20 μmol/l) was 63±17%. Rats fed a diet rich in fish oil for 5 days showed a markedly lower platelet aggregation in response to 20 μmol/l ADP (7±1%, $p<0.01$) indicating a potent platelet aggregation inhibitory effect of fish oil.

After 15 minutes of ischaemia and 10 minutes of reperfusion, the force of cardiac contraction was markedly less and the mean coronary perfusion pressure was markedly higher in hearts from both control and fish oil groups compared with the pre-ischaemia values. However, the changes in the rats fed fish oil were less pronounced than those in the control group ($p<0.05$). Heart rate in the control group (246±12 beats/minute, n=9) was similar to that in the fish oil group (229±9 beats/minute, n=8). A representative experiment from each group is shown in Figure 4. During reperfusion, ventricular arrhythmias (tachycardia and fibrillation) developed in 78% of the hearts in the control group, but in only 38% of hearts in the fish oil group ($p<0.005$). The effects of feeding fish oil were attenuated by the cyclooxygenase inhibitor indomethacin. We thus postulate that the effects of n-3 FA may be mediated by alterations in arachidonic acid metabolism.

Creatine kinase in coronary effluents was measured as a reflection of myocardial injury. As shown in Figure 5, creatine kinase in the coronary effluent was 5-7-fold higher than the basal value during reperfusion in the control group of hearts (12±3 IU/l, n=9), whereas creatine kinase in the coronary effluents increased only 3-4-fold from basal levels during reperfusion in the fish oil group (15±3 IU/l, n=8). The difference in creatine kinase release between the two groups of hearts (measured as the area under the curve) was significant ($p<0.05$).

Immunoreactive TXB_2 release in the coronary effluents was seen in the first minute of reperfusion and then returned to baseline in both groups of hearts. However, the levels of TXB_2 in the fish oil group were lower than those in the control group during the entire period of the procedure ($p<0.05$, Fig. 6).

Our measurements of phospholipids show clearly that short-term (5-day) administration of fish oil to rats increases the myocardial and plasma levels of long-chain n-3 FA and reduces the level of n-6 FA. These changes are associated with a decrease in platelet aggregation, presumably related to altered phospholipid

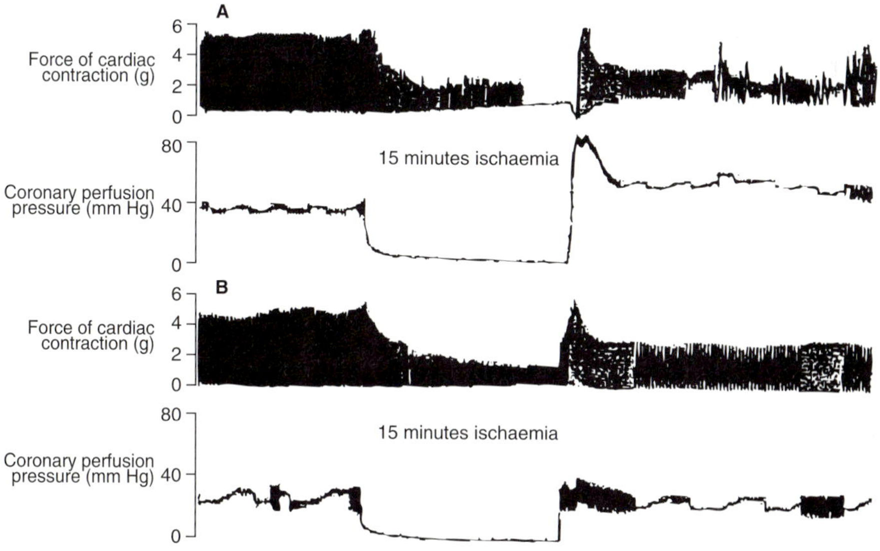

Fig. 4. Representative examples of cardiac dynamics in a heart from a rat fed a control diet (A) and from a rat fed a diet supplemented with fish oil (B). Both hearts were exposed to ischaemia (15 minutes) and reperfusion (10 minutes). Ischaemia-reperfusion was associated with a marked decline in the force of cardiac contraction, an increase in coronary perfusion pressure and the appearance of ventricular arrhythmias. These changes were less marked in the heart from the rat receiving fish oil.

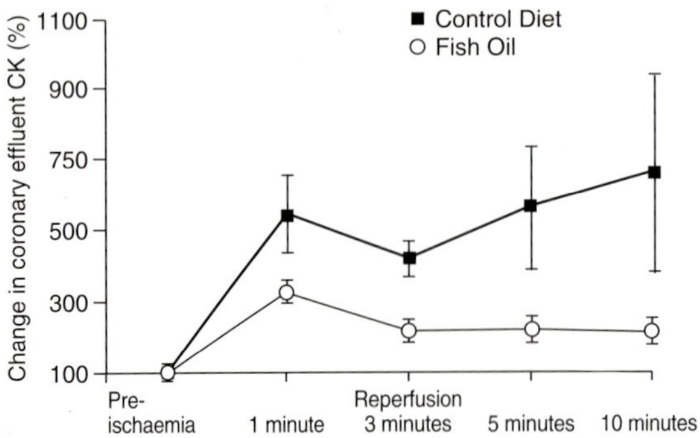

Fig. 5. Effects of dietary supplementation with fish oil on release of creatine kinase (CK) in the coronary effluent following ischaemia-reperfusion. CK release, expressed as a percentage of pre-ischaemic levels, was significantly less ($p<0.01$) in the coronary effluent of rats fed a diet rich in fish oil compared with rats fed a control diet at all time points during reperfusion. Values are means±SEM for eight rats in each group.

content of platelet membranes. Our study also demonstrates that short-term dietary supplementation with fish oil for 5 days significantly attenuates the myocardial dysfunction caused by ischaemia and reperfusion. The incidence of ventricular arrhythmias in isolated hearts subjected to ischaemia and reperfusion also decreased. Furthermore, myocardial creatine kinase release in the coronary effluent following ischaemia was less, indicating that cardiac injury was attenuated.

In other studies, rats were fed the same fish oil with a lower final fat content (5-7%) for 4-5 weeks. Isolated hearts from these rats also exhibited the same

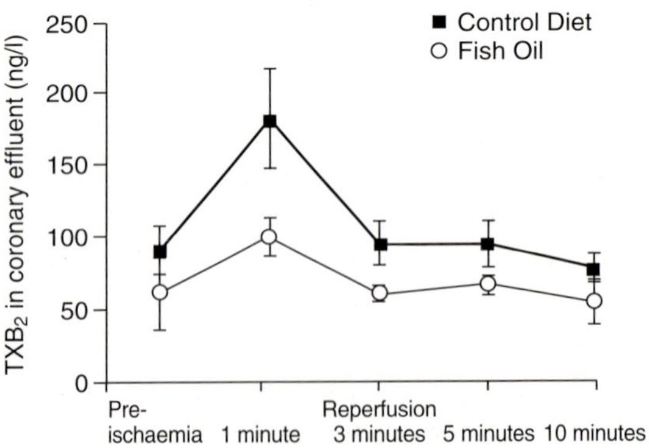

Fig. 6. Effects of dietary supplementation with fish oil on immunoreactive thromboxane B_2 (TXB_2) in the cardiac effluent following ischaemia-reperfusion. TXB_2 release, expressed as mean±SEM (n=8), was significantly less in the coronary effluents of rats fed a diet rich in fish oil compared with those fed a control diet ($p<0.05$).

cardioprotection against ischaemia and reperfusion, even when ischaemia was prolonged to 25 minutes and reperfusion to 20 minutes.[31]

In summary, these results demonstrate that dietary supplementation with fish oil protects against myocardial dysfunction and injury, as well as against arrhythmias caused by ischaemia and reperfusion. These observations provide a mechanistic basis for the association between n-3 FA and SCD.

Potential Mechanisms of the Cardioprotective Effects of Fish Oil

In other recent investigations, we have studied the mechanisms behind the cardioprotective effects of fish oil. We postulated that the reduction in ischaemia–reperfusion-mediated myocardial dysfunction in rats fed fish oil may relate to the modulation of coronary vascular tone. To examine this hypothesis, we incubated rat aortic rings with n-3 FA *in vitro* and examined endothelium-dependent relaxation. Relaxation of these n-3 FA-treated rings in response to both acetylcholine (ACh) and the Ca^{2+} ionophore A23,187, was enhanced, indicating either increased synthesis or diminished breakdown of nitric oxide (NO).[32] This response was blunted both by a NO inhibitor and by indomethacin, suggesting that, in addition to the L-arginine-NO-pathway, the cylooxygenase pathway is also involved in increased relaxation of aortic rings.

In other studies, we identified a marked reduction in the potential of neutrophils and aortas from rats fed fish oil to generate superoxide anions, without a concurrent increase in NO synthase activity.[33] These observations suggest that the increased NO in response to fish oil may be due, not to increased NO formation, but to decreased NO breakdown, as superoxide anions are known to degrade NO. A decrease in superoxide generation by human neutrophils was also detected after dietary supplementation with fish oil,[26] as well as after incubation *in vitro* with n-3 FA.[34] The effect of n-3 FA on superoxide generation in these experiments was abolished by coincubation of cells with cyclooxygenase inhibitors, but not NO synthase inhibitors.

An increase in n-3 FA leads to the formation of TXA_3, and prostaglandin (PG)I_3, and to a concurrent reduction in the formation of TXA_2 and PGI_2. While TXA_3 is inactive, PGI_3 is as active as PGI_2. We also found that myocardial production of TX was lower in rats given fish oil and the PGI_2/TXA_2 production was higher.[35] This modified metabolism of eicosanoids may contribute to the protective effects exerted by n-3 FA against ischaemia and reperfusion, as well as to a state of vasorelaxation. In addition, PGI_2 enhances NO release and potentiates its activity. PGI_3, like PGI_2, reduces superoxide radical generation, which may enhance the activity of preformed NO. TXA_2 has been shown to be arrhythmogenic and PGF_2 is an endogenous anti-arrhythmic substance,[36] implying that myocardial prostanoid balance may be one important factor involved in the genesis of cardiac arrhythmias after ischaemia and reperfusion. The attenuation of the cardioprotective effect of fish oil by indomethacin may also have other explanations. Indomethacin can shunt arachidonic acid metabolism towards the lipoxygenase pathway, leading to an increase in the synthesis of leukotrienes, which are potent vasoconstrictors[37] and which can potentiate the coronary vasoconstrictive effect of TXA_2.[38]

There is increasing evidence to suggest that oxygen free radicals and endogenous antioxidant defence systems, such as SOD, play a major role in the pathogenesis of reperfusion injury.[39] We found that myocardial manganese superoxide dismutase (MnSOD) activity was higher in rats fed fish oil.[35] An increase in the activity of endogenous myocardial antioxidative defence systems, such as MnSOD, may be an important factor in determining the vulnerability of the myocardium to arrhythmia. In summary, these observations suggest that the major mechanism behind the protective effect of n-3 FA may be the synthesis of PGI_3 and a diminished synthesis of TXA_2.

Thoughts on Coronary Plaque Rupture, FA Content of Atherosclerotic Plaques and the Role of Fish Oil

Rupture of an atherosclerotic plaque is believed to be the precipitating event in most episodes of coronary artery occlusion. A vulnerable plaque contains much extracellular fat, derived from macrophage foam cells.[40] Most ruptures occur in the plaque periphery, at sites heavily infiltrated with macrophages. It has been suggested that the release of proteolytic enzymes from macrophages may contribute to the weakening of the collagen cap. n-3 FA have been shown to suppress the release of various substances from macrophages, including proteolytic enzymes. A high content of n-3 FA in plaque macrophages could therefore make the plaque less vulnerable. We found that EPA decreased the production of inducible NO in stimulated macrophages and improved the viability of these cells.[41] SOD also improved cell viability, indicating that superoxide may also contribute to cell death, possibly by formation of peroxynitrate and hydroxyl radicals from the reaction between superoxide and NO. It is therefore possible that n-3 FA may increase the activity of the constitutive NO in endothelial cells, mainly by decreasing superoxide activity, but in contrast may decrease the inducible NO activity in macrophages, mainly by inhibiting NO synthase.

Importance of Antioxidants

The antioxidant content of fish oil has major importance not only in preventing the oxidation of the fish oil itself, but also for its *in vivo* effects. The antioxidant content of fish oil was shown to influence the effect of fish oil on cardiovascular risk factors, such as triglycerides and fibrinogen,[18] as well as blood glucose[29] and myocardial malondialdehyde (Jokela *et al.*, unpublished data) (Fig. 7). An inadequate antioxidant content may also decrease, rather than increase, SOD activity.[42]

Fish Oil and Coronary Mortality

Several studies in patients with previous myocardial infarction have demonstrated beneficial effects of fish oil on subsequent morbidity and mortality.[15,43] Recently, however, Ascherio *et al.*[44] found no association between fish intake and IHD events in a large observational study in normal healthy subjects. This result contrasts with the results of many other studies. In addition to the explanations offered in their paper and in an accompanying editorial,[45] there are other possibilities for the discrepancy between different studies.

First, the study by Ascherio *et al.*[44] was based on a food-frequency questionnaire, and questionnaire-based studies have inherent flaws. Second, although the intake of fish was high in the population studied, the mean intake of n-3 FA was modest, indicating that most of the fish was non-fatty and contained only small amounts of n-3 FA. Fish intake in the highest quintile was 5.9 servings of fish/week, but the median intake of n-3 FA was only 0.58 g/day. In the DART-study,[15] the intake of EPA alone was 2.5 g/week indicating a higher intake of total n-3 FA in these patients, although the intake of fatty fish was only two servings/week. In this randomized controlled intervention study,[15] intake of fish resulted in a 29% reduction in total mortality primarily due to a decrease in cardiac death. It is thus possible that even the dose of n-3 FA in the population consuming the greatest amount of fish in the Ascherio study[44] may not have been high enough. Certainly most risk factors for IHD known to be modulated by n-3 FA in fish oil show no change with this small amount of n-3 FA.

The intake of n-3 FA, although beneficial in most studies, may be regarded as a

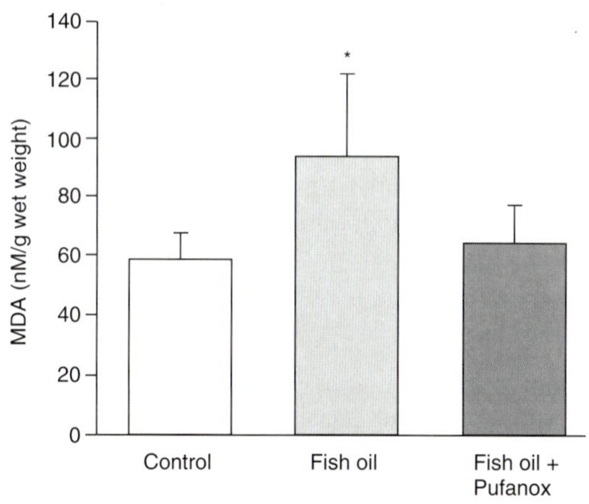

Fig. 7. Malondialdehyde (MDA) in the heart of control rats and rats receiving an ordinary fish oil supplement containing vitamin E (1 mg/g) and stabilized fish oil containing the antioxidant Pufanox. * Indicates a significant difference from controls ($p<0.05$).

double-edged sword. While fish intake may modify some risk factors for IHD, it may reduce antioxidant protection leading to increased peroxidation of lipoproteins and production of cytotoxic derivatives.[18] If the intake of n-3 FA is not combined with adequate intake of antioxidants, many of the positive effects of these FA may be attenuated. In the Cretan Mediterranean diet study,[46] the increased intake of antioxidants with fruit and vegetables, along with high intake of n-3 FA, was supposed to have been important in the 70% reduction in coronary events and death in patients with previous myocardial infarction. A relatively small intake of adequate natural antioxidants by fish-consuming subjects in the Ascherio study[44] may account for the failure to see any benefit from n-3 FA consumption.

Lastly, the Ascherio study was conducted over 6 years. In the DART study, which lasted only 2 years, the beneficial effect of fish oil appeared after a few months. Experience from Norway during World War II indicates that a change in diet results in a very rapid decrease in cardiac mortality. Furthermore, the beneficial effect of the Cretan Mediterranean diet appeared as early as 2 months after dietary modification.[46] These observations suggest that n-3 FA consumption results in early benefit. However, beyond the first 2 years of follow-up, other factors may blunt the early benefit. Notably, most secondary prevention trials in patients with IHD have lasted between 30 days and 2 years in order to define early benefit. Kaplan-Meier morbidity and mortality analyses would have helped discern any early benefit from intake of n-3 FA.

Conclusions

Our studies show that n-3 FA are decreased in the coronary arteries in SCD victims, n-3 FA are cardioprotective in the experimental setting and an intact cyclooxygenase pathway is essential for the beneficial effect of n-3 FA. In addition, n-3 FA increase MnSOD activity, resulting in decreased superoxide anion activity and decreased breakdown of NO, which may also be cardioprotective. Lastly, intake of at least moderate amounts of n-3 FA with adequate antioxidant content may be necessary for their effects to be manifest.

Summary

To determine the role and potential mechanisms of n-3 fatty acids (FA) in sudden cardiac death (SCD), we studied the FA composition of human coronary arteries in 30 individuals who died of SCD and 29 controls who died of other causes. The levels of saturated FA were increased, whereas n-3 FA were decreased in victims of SCD, suggesting that an increase in saturated FA and a decrease in n-3 FA may be of importance in the pathogenesis of SCD. While linoleic acid was markedly increased, the other n-6 FA were decreased in SCD victims indicating that an impaired metabolism of linolenic acid, possibly due to decreased delta-6-desaturase activity, may also be important in SCD.

To elucidate the potential role of the n-3 FA deficiency in the pathogenesis of SCD, Sprague-Dawley rats were fed with a stabilized fish oil and isolated hearts were subjected to global ischaemia and reperfusion. In control hearts, ischaemia-reperfusion resulted in a marked decrease in cardiac contractile force, an increase in coronary perfusion pressure, fatal arrhythmias and the release of creatine kinase and thromboxane. Feeding the rats with fish oil protected against the myocardial dysfunction induced by ischaemia and reperfusion. The frequency of fatal arrhythmias was 38% in rats fed fish oil compared with 78% in control rats.

In other studies, *in vitro* incubation of rat aortic rings with n-3 FA enhanced endothelium-dependent relaxation. The enhanced relaxation was blocked by cyclooxygenase or nitric oxide (NO) synthase blockers. n-3 FA had no effect on NO synthase activity, but increased manganese superoxide dismutase activity and decreased formation of superoxide radicals, both of which would enhance the activity of preformed NO and result in increased vasorelaxation.

In conclusion, these studies show that n-3 FA are decreased in the coronary arteries of victims of SCD and that these acids are cardioprotective in an experimental model of ischaemia-reperfusion. The cardioprotection appears to be related to alterations in arachidonic acid metabolism, and perhaps to a prolonged half life of NO.

References

1. Leaf A., Weber P.C.: A new era for science in nutrition. Am. J. Clin. Nutr. 1987; 45: 1048-1053
2. Miettinen T., Naukkarinen V., Huttunen J., Mattila S., Kumlin T.: Fatty acid composition of serum lipids predicts myocardial infarction. Br. Med. J. 1982; 285: 993-996
3. Luostarinen R., Boberg M., Saldeen T.: Fatty acid composition in total phospholipids of human coronary arteries in sudden cardiac death. Atherosclerosis 1993; 99: 187-189
4. Rapp J.H., Connor W.E., Lin D.S, Porter J.M.: Dietary eicosapentaenoic acid and docosahexaenoic acid from fish oil. Their incorporation into advanced human atherosclerotic plaques. Arterioscler. Thromb. 1991; 11: 903-907
5. Kim D.N., Schmee J., Lee C.S., Eastman A., Ross J.S., Thomas W.A.: Comparison of effects of fish oil and corn oil supplements on hyperlipidemic diet induced atherogenesis in swine. Atherosclerosis 1991; 89: 191-201
6. Saldeen P., Saldeen T.: Increased synthesis of thromboxane in atheramatous vessels. Thromb. Res. 1983; 31: 591-597
7. Mehta J., Lawson D., Mehta P., Saldeen T.: Increased prostacyclin and thromboxane A2 biosynthesis in atherosclerosis. Proc. Natl. Acad. Sci. USA 1988; 85: 4511-4515
8. Saldeen T., Saldeen P., Nichols W., Lawson D., Nicolini F., Mehta J.: Increased production of thromboxane A_2 by coronary arteries after thrombolysis. Am. Heart. J. 1993; 125: 277-284
9. Battistini B., Botting R., Bakhle Y.: COX-1 and COX-2: Toward the development of more selective NSAIDs. Drug News Perspect. 1994; 7: 501-512
10. Bjorneboe A., Soyland E., Bjorneboe G-E., Rajka G., Drevon C.A.: Effect of n-3 fatty acid supplementation to patients with topic dermatitis. J. Int. Med. 1989; 225: 233-236
11. Bach R., Schmidt U., Jung F., Kieswetter H., Hennen B., Wenzel E., Schieffer H., Bette L., Heyden S.: Effects of fish oil capsules in two dosages on blood pressure platelet functions, haemorheological and clinical chemistry parameters in apparently healthy subjects. Ann. Nutr. Metab. 1989; 33: 359-367
12. Wahle K.W.J., Brown J.E.: Plasma lipid peroxidation and vitamin E supplementation during high intakes of fish-oil fatty acids. Fat. Sci. Technol. 1990; 92: 326-330

13. Müllertz A., Holmer G., Grondahl-Hansen J.: Increased concentration of plasminogen activator inhibitor type-1 in plasma after intake of fish oil. Fibrinolysis 1990; 4: 86-88
14. Nair P.P., Judd J.T., Berlin E., Taylor P.R., Shami S., Sainz E., Bhagavan H.N.: Dietary fish oil-induced changes in the distribution of α-tocopherol, retinol, and β-carotene in plasma, red blood cells, and platelets: modulation by vitamin E. Am. J. Clin. Nutr. 1993; 58: 98-102
15. Burr M.L., Gilbert J.F., Holliday R.L.: Effects of changes in fat, fish and fibre intake on death and myocardial reinfarction: Diet and reinfarction trial (DART). Lancet 1989; ii: 757-761
16. Saldeen T., Wallin R., Alving B., Marklinder I.: Effect of fish oil in bread on fatty acids in plasma phospholipids and on serum triglycerides. In: Lambertsen G. (Ed.): *Lipids from the Sea. Lipidforum*. Bergen, Norway; 1994: 77 (Abstract)
17. Haglund O., Wallin R., Luostarinen R., Saldeen T.: Effects of a new fluid fish oil concentrate, ESKIMO-3, on triglycerides, cholesterol, fibrinogen and blood pressure. J. Intern. Med. 1990; 277: 347-353
18. Haglund O., Luostarinen R., Wallin R., Wibell L., Saldeen T.: The effects of fish oil on triglycerides, cholesterol, fibrinogen and malondialdehyde in humans supplemented with vitamin E. Eur. J. Nutr. 1991; 121: 165-169
19. Haglund O., Luostarinen R., Wallin L., Saldeen T.: Effects of fish oil on triglycerides, cholesterol, lipoprotein (a), atherogenic index and fibrinogen. Influence of degree of purification of the oil. Nutr. Res. 1992; 12: 455-468
20. Haglund O.: Effects of fish oil on risk factors for cardiovascular disease. Comprehensive Summaries of Uppsala Dissertations from the Faculty of Medicine. 1993: 428 (Thesis)
21. Haglund O., Hamfelt A., Hambraeus L., Saldeen T.: Effects of fish oil supplemented with pyridoxine and folic acid on homocysteine, atherogenic index, fibrinogen and plasminogen activator inhibitor-1 in man. Nutr. Res. 1993; 13: 1351-1365
22. Haglund O., Wallin R., Wretling S., Hultberg B., Saldeen T.: Effects of fish oil alone and combined with long chain (n-6) fatty acids on some coronary risk factors in man. J. Nutr. Biochem. 1995; In press
23. Haglund O., Mehta J., Saldeen T.: Effects of fish oil on some parameters of fibrinolysis and lipoprotein (a) in healthy subjects. Am. J. Cardiol. 1994; 74: 189-192
24. Haglund O., Mehta J., Saldeen T.: Effect of fish oil on some parameters of fibrinolysis. In: Glas-Greenwalt (Ed.): *Fibrinolysis in Disease*. Miami, Florida; CRC Press, 1995: 102-109
25. Luostarinen R., Siegbahn A., Saldeen T.: Effect of dietary fish oil supplemented with different doses of vitamin E on neutrophil chemotaxis in healthy volunteers. Nutr. Res. 1992; 12: 1419-1430
26. Luostarinen R., Saldeen T.: Dietary fish oil decreases superoxide generation by human neutrophils. Relation to cyclooxygenase pathway and lysosomal enzyme release. In: *Studies on (n-3) Polyunsaturated Fatty Acids. With Special Reference to Cardiovascular Disease.* Comprehensive Summaries of Uppsala Dissertations from the Faculty of Medicine 1995: 588
27. Luostarinen R.: Studies on (n-3) polyunsaturated fatty acids. With special reference to cardiovascular disease. Comprehensive Summaries cf Uppsala Dissertations from the Faculty of Medicine 1995: 588
28. Saldeen T., Luostarinen R., Haglund O., Wallin R.: N-3 fatty acids and ischaemic heart disease. Proceedings of the 17th Nordic Lipid Symposium. Bergen, Norway; Lipidforum, 1993; 20-34
29. Luostarinen R., Wallin R., Wibell L., Saldeen T.: Vitamin E supplementation counteracts the fish oil-induced increase of blood glucose in humans. Nutr. Res. 1995; 15: 953-968
30. Yang B., Saldeen T., Nichols W., Mehta J.: Dietary fish oil supplementation attenuates myocardial dysfunction and injury caused by global ischemia and reperfusion in isolated rat hearts. J. Nutr. 1993; 123: 2067-2074
31. Yang B., Saldeen T., Bryant J., Nichols W., Mehta J.: Long-term dietary fish oil supplementation protects against ischemia-reperfusion-induced myocardial dysfunction in isolated rat hearts. Am. Heart J. 1993; 126: 1287-1292

32. Lawson D., Mehta J., Saldeen K., Mehta P., Saldeen T.: Omega-3-polyunsaturated fatty acids augment endothelium-dependent vasorelaxation by enhanced release of EDRF and vasodilator prostaglandins. Eicosanoids 1991; 4: 217-223
33. Bryant J., Yang B., Mehta P., Saldeen T., Mehta J.: Dietary fish oil decreases superoxide radical generation without affecting nitric oxide synthase activity: a mechanism of vasorelaxation. J. Am. Coll. Cardiol. 1993; 21: 430 (Abstract)
34. Chen L.Y., Lawson D.L., Mehta J.L.: Reduction in human neutrophil superoxide anion generation by n-3 polyunsaturated fatty acids: Role of cyclooxygenase products and endothelium-derives relaxing factor. Thromb. Res. 1994; 76: 317-322
35. Luostarinen R., Wallin R., Saldeen T.: Dietary n-3 fatty acids increase superoxide dismutase activity and decrease thromboxane production in the rat heart. In: *Studies on n-3 Polyunsaturated Fatty Acids. With Special Reference to Cardiovascular Disease.* Comprehensive Summaries of Uppsala Dissertations from the Faculty of Medicine. 1995: 588
36. Parratt J., Wainwright C., Coker S., Zeitlin I.: Eicosanoids and cardiac arrhythmias. Biomed. Biochim. Acta 1988; 47: 13-18
37. Wargovich T.J., Mehta J.L., Nichols W.W., Pepine C.J., Conti C.R.: Reduction in blood flow in normal and narrowed coronary arteries of dogs by leukotriene C4. Am. Coll. Cardiol. 1985; 6: 1047-1051
38. Nichols W.W., Mehta J.L., Thompson L.V., Donnelly W.H.: Synergistic effects of LTC4 and TXA_2 on coronary flow and myocardial function. Am. J. Physiol. 1988; 255: H153-H159
39. Werns S., Shea M., Lucchesi B.: Free radicals and myocardial injury: pharmacologic implications. Circulation 1986; 74: 1-5
40. Falk E.: Why do plaques reputre? Circulation 1992; 86 (Suppl. 3): 30-42
41. Haglund O., Dutertre Y., Saldeen T: Eicosapentaenoic acid decreases nitric oxide activity and increases cell viability in stimulated macrophages. Nutr. Res. 1995. In press
42. L'Abbé M., Trick K., Beard-Rogers J.: Dietary (n-3) fatty acids affect rat heart, liver and aorta protective enzyme activities and lipid peroxidation. J. Nutr. 1991; 121: 1331-1340
43. Dolocek T.A., Grandits G.: Dietary polyunsaturated fatty acids and mortality in the multiple risk factor intervention trial (MRFIT). World Rev. Nutr. Diet 1991; 66: 205-216
44. Ascherio A., Rimm E.B., Stampfer M.J., Giovannuci E.L., Willett W.C.: Dietary intake of marine n-3 fatty acids, fish intake, and the risk of coronary disease among men. N. Engl. J. Med. 1995; 332: 977-982
45. Katan M.B.: Fish and heart disease. N. Engl. J. Med. 1995; 332: 1024-1025
46. de Lorgeril M., Renaud S., Marelle N., Sallen P., Martin J.L., Monjaud I., Gouidollet J., Touboul P., Delaye J.: Mediterranean alpha-linolenic acid-rich diet in secondary prevention of coronary heart disease. Lancet 1994; 343: 1454-1459

S.D. Kristensen, E.B. Schmidt, R. De Caterina, S. Endres
n-3 Fatty Acids: Prevention and Treatment in Vascular Disease
Bi & Gi Publishers, Verona - Springer Verlag, London, 1995

13. α-Linolenic Acid in the Prevention of Coronary Heart Disease

S. Renaud

Inserm, Unit 63, 22 Avenue Doyen Lépine, Bron Cedex, France

Introduction

Dietary habits, especially the intake of saturated fat, appear to be the main environmental factor associated with coronary heart disease (CHD).[1] Nevertheless, most of the trials in which patients' diet was modified either before (primary) or after (secondary) a first myocardial infarction did not show the expected preventive effects.[2]

The most recent dietary trial involved 9057 randomized patients from psychiatric hospitals in Minnesota, USA.[3] After a mean follow-up of 4.5 years, no beneficial effects on CHD and total mortality were observed. The number of myocardial infarctions and sudden deaths in the experimental group was 131, compared with 121 in the control group. There were a total of 269 deaths in the experimental group compared with 248 in the control group. Nevertheless, serum cholesterol levels decreased by 15.4% in the experimental group, owing to a lowering of the intake of saturated fat from 18.3% to 9.2% of calories. Conversely, the intake of polyunsaturated fatty acids, mostly linoleic acid, increased from 5.2% to 14.7% of calories, increasing the polyunsaturated:saturated (P:S) fatty acid ratio from 0.28 to 1.6. In primary prevention, the only trial in which a significant reduction (47%) in fatal and nonfatal coronary events had been observed was associated with a P:S ratio of only 0.7 in the experimental group,[4] and serum cholesterol was reduced by not more than 10% compared with the controls.[5] The diet modifications consisted mainly of a reduction in the saturated fat intake and a slight increase in the intake of polyunsaturated fat. It was also recommended that the experimental group eat more fish and cooked using polyunsaturated oil, such as soybean oil, which was used in the first Oslo trial.[6] Thus, in Hjermann *et al.*'s trial[5] the dietary changes were much less dramatic than those in the Minnesota survey,[3] although the reduction in the intake of saturated fat in the two trials was probably similar. Unfortunately, the diet composition was not reported in detail in either of these two trials, but it can be speculated that in the Oslo trial the consumption of fish, as well as that of linolenic acid supplied by soybean oil was substantially greater than that in the Minnesota trial. Soybean and rapeseed oil are the only two oils containing between 6% and 8% linolenic acid that are available commercially for human consumption. Linolenic acid (18:3 n-3) is the precursor of the n-3 fatty acids eicosapentaenoic acid (EPA) (20:5 n-3) and docosahexaenoic acid (DHA) (22:6 n-3), which are found in fish and marine mammals. In a randomized trial by Burr *et al.* involving 2033 men, it was observed that eating at least two portions/week of fatty fish, such as mackerel, herring, kipper, sardine, salmon and trout, could reduce total mortality by 29% after a myocardial infarction.[7] Nevertheless, the fish supplement did not provide protection aginst nonfatal myocardial infarction.

In the trial by Hjermann *et al.*,[5] as well as that by Burr *et al.*,[7] a reduction in mortality was observed as early as in the first year of the trial. Thus, it can be speculated that the diets used in these trials had an effect on thrombosis rather than on atherosclerosis, which is known to require years to develop. The question raised by these trials, in which patients increased their intake of n-3 fatty acids, is whether a higher level of linolenic acid, the precursor of the fatty acids EPA and DHA (the fatty acids presumably active in haemostasis), can also be associated with protective effects against CHD.

Early Trials Involving Linolenic Acid

The role of linolenic acid in the prevention of thrombosis was first hypothesized in 1964 by Owren and colleagues in a paper published in *The Lancet.*[8] These investigators emphasized that thrombosis was the most important process determining morbidity and mortality of patients with atherosclerosis. They also underlined that the initial stage of thrombus formation depended on platelet functions and that, in atherosclerosis, these functions were increased. In their study in diabetic and atherosclerotic patients, they found that platelet adhesiveness could be reduced by administration of soybean oil, but not by corn oil and safflower oil, which contain linoleic acid, but no linolenic acid. By contrast, the lowering of platelet adhesiveness by soybean oil could be reproduced when linseed oil, which contains very large amounts of linolenic acid, or purified linolenic acid, were introduced to the diet. However, cod liver oil, which is rich in EPA and DHA, could not reproduce the effect of linolenic acid on platelet adhesiveness. Thus it was postulated that the effect of soybean oil was essentially due to linolenic acid *per se*. Moreover, in a subsequent trial involving survivors of acute myocardial infarction, Owren and his colleagues did not confirm that platelet adhesiveness could be decreased by refined linseed oil in comparison with corn oil.

In the same period, however, Nordoy observed that in the rat, linseed oil could significantly decrease platelet adhesiveness[9] as well as thrombosis induced by ADP.[10] The conclusion of Owren and his colleagues was that "A possible prophylactic and therapeutic effect of linolenic acid had to be determined by controlled clinical trials". The first clinical trial evaluating the effect of a diet enriched with linolenic acid by soybean oil was that of Leren[6] from the Oslo group. In this secondary prevention trial, Leren observed that coronary events were reduced significantly by 23%, and cardiac mortality by 25%, although this latter result was not statistically significant.

Linolenic Acid and Platelet Aggregation in Healthy Populations

To determine whether platelet functions in man, especially aggregation, could be influenced by the intake of dietary fats, as has been observed in animal studies[11] and in studies by Owren in atherosclerotic patients,[8] we studied groups of farmers from different regions of France and the UK between 1976 and 1980.[12,13] Venepuncture, preparation of samples, platelet aggregation and clotting activity were performed in a mobile laboratory that could easily be moved from one area to another. At the same time, dietary habits were carefully determined using different techniques, in particular chemical analysis of a duplicate sample of food. The results obtained following analysis of 396 subjects from 16 groups studied in France and the UK are summarized in Table I.

As has been observed by several investigators,[14] levels of saturated fatty acids were not significantly related, on an individual basis, with serum cholesterol. By contrast, as in previous studies, there was a significant positive correlation between the levels of saturated fatty acids and the clotting activity of platelets, and also between the levels of saturated fatty acids and the response of platelets to aggregation by thrombin.[12] Furthermore, levels of oleic acid were significantly inversely related to ADP-induced aggregation.[12]

As shown in Table I, the intake of linoleic acid was positively associated with ADP-induced aggregation and high density lipoprotein (HDL)-cholesterol, but inversely related to serum cholesterol. Linoleic acid is well known for lowering total cholesterol, while slightly increasing HDL-cholesterol. Its untoward effect on ADP-induced aggregation has been emphasized recently.[15] Linolenic acid was strongly inversely related to both platelet clotting activity and platelet aggregation in response to thrombin.

Concerning the effect of dietary calcium, we have shown that, in rabbits, a higher

Table I. Relationship between nutrients and blood parameters in 396 French and British farmers. The table shows standardized partial regression coefficients adjusted for smoking. The nutrients were evaluated by chemical analysis of a duplicate sample of food over a 24-hour period. Obtained by multivariate analysis.

	Platelet tests			Lipaemia	
Diet	**F_3-CT**	**THR**	**ADP**	**Chol**	**HDL**
Sat	0.30^{***}	0.17^{***}			
18:1			-0.10^{*}		
18:2			0.13^{**}	-0.27^{***}	0.12^{*}
18:3	-0.31^{***}	-0.31^{***}			
Calcium		-0.10^{*}		-0.11^{*}	
Alcohol			-0.11^{*}		0.13^{*}

Abbreviations: F_3-CT=clotting activity of platelets (the inverse of the clotting time), THR=thrombin induced aggregation, ADP=adenosine diphosphate induced aggregation, Chol=serum cholesterol, HDL=high-density lipoprotein cholesterol, Sat=saturated fatty acids (14:0 + 16:0 + 18:0), 18:1=oleic acid, 18:2=linoleic acid, 18:3=α-linolenic acid. $^{*}p<0.05$, $^{**}p<0.01$, $^{***}p<0.001$.

level of calcium decreased platelet reactivity to thrombin and serum cholesterol, probably by promoting the faecal excretion of saturated fatty acids.[16] Regarding alcohol, it is well known that this decreases platelet reactivity to ADP[17] and increases the level of HDL-cholesterol.

The study involving French and British farmers indicates that the clotting activity of platelets and their reactivity to thrombin were more closely related to the intake of saturated fatty acids than to serum cholesterol; an observation that supported those of previous studies.[12] The study also confirms previous results reported by Owren *et al.*,[8] which suggested that linolenic acid was the main dietary fatty acid to inhibit the platelet functions increased by the intake of saturated fatty acids, although they used different conditions.

Owren's results have also been confirmed following long-term modification of the diet of French farmers in the Moselle region.[18] Intake of rapeseed oil (deprived of erucic acid) and rapeseed margarine (made by Astra-Calvé, France, for our studies) decreased platelet clotting activity and platelet reactivity to thrombin more efficiently than sunflower oil and margarine. Only rapeseed (oil and margarine) contained a sizeable amount (6-8%) of linolenic acid.

The evaluation of dietary habits is always a difficult task, even when performed by weighing the food ingested and chemical analysis of a duplicate sample, as was performed in our studies. The fatty acids consumed can be confirmed by gas-liquid chromatography of plasma from all subjects under fasted conditions. Plasma from the 396 subjects reported in Table I was analysed using this method. Table II shows the results of these analyses, in particular the relationship between the intake of the main fatty acids and the level of selected fatty acids in plasma.

It was found that saturated fatty acids were not significantly related to plasma saturated fatty acids but rather to the following: first, 16:1 n-7 by desaturation of 16:0, as we have reported recently in the rat;[19] second, 20:3 n-9 by desaturation of 18:0; third, 20:5 n-3 for reasons that are unclear as it is independent of the intake of 18:2 and 18:3 n-3 (it could be associated with highly saturated dairy products that contain some amounts of 20:5 n-3).

Intake of linoleic acid was inversely related to the level of most fatty acids, but positively related to its own level, in plasma. This observation indicates clearly that a high intake of linoleic acid will decrease the plasma level of 18:3 n-3 as well as its desaturation and elongation to 20:5 n-3 and other metabolites. This has been confirmed recently by Emken *et al.*, using deuterium-labelled fatty acids in man.[20] Linolenic acid in the diet was mostly associated with its own level in plasma, but also with 20:5 n-3.

The relationship between plasma fatty acids and the blood variables examined in the 396 individuals is shown in Table III. Palmitoleic acid (16:1) in plasma was positively associated with the level of total serum cholesterol, confirming the results obtained by Cambien *et al.*[21] The platelet function tests, clotting activity and aggregation of platelets in response to thrombin were positively correlated with 20:3 n-9 in plasma, a fatty acid derived from stearic acid (18:0), which is probably

Table II. Relationship between nutrients (chemical analysis) and plasma total lipid fatty acids in 396 French and British farmers. The table shows standardized partial regression coefficients (adjusted for smoking). Obtained by multivariate analysis.

	Plasma fatty acids						
Diet	**16:0**	**16:1**	**18:1**	**18:2**	**18:3 (n-3)**	**20:3 (n-9)**	**20:5 (n-3)**
Sat		0.13**				0.23***	0.36***
18:1			-0.18***	-0.12**	-0.12**		-0.14*
18:2	-0.09*	-0.31***	-0.58***	0.50***	-0.22***	-0.31***	-0.22***
18:3			0.10*		0.67***	-0.10**	0.25***
Alcohol	0.31***	0.11*		-0.17**	-0.12**	0.19**	0.15**

Abbreviations: as in Table I. $^{*}p<0.05$, $^{**}p<0.01$, $^{***}p<0.0001$.

Table III. Relationship between plasma total lipid fatty acids and blood parameters in 396 (16 groups) French and British farmers. The table shows standardized partial regression coefficients. Obtained by multivariate analysis.

	Platelet tests			Lipaemia	
Plasma	F_3-CT	THR	ADP	Chol	HDL
16:1				0.36^{***}	
18:0			0.11^{*}		
18:1					-0.27^{***}
18:3 (n-3)	-0.35^{***}	-0.32^{***}			
20:3 (n-9)	0.12^{**}	0.12^{**}	-0.19^{**}		
20:4 (n-6)			0.18^{**}		0.18^{**}
20:5 (n-3)				0.18^{**}	0.19^{**}
22:5 (n-3)	0.12^{**}		0.13^{**}	-0.10^{*}	

Abbreviations: as in Table I. $^{*}p<0.05$, $^{**}p<0.01$, $^{***}p<0.0001$.

directly involved in the increased platelet reactivity to thrombin in response to a high intake of saturated fat.[22] Finally, the inhibitory effects of dietary linolenic acid *per se* on platelet functions were confirmed by the observation that only linolenic acid in plasma was highly significantly inversely related to platelet functions, and not EPA or DHA (data not shown).

The Diet of the Cretan Population

The Seven Country Study investigated food consumption patterns in the seven countries during the 1960s.[23] After 5, 10 and 15 years of follow-up, the Cretan cohort had the lowest mortality rate from CHD, with a rate 95% less than the other Mediterranean cohorts and 98% less than those from northern Europe.[24] Even mortality from all causes was more than 50% lower than that of the other Mediterranean and non-Mediterranean cohorts. Compared with the other groups or countries, the diet in Crete was characterized by a high intake of bread, legumes, vegetables, fruit and olive oil, but a lower intake of meat and a moderate consumption of fish and red wine.[24,25] After analysing the results of dietary surveys performed in the 1960s, no foodstuffs appeared to be especially responsible for this remarkable protection. Nevertheless, a recent evaluation of the fatty acid composition of cholesterol esters by Sandker *et al.*[26] confirmed that the Cretan cohort consumed less saturated fatty acids and linoleic acid, but more oleic acid and much more linolenic acid (a threefold higher level in plasma) than the Zutphen cohort in the Netherlands. Despite a low intake of saturated fatty acids (8% of energy), levels of serum cholesterol were not lower in the Cretan cohort than in the nine other Mediterranean cohorts, owing to a low intake of linoleic acid (3-4% of energy).[27] This low level of linoleic acid would not compete for accumulation and desaturation with linolenic acid, moderate levels of which are consumed in the form of olive oil (23% of energy), vegetables and salads such as purslane, all containing linolenic acid. As shown by our studies of French farmers in Moselle[28] and more recently by Emken *et al.*,[20] when the intake of linoleic acid accounts for less than 5% of calorie intake, linolenic acid can accumulate in plasma and be elongated and desaturated efficiently.

Duplication of the Cretan Diet in Lyon: A Randomized Secondary Prevention Trial

In a randomized trial conducted in Lyon, the effect of the Cretan diet on secondary prevention of CHD was investigated.[29] Six weeks after a first myocardial infarction, 600 patients were randomized into a control and an experimental group. Treatment for the myocardial infarction was similar, only the diet differed between the two groups. The control group was advised by their cardiologist and the hospital dietitians to use a prudent diet low in saturated fat, but enriched in linoleic acid by the use of polyunsaturated (sunflower) oil and margarine. The experimental group was persuaded to adopt a diet closer to that of the Cretan population through changes summarized in the form of six commandments:

- more bread
- more vegetables and legumes
- more fish
- less meat (beef, lamb, pork) - replaced by poultry
- fruit to be eaten daily
- no butter and cream - replaced by the supplied margarine.

In a large part of France, as well as in other northern countries, it is almost impossible for subjects or patients to consume at least a glass of olive oil per day, and especially to use olive oil at breakfast on bread with coffee. In addition, to supply the 2 g of linolenic acid needed each day, a large amount of vegetables, salads and walnuts are required. Rapeseed (canola) oil (deprived of erucic acid) is the only oil that has even lower levels of saturated fatty acids than olive oil (8% in rapeseed *versus* 14% in olive oil) and is rich in oleic acid compared with olive oil (55% *versus* 70%). In addition, rapeseed oil contains much more linolenic acid (8% *versus* 0.6%) than olive oil.

The advantage of margarines is that their composition can, in principle, be modified to suit our purpose exactly. Even the level of *trans* fatty acids can be reduced to a minimum. Owing to the unique cooperation of Astra-Calvé (Unilever, France), we designed a margarine with a rapeseed oil base that was close to olive oil in composition, enriched in linolenic acid, but with a taste similar to that of butter. The level of *trans* fatty acids was kept to 6-7% and came only from 18:1. This margarine used in the secondary prevention trial had already been used by French farmers in the Moselle region in 1979.[28] It was supplied free to the patients (and their families) of the experimental group for use on bread and for meal preparation. In the experimental group, the specially prepared margarine replaced the butter and cream consumed by the control group (17 g/day) almost completely.

Dietary surveys and analyses of fatty acid composition of plasma, performed at 8, 52 and 104 weeks, confirmed that most of the patients followed the diet prescribed. As shown in Table IV, changes were observed in the levels of the main fatty acids in the plasma of patients 8 weeks after commencing the special diet and were similar to levels reported at 52 weeks. In brief, the plasma of the experimental group contained significantly higher levels of 18:1, 18:3 n-3, 20:5 n-3 and a lower level of 18:2 n-6 than that of the control group.

At 8, 52, 104 weeks lipaemia, evaluated by measuring the level of total cholesterol, and levels of HDL-cholesterol, triglyceride, apoproteins A_1 and B, and lipoprotein (a) were identical in the two groups. By contrast, death from all causes, cardiac death and non-fatal myocardial infarction were all reduced from 70% to 76% in the experimental group.[29] The number of all the additional cardiovascular events that required hospitalization, such as unstable angina, cardiac insufficiency, stroke and thromboembolism, was also decreased by the same proportion in the experimental group; thus the sum of all the cardiovascular events was reduced by

Table IV. Proportion of fatty acids in plasma total lipids at 8 and 52 weeks.

Group	Control		Experimental	
	Week 8	Week 52	Week 8	Week 52
18:1 n-9	19.0 ± 0.2	19.5 ± 0.3	22.1 ± 0.2***	21.8 ± 0.3***
18:2 n-6	29.8 ± 0.4	29.1 ± 0.5	27.3 ± 0.3***	27.3 ± 0.5**
18:3 n-3	0.39 ± 0.01	0.37 ± 0.02	0.65 ± 0.02***	0.62 ± 0.03***
20:5 n-3	0.75 ± 0.04	0.76 ± 0.05	0.92 ± 0.03***	1.03 ± 0.06***

Values are mean ± SE. **$p<0.01$, ***$p<0.001$. Adapted with permission from Renaud *et al.*[27] and de Lorgeril *et al.*[29]

76%.[27] Perhaps the most surprising finding was that the protection against all cardiovascular events was obvious after only 2 months of the experimental diet. This effect could not have been through a reduction in atherosclerosis, as cholesterol levels were similar in the two groups. Furthermore, trials using cholesterol-lowering drugs have shown that a period of 3 years is required before these drugs produce an effect on mortality and recurrences.[30] As observed in the trials by Burr *et al.*[7] and Leren,[6] the protection developing within the first year is due to an effect on thrombosis, possibly on ventricular fibrillation, as shown in animal studies.[31] In that regard, it is of interest to emphasize that rapeseed oil seems to be the most efficient oil,[32] even more efficient than fish oil,[33] at least in the rat, in preventing arrhythmia and ventricular fibrillation.

Conclusions

As postulated by Owren in 1964,[8] linolenic acid seems to be the most efficient fatty acid in man in lowering at least some platelet function tests, such as aggregation in response to thrombin and platelet clotting activity, in addition to platelet adhesiveness,[8] which was confirmed in the rat by Nordoy.[9] In secondary prevention trials, Leren was the first to show that linolenic acid, supplied by soybean oil, significantly reduced coronary events by 23% and mortality by 25%.[6] Under the conditions used in our trial in Lyon, France, which duplicated the diet

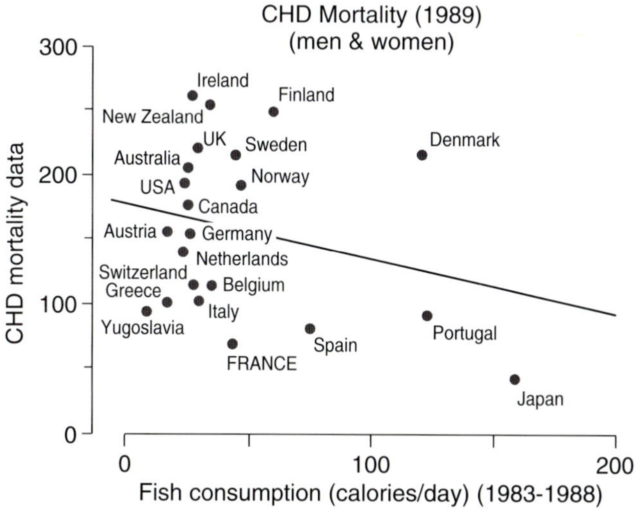

Fig. 1. Relationship between the mortality rate from coronary heart disease (CHD) (mean, men and women) in 1989, as reported by World Health Organization,[36] and the consumption of fish in the countries from the Organization for Economic Co-operation and Development.[37] r=-0.26.

eaten in Crete by using rapeseed oil and margarine, and more vegetable foodstuffs and red wine, nonfatal myocardial infarction and death from all causes were reduced by more than 70% in the patients on the special diet. Although further studies are required, rapeseed oil, because it contains much less linoleic acid and more oleic acid than soybean oil, may be much more efficient in delivering to the human body linolenic acid, which can be accumulated and transformed into its metabolites.[20] In addition, the larger consumption of fruits, vegetables and wine may protect the polyunsaturated fatty acids from peroxidation.

Nevertheless, in the context of the protection afforded by n-3 fatty acids, it is significant that the two populations with the lowest mortality rate from CHD and the greatest life expectancy in the world, the Cretan cohort of the Seven Country Study and the Japanese, have a high consumption of linolenic acid. In Japan, linolenic acid is supplied by rapeseed oil (36% of all fat consumption) and by soybean oil (35%) so that the plasma fatty acid composition of the Japanese is very similar to that of the experimental group from the Lyon diet heart study.[27]

Finally, it has to be emphasized that the Diet and Reinfarction (DART) trial, which investigated the effect of fish or fish oil on death and myocardial infarction, reduced total mortality by only 29% and was not associated with a lowering of non-fatal acute myocardial infarction.[7] When considering the recent consumption of fish in industrialized countries (Fig. 1), an inverse relationship between fish consumption and mortality rate from CHD was not found, as has been emphasized by Crombie *et al.*[34] These results suggest that linolenic acid could be more efficient in protecting against CHD than EPA or DHA, or that linolenic acid is required in addition to fish for effective protection. Even the Eskimos, at least the Canadian Inuits, whose low rate of CHD is well known, appear to have a three- to fourfold higher level of linolenic acid in their red cells than the Canadians in Vancouver.[35]

Summary

Previous dietary trials to prevent ischaemic heart disease (IHD), either before or after a first myocardial infarction, have been shown to reduce mortality only when n-3 fatty acids, either linolenic acid (soybean oil) and/or eicosapentaenoic acid (fish oil), were included in the diet. In contrast, trials using high levels of linoleic acid to decrease serum cholesterol did not reduce IHD.

The hypothesis formulated in 1964 by P.A. Owren was that linolenic acid was the fatty acid most efficient at decreasing platelet adhesiveness, which is enhanced by a diet of saturated fat.[8] In the 1970's, we confirmed, in a study of a rural population in France and the UK, that linolenic acid was the only fatty acid that could lower the clotting activity of platelets and the response of platelets to aggregation by thrombin.[12,13]

In the Seven Countries Study, Crete was associated with a mortality rate from IHD that was 94-98% lower than that of Northern Europe or the USA.[1] In Crete, serum lipids contain a lower level of linoleic acid, but a threefold higher level of linolenic acid, compared with The Netherlands. We have recently conducted a randomized trial involving 600 patients following a first myocardial infarction.

The diet used in this trial was adapted from Crete and included a high intake of α-linolenic acid (0.8% *versus* 0.3% energy), supplied by rapeseed oil-based margarine. After 1 and 2 years, levels of serum lipids were similar in the two groups. After a mean follow-up period of 27 months, cardiac death plus non fatal-myocardial infarctions were reduced by 74%, in the experimental group. The number of cardiovascular events requiring hospitalization (unstable angina, heart failure, stroke, embolism) plus the number of fatal and non-fatal myocardial infarctions was reduced by 76% and total mortality by 70% in the experimental group. This protection was observed as early as 2 months after diet modification, suggesting primarily an effect on thrombosis.

The remarkable protection observed in that intervention trial seems to be concordant with the high intake of linolenic acid in Crete and Japan, the two populations with the greatest life expectancy in the world. It could also explain part of the protection from CHD in Eskimos, at least the Canadian Inuits, who also have a high level of linolenic acid in their blood.

References

1. Keys A.: Coronary heart disease in seven countries. Circulation 1970; (Suppl. 1): 1-211
2. Renaud S., de Lorgeril M.: Dietary lipids and their relation to ischaemic heart disease: from epidemiology to prevention. J. Intern. Med. 1989; 225 (Suppl. 1): 39-46
3. Frantz I.D. Jr., Dawson E.A., Ashman P.L., Gatewood L.C., Bartsch G.E., Kuba K., Brewer E.R.: Test of effect of lipid lowering by diet on cardiovascular risk. The Minnesota Coronary Survey. Arteriosclerosis 1989; 9: 129-135
4. Hjermann I.: Dietary prevention of coronary heart disease. In: Somogy J.C., Renaud S., Astier-Dumas (Eds.) *Emerging Problems in Human Nutrition*. Karger, Basel; Biblthca. Nutr. Dieta., 1987; 40: 28-32
5. Hjermann I., Holme I., Leren P.: Oslo study and antismoking trial. Results after 102 months. Am. J. Med. 1986; 80 (Suppl. 2A): 7-11
6. Leren P.: The Oslo diet-heart study. Eleven year report. Circulation 1970; 42: 935-942
7. Burr M.L., Fehily A.M., Gilbert J.F., Rogers S., Holliday R.M., Sweetnam P.M., Elwood P.C., Deadman N.M.: Effects of changes in fat, fish and fibre intakes on death and myocardial reinfarction: diet and reinfarction trial (DART). Lancet 1989; 2: 757-761
8. Owren P.A., Hellem A.J., Ödeguard A.: Linolenic acid for the prevention of thrombosis and myocardial infarction. Lancet 1964; 2: 975-979
9. Nordoy A.: The influence of saturated fat, cholesterol corn oil and linseed oil on the ADP-induced platelet adhesiveness in the rat. Thromb. Diath. Haemorrh. 1965; 13: 543-549
10. Nordoy A.: The influence of saturated fats, cholesterol corn oil and linseed oil on experimental venous thrombosis. Thromb. Diath. Haemorrh. 1965; 13: 244-256
11. Renaud S., Godu J.: Induction of large thrombi in hyperlipemic rats by epinephrine and endotoxin. Lab. Invest. 1969; 21: 512-518
12. Renaud S., Morazain R., Godsey F., Dumont E., Thevenon C., Martin J.L., Mendy F.: Nutrients, platelet function and composition in nine groups of French and British farmers. Atherosclerosis 1986; 60: 37-48
13. Renaud S., Morazain R., Godsey F., Dumont E., Symington I.S., Gillanders E.M., O'Brien J.R.: Platelet function in relation to diet and serum lipids in British farmers. Br. Heart J. 1981; 46: 562-570
14. Jacobs D.R. Jr, Anderson J.T., Blackburn H.: Diet and serum cholesterol. Do zero correlations negate the relationship? Am. J. Epidemiol. 1979; 110: 77-87

15. Renaud S.: Linoleic acid, platelet aggregation and myocardial infarction. Atherosclerosis 1990; 80: 255-256
16. Renaud S., Ciavatti M., Thévenon C., Ripoll J.P.: Protective effects of dietary calcium and magnesium on platelet function and atherosclerosis in rabbits fed saturated fat. Atherosclerosis 1983; 47: 187-198
17. Renaud S., Beswick A.D., Fehily A.M., Sharp D.S., Elwood P.C.: Alcohol and platelet aggregation: the Caerphilly prospective heart disease study. Am. J. Clin. Nutr. 1992; 55: 1012-1017
18. Renaud S., Godsey F., Dumont E., Thévenon C., Ortchanian E., Martin J.L.: Influence of long-term diet modification on platelet function and composition in Moselle farmers. Amer. J. Clin. Nutr. 1986; 43: 136-150
19. Renaud S., Ruf J.C., Petithory D.: The positional distribution of fatty acids in palm oil and lard influences their biologic effects in rats. J. Nutr. 1995; 125: 229-235
20. Emken E.A., Adlot R.O., Gulley R.M.: Dietary linoleic acid influences desaturation and acylation of deuterium-labeled linoleic and linolenic acids in young adult males. Biochim. Biophys. Acta 1994; 1213: 277-278
21. Cambien F., Warnet J.M., Vernier Y.M., Ducimetière P., Jacqueson A., Flament C., Orssaud G., Richard J.L., Claude J.R.: An epidemiological appraisal of the associations between the fatty acids esterifying serum cholesterol and some cardiovascular risk factors in middle-aged men. Am. J. Epidemiol. 1988; 127: 75-86
22. Lagarde M., Burtin M., Rigaud M., Sprecher H., Dechavanne M., Renaud S.: Prostaglandin E2-like activity of 20:3 omega-9 platelet lipoxygenase end-product. FEBS Lett. 1985; 181: 53-56
23. Kromhout D., Keys A., Aravanis C., Buzina R., Fidanza F., Giampaoli S., Jansen A., Menotti A., Nedeljkovic S., Pekkarinen M., Simic B.S., Toshima H.: Food consumption patterns in the 1960s in seven countries. Am. J. Clin. Nutr. 1989; 49: 889-894
24. Keys A., Menotti A., Aravanis C., *et al.*: The Seven Countries Study: 2289 deaths in 15 years. J. Prev. Med. 1984; 13: 141-154
25. Keys A., Aravanis C., Sdrin H.: The diets of middle-aged men in two rural areas of Greece. Voeding 1966; 27: 575-586
26. Sandker G.N., Kromhout D., Aravanis C., Bloemberg B.P.M., Mensink R.P., Karalias N., Katan M.B.: Serum cholesterol ester fatty acids and their relation with serum lipids in elderly men in Crete and the Netherlands. Eur. J. Clin. Nutr. 1993; 47: 201-208
27. Renaud S., de Lorgeril M., Delaye J., Guidollet J., Jacquard F., Mamelle N., Martin J.L., Monjaud I., Salen P., Touboul P.: The Cretan Mediterranean diet for prevention of coronary heart disease. Am. J. Clin. Nutr. 1995; 61 (Suppl.): 1060S-1067S
28. Renaud S., Godsey F., Dumont E., Thévenon C., Ortchanian E., Martin J.L.: Influence of long-term diet modification on platelet function and composition in Moselle farmers. Am. J. Clin. Nutr. 1986; 43: 136-150
29. de Lorgeril M., Renaud S., Mamelle N., Salen P., Martin J.L., Monjaud I., Duidollet J., Touboul P., Delaye J.: Mediterranean alpha-linolenic acid-rich diet in secondary prevention of coronary heart disease. Lancet 1994; 343: 1454-1459
30. Scandinavian Simvastatin Survival Study Group.: Randomised trial of cholesterol lowering in 4444 patients with coronary heart disease: the Scandinavian Simvastatin Survival Study (4S). Lancet 1994; 344: 1383-1389
31. Riemersma R.A., Sargent C.A.: Dietary fish oil and ischaemic arrhythmias. J. Intern. Med. 1989; 225 (Suppl. 1): 111-116
32. McLennan P.L., Dallimore J.A.: Dietary canola oil modifies myocardial fatty acids and inhibits cardiac arrhythmias in rats. J Nutr. 1995; 125: 1003-1009

33. Siebert B.D., McLennan P.L., Woodhouse J.A., Charnock J.S.: Cardiac arrhythmia in rats in response to dietary n-3 fatty acids from red meat, fish oil and canola oil. Nutr. Res. 1993; 13: 1407-1418
34. Crombie I.K., Mcloone P., Smith W.C.S., Thomson M., Tunstall Pedoe H.: International differences in coronary heart disease mortality and consumption of fish and other foodstuffs. Eur. Heart J. 1987; 8: 560-563
35. Innis S.M.: Sources of omega 3 fatty acids. In Galli C. and Simopoulos A. P. (Eds.) *Biological Effects and Nutritional Essentiality*. New York; Plenum Press, 1989: 135-146
36. World Health Organization: World Health Statistics Annual. World Health Organization; Geneva 1991
37. Organization for Economic Co-operation and Development (OECD): Food consumption statistics. Paris; OCDE Publications, 1991

Safety,
Preparation and New Indications
for n-3 Fatty Acids

S.D. Kristensen, E.B. Schmidt, R. De Caterina, S. Endres
n-3 Fatty Acids: Prevention and Treatment in Vascular Disease
Bi & Gi Publishers, Verona - Springer Verlag, London, 1995

14. Dietary Fish Oil in Renal Transplant Recipients Treated With Cyclosporine A: A 4-Year Follow-Up

J.J. Homan Van Der Heide, H.J.M. Bilo, A.J.M. Donker, A.M. Tegzess

Renal Transplant Division, Department of Internal Medicine, University Hospital, Groningen, The Netherlands

Introduction

In recent years, cyclosporine A (CsA) has become the cornerstone of immunosuppression in transplantation medicine.[1,2] Considerable side-effects have been observed following treatment with CsA, the most important being nephrotoxicity,[3,4] which occurs at therapeutic blood levels.[5]

Altered renal haemodynamics have been shown to play an important role in CsA-induced renal dysfunction. A dose-dependent, initially reversible decrease in glomerular filtration rate (GFR) and effective renal plasma flow (ERPF),[6-8] is often accompanied by a rise in blood pressure.[9,10] These haemodynamic changes are probably due to constriction of the afferent arterioles.[11,12] An increase in the production of thromboxane A_2 (TXA_2), a potent vasoconstrictive and platelet pro-aggregatory substance, has been demonstrated to occur during CsA-induced renal dysfunction.[13,14] In addition, lipoxygenase pathway-derived vasoconstrictor sulfidopeptide leukotrienes, such as leukotriene (LT)C_4 and LTD_4, have been implicated recently in CsA-induced renal vasoconstriction.[15] Thus, CsA appears to disturb the balance between vasodilation and vasoconstriction, induced by arachidonic acid-derived eicosanoids. In addition, fish oil has been shown to exert effects on the immune system. Although the effects of fish oil on the immune response have not yet been clarified, its potential uses are gaining increasing attention. It has been demonstrated that dietary fish oil reduces the generation of several cytokines, including interleukin (IL)-1,[16,17] IL-2,[17] IL-6[16,17] and tumour necrosis factor (TNF)-

α.[15,16] The effect of fish oil on the generation of cytokines may lead to a decrease in the production of LTB_4, which occurs as a result of the inhibition of the 5-lipoxygenase pathway by n-3 fatty acids (FA).[18] Furthermore, administration of fish oil has been shown to enhance the immunosuppressive effects of CsA in a cardiac allograft model,[19-21] and to inhibit delayed-type hypersensitivity.[21]

We have recently demonstrated that administration of n-3 FA (3 g/day) to CsA-treated renal transplant patients during the first postoperative year has beneficial effects on renal function, mean arterial blood pressure (MAP) and the occurrence of rejection episodes.[22] We have therefore evaluated these variables in the same group of patients, 24 and 48 months after transplantation.

Patients and Methods

Study design

The study was a randomized and, initially, double-blind comparison between fish oil (6 g/day; 30% eicosapentaenoic acid (EPA; C20:5 n-3) and 20% docosahexaenoic acid (DHA; C22:6 n-3) as their ethyl esters, with vitamin E (1 IU/g fish oil) added as an antioxidant (Kortman Intradal BV, Amersfoort, The Netherlands), and coconut oil (6 g/day, containing medium-chain saturated fatty acids (63% C8:0 and 36% C10:0) with vitamin E (1 IU/g coconut oil) and fish perfume (0.25%) (Kortman Intradal BV, Amersfoort, The Netherlands). Fish oil and coconut oil were administered in capsules (0.5 g) containing n-3 FA (50%), delivered in three daily doses of four capsules, which were ingested at meal times.

Sixty-six primary cadaveric renal transplant recipients were given a trial number directly prior to grafting. The number corresponded to the treatment regimen, and fish oil or coconut oil were administered for the first 90 days following grafting. Oil ingestion was started 3 days postoperatively. After 3 months the code was broken; patients ingesting fish oil (n=33, EPA+ group) continued to do so until month 24, when ingestion of fish oil was stopped. Oil ingestion was stopped in patients assigned to coconut oil (n=33, EPA- group) after 3 months. The latter cohort of patients served as a control group in all further clinical and laboratory follow-up investigations. A full clinical and laboratory evaluation was performed 12 months, 24 months and between 4-5 years postoperatively. Routine follow-up was performed by physicians who were unaware of any oil ingestion.

Patients ingesting non-steroidal anti-inflammatory drugs, including acetylsalicylic acid, were not included in the trial. In the case of persistent hypertension, patients were treated with a ß1-selective blocker, which, if necessary, was combined with a diuretic or a centrally acting vasodilatory agent, such as clonidine. Calcium channel blockers, such as nifedipine, were regarded as an antihypertensive rescue therapy instead of a first choice drug, in view of their potential effects on several study variables, such as renal haemodynamics,[23,24] and their enhancement of the immunosuppressive action of CsA.[25] Antihypertensive or diuretic agents were prescribed at the judgement of the physician in charge of the patient at that particular time, according to generally accepted standards, but administration was not strictly protocolled. After grafting, patients adhered to a diet containing fluid (2.5 l/day) and sodium chloride (3 g/day) during hospitalization. The intake of protein, potassium and fatty acids was unrestricted. After discharge, patients were urged to maintain a restricted intake of sodium.

Administration of CsA

CsA was administered intravenously (3 mg/kg body weight/day) for the first 72 hours, starting 6 hours after revascularization of the graft. This was followed by oral administration of CsA (10 mg/kg body weight/day), delivered in three daily doses, and subsequently slowly reduced. All patients received prednisolone (20 mg/day) from day 1 onwards. This dose was reduced by 2.5 mg every 2 weeks until a maintenance dose of 10 mg was reached.

Assays

- *CsA levels*: CsA whole-blood 8-hour trough levels were measured using a monoclonal, specific, radioimmunoassay (Sandoz, Basle, Switzerland). This assay was performed three times per week during hospitalization. The same assay was performed twice weekly on regular outpatient controls for 2 months postoperatively, followed by once a week for a further 2 months. From month 4, the assay was performed every 4 months until 48 hours after the transplant.

- *Renal function*: renal function tests were performed using simultaneous determinations of the ^{125}I-iothalamate and ^{131}I-hippuran clearance rates for GFR and ERPF, respectively.[26] Coefficients of variation of day to day determinations of ^{125}I-iothalamate (GFR) and ^{131}I-hippuran (ERPF) clearance rates were 2.2 and 5.0%, respectively.[26] Filtration fraction (FF) was calculated as GFR divided by ERPF. Clearance rate was expressed as ml/min/1.73m^2. Protein content was determined prior to the isotope clearance studies from urine samples collected over 24 hours. Blood pressure was measured using a Hawksley random zero sphygmomanometer after a rest period of at least 15 minutes in a supine position. MAP was calculated as (systolic pressure + 2 x diastolic pressure) ÷ 3.
  Delayed postoperative graft function was defined as the number of postoperative days in which a diuresis of less than 1000 ml was measured in the absence of a decrease in levels of serum creatinine, with an optimal hydration in the peri-operative phase maintained in all patients.

- *Leukotriene analysis*: neutrophils were isolated from peripheral blood (20 ml) drawn into EDTA. Erythrocytes were sedimented with gelatine (0.3% w/v). The buffy coat was separated on gelatine (0.3 w/v) and neutrophils were subsequently isolated on Percoll (d=1.077 g/ml). Residual erythrocytes were lysed with hypotonic ammonium chloride. Neutrophils (10^7 cells/ml) were preincubated in Dulbecco's medium for 30 minutes at 37°C. Calcium chloride was then added to a final concentration of 2 mM and cells were stimulated with the calcium ionophore A-23187 (10 μM) for a further 10 minutes. Cells were centrifuged (1 minute at 11,000 g) and finally, prostaglandin B_2 was added to the supernatant as an internal standard for high performance liquid chromatography (HPLC) measurements. LTs were separated and quantified using a C_{18} column.[27,28] LT measurements were performed prior to transplantation and 6 months after grafting in two groups of eight patients, randomly selected from both experimental and control groups.

Compliance and rejection

Compliance with fish oil ingestion was determined by analysis of plasma cholesterol esters after preparation of an extract of total plasma lipids and isolation of the cholesterol ester fraction using amino propyl-silica columns; the fatty acid composition was determined by capillary gas chromatography.[29] This was performed prior to transplantation and 6 months postoperatively.

Rejection was suspected when levels of serum creatinine rose, or did not improve further, over 3 consecutive days in the absence of excessive CsA whole-blood trough levels. The diagnosis of rejection was established using clinical variables (such as graft swelling, tenderness, sodium retention, blood eosinophilia and fever) and serial ultra-sonography, and was confirmed by a percutaneous renal biopsy prior to the initiation of rejection treatment in all cases.

Statistics

All values are expressed as median values, except when indicated otherwise, with their ranges within parentheses. The statistical significance of values from unpaired tests was calculated using the Mann-Whitney U test, while values from paired tests were compared using a two-sided Wilcoxon test. Dichotome variables were tested with a χ^2 analysis. A value of $p<0.05$ was considered to be statistically significant.

Results

Of the 66 patients included in the trial, 52 patients had an evaluable renal function after 4 years. In the group treated with fish oil, three grafts were lost from the follow-up study (one due to technical failure, while two were lost due to acute/chronic rejection). In the control group, nine grafts were lost (one due to a technical failure, six due to therapy-resistant rejection, while two patients died with functioning graft). All surviving patients with a functioning graft participated in the analysis of renal function and MAP, while all surviving patients initially included in the trial participated in the graft survival analysis. Both groups were comparable in donor and patient characteristics, with the exception of the incidence of acute postoperative oligo-anuria, which was significantly less in the group treated with fish oil (Table I).

Compliance to ingestion of fish oil was confirmed by analysing plasma-cholesterol esters after 6 months. In the EPA+ group, the 20:5 n-3 content increased from 0.39 (0.18-1.67) Mol % prior to grafting to 4.7 (0.89-10.31) Mol % ($p<0.0001$) after 6 months postoperatively. No major changes were observed in the control group: [0.47 (0.12-0.97) to 0.53 (0.12-2.24) Mol %]. These data indicate an overall good compliance with the fish oil treatment.

The dose and whole-blood trough levels of CsA in both groups are shown in Table II. These data demonstrate that the dose and whole-blood trough levels of

Table I. Demographics of patients treated with fish oil (EPA+) or coconut oil (EPA-) and their corresponding donors.

	EPA+ (n=33)	**EPA– (n=33)**
Donor age (years)	47 (4-61)	42 (5-65)
Donor sex (% male)	56	67
Recipient age (years)	41 (17-69)	47 (19-67)
Recipient sex (% male)	64	59
Duration of dialysis (months)	56	48
MM HLA-A**	56%	58%
MM HLA-B**	60%	41%
MM HLA-DR**	18%	26%
Current PRA	8.2% (0-76)	8.5% (0-80)
Max PRA	22.5% (0-99)	13.5% (0-99)
Warm ischaemia (min)	36 (15-70)	35 (20-74)
Cold ischaemia (hours)	26 (11-40)	29 (12-52)
Delayed function (days)	0.9 (0-10)*	1.6 (0-14)

Abbreviations: MM=mismatch, PRA=panel reactive antibodies. Data are shown as median values and ranges in parentheses; percentage values are expressed as mean. *$p<0.05$ (Mann-Whitney U test), **two mismatches on each locus (HLA-A, HLA-B and HLA-DR)=100%.

Table II. CsA- dose and whole-blood 8-hour trough levels in patients treated with fish oil (EPA+) or coconut oil (EPA-), 12, 24 and 48 months postoperatively.

	CsA dose (mg/kg BW)		
	12 months	**24 months**	**48 months**
EPA+	4.5 (3-8)	4.5 (1.5-6.5)*	3.0 (1-6)
EPA-	4 (1.3-10)	3.8 (1-7.5)*	3.2 (1-6)
	CsA levels (ng/ml)		
EPA+	140 (50-321)	182 (40-420)	110 (75-210)
EPA-	143 (80-245)	155 (30-310)	125 (40-340)

Data are shown as medians with ranges in parentheses. *$p<0.05$ 12 months *versus* 48 months (Wilcoxon test).

CsA were comparable throughout the follow-up period. The data also indicate that the bioavailability of CsA was not changed greatly when it was combined with fish oil or coconut oil (6 g/day).

Figure 1 shows the GFR 1, 3, 6, 12, 24 and 48 months postoperatively for the patient groups receiving fish oil and coconut oil. GFR was significantly higher in patients receiving fish oil than in control patients receiving coconut oil after 3, 6 and 12 months. At 24 months, however, the GFR of the control group continued to increase

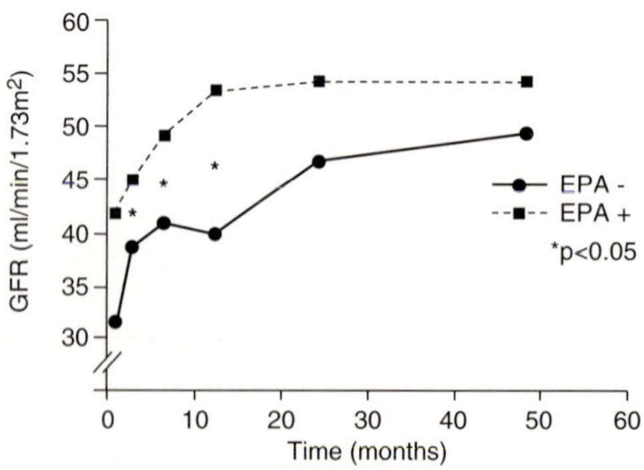

Fig. 1. Glomerular filtration rate (GFR) of patients treated with fish oil (EPA+) and patients treated with coconut oil (EPA-) at 1, 3, 6, 12, 24 and 48 months after transplantation. GFR is expressed as ml/min/ 1.73m^2; *$p<0.05$ EPA+ *versus* EPA- (Mann-Whitney U test).

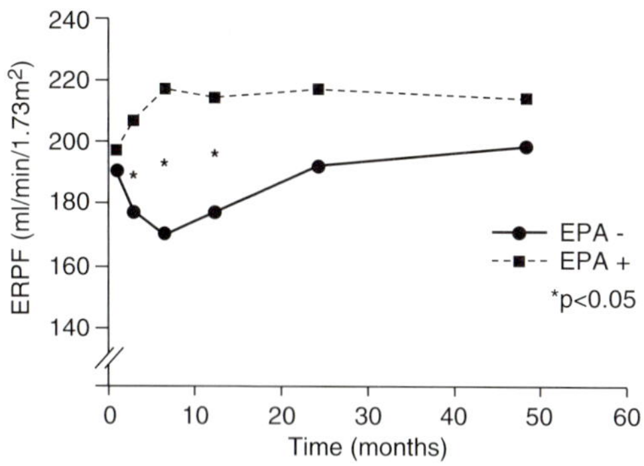

Fig. 2. Effective renal plasma flow (ERPF) of the patients treated with fish oil (EPA+) and patients treated with coconut oil (EPA-) at 1, 3, 6, 12, 24 and 48 months after transplantation. ERPF is expressed as ml/min/1.73m^2. *p<0.05 EPA+ *versus* EPA- (Mann-Whitney U test).

slowly, while in the group treated with fish oil, no further increase in GFR was observed. ERPF was comparable for both groups after 1 month (Fig. 2). Once again, ERPF was significantly higher in the patients receiving, fish oil 3, 6 and 12 months postoperatively and after 12 months, the ERPF in the control group tended to increase further while in the patients receiving fish oil, ERPF remained constant (Fig. 2).

Patients receiving fish oil had a significantly lower MAP than control patients (Table III). Significant differences in MAP were still detectable between the two groups after 24 and 48 months. The cumulative incidence of acute rejection episodes was significantly lower 12 months after grafting in the patients receiving fish oil than in the control patients (24% *versus* 64%, p<0.05).[22] During the following 36 months, no more acute rejection episodes occurred in either group. However, in the group

Table III. Mean arterial pressure (MAP; mmHg) and the percentage of patients treated with antihypertensive agents, including diuretics, in the groups treated with fish oil (EPA+) or coconut oil (EPA-), 12, 24 and 48 months after grafting.

	MAP (mmHg)		
	12 months	**24 months**	**48 months**
EPA+	103 (80-141)	103 (74-140)	100 (70-133)
EPA-	118 (98-131)*	112 (86-133)*	109 (74-144)*

Data are shown as median values with ranges on parentheses; *p<0.05 EPA+ *versus* EPA- (Mann-Whitney U test).

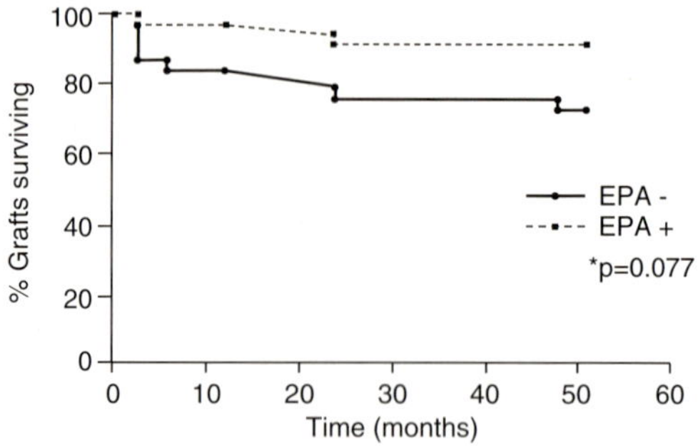

Fig. 3. Kaplan-Meier graft survival estimates of the patients treated with fish oil (EPA+) or patients treated with coconut oil (EPA-).

treated with fish oil, two grafts were lost due to chronic rejection compared with six in the group receiving placebo (p=0.06). Kaplan-Meier graft survival estimates are depicted in Figure 3, and show that there was a tendency towards a better 4-year graft survival in patients receiving fish oil than in placebo-treated controls (p=0.077). The *in vitro* production of LTB_4 and LTB_5 by polymorphonuclear neutrophils (PMNs) stimulated by Ca^{2+}-ionophore in both groups is shown in Table IV.

A significant decrease in the production of LTB_4 was observed in patients receiving fish oil, while LTB_4 levels in the control group remained unchanged. Furthermore, after 6 months, a moderate amount of LTB_5 was detected in the patients receiving fish oil, whereas no detectable levels of LTB_5 were established in the control group. However, no major differences in LTB_4 production were

Table IV. Production of leukotrienes by polymorphonuclear leukocytes (PMNs) (ng/10^7 neutrophils) before transplantation (T=0) and 6 months after grafting (T=6) in patients treated with fish oil (EPA+, n=8) or coconut oil (EPA-, n=8).

	EPA+		**EPA-**	
	T=0	**T=6**	**T=0**	**T=6**
LTB_4	178 (64-250)*	131.8 (46-170)	132.3 (41-190)	124.5 (93-208)
LTB_5	0 (0-0)*	21.3 (3-44)**	0 (0-0)	0 (0-0)

Data are shown as median values with ranges in parentheses. *p<0.05, T=0 *versus* T=6 (Wilcoxon test) and EPA+ *versus* EPA- (Mann-Whitney U test), **p<0.05 EPA+ *versus* EPA- at T=6.

detected between the patients receiving fish oil and the controls at 6 months after grafting. A possible risk following the intake of high amounts of n-3 FA may be impaired haemostasis.[30] Although haemostatic variables were not analysed prospectively, prothrombin time, activated partial thromboplastin time and bleeding time, were determined prior to every percutaneous renal biopsy. No differences in these variables were observed between the patients receiving fish oil and the controls, while all biopsies were uneventful. No difference in postoperative bleeding from either operation wounds or from the urinary tract was observed between the two groups.

Discussion

The aim of this study was to evaluate a long-term follow-up of the effect of dietary supplementation with fish oil on renal function, MAP, the incidence of acute rejection and graft survival in CsA-treated renal allograft recipients.

Patient characteristics in the EPA+ and EPA- group were comparable, with the exception of the median number of days before postoperative diuresis exceeded 1 litre, which was significantly lower in the EPA+ group. This finding cannot be attributed to the ingestion of fish oil, which started 3 days after grafting. However, ingestion of fish oil could have influenced the outcome of the trial. It is well known that postoperative oligo-anuria due to acute tubular necrosis (ATN) is worsened by CsA,[1,31] although it is rather difficult to differentiate between a diagnosis of prolonged ATN, CsA nephrotoxicity and incipient acute cellular rejection. Therefore, all data were analysed excluding the patients with ATN. This method of analysis did not alter the calculated p values, suggesting that the outcome of the trial was not affected by differences in the incidence of postoperative oligo-anuria. A good compliance to the fish oil capsules was demonstrated by the increase in the percentage of n-3 FA in the plasma cholesterol fraction.

As expected, GFR tended to increase with time in both the patients treated with fish oil and the control patients. However, the patients receiving fish oil tended to have a higher GFR after 1 month, and after 3, 6 and 12 months, the difference between the two groups being significant. However, at 24 months, although the patients treated with fish oil still ingested fish oil, no further increase in GFR was detected. Indeed, GFR remained stable for the remainder of the trial, despite cessation of the fish oil at 24 months. In contrast, GFR tended to increase in the placebo-treated patients, resulting in comparable GFR values for both groups from month 24 onwards. ERPF tended to rise immediately in the patients treated with fish oil but tended to decrease initially in the control group. Thus, at 3, 6 and 12 months there was a significant difference in ERPF between the patients receiving fish oil and the controls. Again, the ERPF continued to increase in the control group, while in the patients receiving fish oil, ERPF remained stable from 6 months onwards.

These trends in GFR and ERPF could be explained by differences in the occurrence of both acute and chronic rejection. It is possible that the initial decrease in ERPF was due to a higher incidence of acute rejection in the control group. Furthermore, it is well known that early acute rejection is an important determinant in the development of chronic rejection and long-term graft survival.[32] Thus, it is possible that, after 24 months, a form of selection may have occurred, resulting in a stable renal function of the remaining grafts. Another possible explanation is that stable renal function developed earlier in the patients receiving fish oil than in the control group as a result of the beneficial effects of fish oil. Fish oil may have affected CsA-induced renal dysfunction, of which postoperative grafts are more vulnerable. This is supported by the fact that at 24 and 48 months, the dose of CsA was significantly lower than in the early postoperative phase.

MAP was significantly lower throughout the trial period in the patients receiving fish oil. The lower blood pressure in these patients was not due to a more intensive antihypertensive treatment, as demonstrated by the significant difference in the percentage of patients requiring antihypertensive drugs.[22]

Taken together, the effects observed suggest a more balanced renal haemodynamic situation in the patients treated with fish oil. This cannot be explained by differences in the dose of CsA administered per day or in CsA-trough levels, as both remained comparable between the groups. The latter finding also indicates that, in our study, dietary supplementation with n-3 FA did not influence the bioavailability of CsA. This finding contrasts with a recent study of rats treated with excessive doses of CsA.[33] Nevertheless, it is not completely possible from our data to assess whether the better renal haemodynamic situation in patients treated with fish oil was purely due to direct haemodynamic changes, such as modification of CsA nephrotoxicity, or whether a more indirect effect was responsible, such as an immunologically mediated effect of fish oil. Several arguments exist in favour of both hypotheses. It is well established that dietary supplementation with n-3 FA has moderate effects on renal haemodynamics in a multitude of clinical conditions.[34] Recent evidence suggests that haemodynamic changes induced by fish oil in the kidney predominantly affect efferent vessels,[35] leading to a decrease in FF, as demonstrated in both normal healthy volunteers[36] and patients with chronic renal insufficiency.[34]

Beneficial effects of dietary supplements with fish oil on renal function have been reported in CsA- and fish oil-treated rats, psoriasis vulgaris patients and cardiac allograft graft recipients with stable renal function, which are all clinical or experimental conditions not hampered by the concomitant effect of acute or chronic renal allograft rejection.[37-39]

Although levels of prostaglandins were not measured in our patients, the effects of fish oil on prostaglandin production are likely to have played an important role in the mechanism resulting in improved renal haemodynamics in patients receiving fish oil. Marine n-3 FA inhibit TXA_2 production in humans.[40] EPA appears to compete with arachidonic acid in the cyclooxygenase pathway, thus limiting the production of TXA_2.[41] It remains to be established whether renal function can be protected completely through this interference. Complete inhibition of TXA_2-production by an inhibitor of thromboxane synthetase did not restore GFR to control levels in CsA-treated rats.[14] Two studies investigating short-term intervention with inhibitors of thromboxane synthetase in CsA-treated renal transplant recipients have been published recently. In one study, renal function remained unaffected, although production of TXB_2 was blocked by 81%.[42] In the other study, a moderate increase in the GFR was observed following a 90% reduction in the production of TXB_2.[43] This suggests that other mechanisms are also involved in the loss of renal function induced by CsA. Interestingly, the combination of a thromboxane- and a leukotriene C_4/D_4-receptor antagonist completely prevented a reduction in renal plasma flow in CsA-treated rats.[15] Moreover, it has been demonstrated that dietary supplementation with fish oil decreases the generation of both LTB_4 and LTC_4.[44] Thus, the combined effect of dietary fish oil-derived cyclooxygenase and lipoxygenase metabolites on CsA-induced renal dysfunction might contribute to the favourable haemodynamic situation of the patients treated with fish oil. Nevertheless, due to the design of the trial we cannot conclude that a total protection of renal function was established, or assess the exact role of various cyclooxygenase metabolites.

An observation of particular interest is that the patients treated with fish oil exhibited a significantly lower cumulative incidence of acute rejection episodes during the first postoperative year than control patients. This observation might explain the trend towards a favourable 4-year period of graft survival in the fish oil-treated patients. It should, however, be emphasized that a trial of this size is not absolute proof of an enhancement in graft survival.

The possible mechanisms for the immunosuppressive action of fish oil remain highly speculative and were not the focus of this study. Nevertheless, there have been a number of reports that suggest immunomodulating effects of dietary fish oil, as reviewed elsewhere.[45,46] It is possible that these effects are, at least partially, located in the effector pathway of the immune response. For example, the anti-inflammatory effects of fish oil, all well recognized in a wide number of experimental settings,[47] might have modified the course of events in a rejecting renal allograft. This hypothesis is in agreement with the effects of fish oil on the cyclo- and lipoxygenase pathways, and its subsequent effects on the generation of eicosanoids, all three compounds being important in the sequence of renal allograft rejection.[48] Our data show a decrease from baseline values in the generation of LTB_4 by PMNs stimulated with Ca^{2+} ionophores in the patients treated with fish oil, as well as moderate production of LTB_5. Such a change in the LT profile has recently been associated with a marked reduction in chemotactic properties,[18] as well as a reduction in the production of TNFα and IL-1,[16] which may be important in the rejection process. Conversely, no difference in the level of LTB_4 generated by

PMNs was detected between the two groups. This may have been due to the small number of patients used to perform this analysis. Furthermore, a decrease in the production of TXA_2 may be important, not only in CsA nephrotoxicity, but also in the rejection process.[49-52] Another possible explanation for the reduced incidence of acute and chronic rejection could be an increase in the immunosuppressive activity of CsA in the presence of fish oil, such as that observed in a cardiac allograft model.[19-21] It was shown recently that cisplatinum reaches a higher intracellular concentration when administered concomitantly with docosahexaenoic acid.[53] It could be argued that a similar phenomenon occurs with a combination of CsA and fish oil, resulting in an increase in immunosuppressive activity without changes in whole-blood trough levels. This theory, however, remains speculative.

In summary, the data presented here demonstrate that fish oil (6 g/day) exerts a favourable effect on renal haemodynamics, MAP and the incidence of acute rejection in CsA-treated renal transplant recipients during the first postoperative year. From 24 to 48 months postoperatively, renal function is comparable in control and treated patients, due to a slow increase in renal function in the control group. In addition, there is a trend towards better graft survival in the patients treated with fish oil.

We conclude that dietary fish oil (6 g/day; 50% long-chain n-3 FA) is a highly useful and safe adjuvant therapy for postoperative CsA-treated renal transplant recipients. The present data suggest, however, that the period of fish-oil ingestion could be limited to the first postoperative year.

Summary

Previously we demonstrated that ingestion of dietary fish oil for 1 year has a beneficial effect on renal haemodynamics and the incidence of rejection in postoperative cyclosporine A (CsA)-treated transplant recipients. We therefore investigated the long-term effect of dietary supplementation with fish oil on renal function, blood pressure and the incidence of acute rejection episodes in CsA-treated renal transplant recipients. In a randomized, initially placebo-controlled double blind trial, 33 primary cadaveric CsA-treated renal transplant recipients ingested 6 g fish oil daily (30% C20:5 n-3 and 20% C22:6 n-3; EPA + group), during the first 2 postoperative years, while another 33 renal graft recipients ingested 6 g coconut oil daily (63% C8:0 and 36% C10:0; EPA- group), for 3 months. Patients were HLA-DR matched, had identical panel of reactive antibodies and donor and recipient demographics. Renal function tests were performed using simultaneous determinations of the ^{125}I-iothalamate and ^{131}I-hippuran clearances for glomerular filtration rate (GFR) and effective renal plasma flow (ERPF), respectively, at 1, 3, 6, 12, 24, and 48 months. Twelve months after grafting, the fish oil-treated patients had a higher GFR (EPA + 53 *versus* EPA- 40 ml/min/1.73m^2, $p<0.05$) and ERPF (EPA+ 214 *versus* EPA- 178 ml/min/1.73m^2, $p<0.05$). After 48 months, no significant difference between these variables was observed (EPA+ 54 *versus* EPA- 49 ml/min/1.73m^2, and ERPF (EPA+ 214 *versus* EPA- 198 ml/min/1.73m^2). From the twelfth month, GFR and ERPF remained stable in the fish oil treated patients, while these variables tended to rise slowly in the control group. Four year graft survival tended to be better the EPA+ group than in the EPA- group (91% *versus* 72%; $p<0.077$). Mean arterial blood pressure (MAP) was significantly lower in the fish oil-treated patients during the entire trial period (EPA+ 100 *versus* EPA- 109 mmHg, $p=0.044$ at 48 months).

We conclude that daily administration of 6 g fish oil has a beneficial effect on renal haemodynamics, MAP and the incidence of rejection episodes during the first postoperative year. After cessation of the fish oil ingestion, no differences in renal function could be detected. Thus, dietary fish oil appears to be a safe and useful adjuvant therapy for CsA-treated renal transplant recipients, in whom it seems that most gain occurs during the first postoperative year.

References

1. Canadian Multicenter Transplant Study Group. A randomized clinical trial of cyclosporine in cadaveric renal transplantation. N. Engl. J. Med. 1983; 309: 809-815
2. European Multicenter Trial Group. Cyclosporine in cadaveric renal transplantation: one year follow-up of a multi-center trial. Lancet 1983; ii: 986-989
3. Calne R.Y., Thiru S., McMaster P., *et al.*: Cyclosporin A in patients receiving renal allografts from cadaveric donors. Lancet 1978; ii: 1323-1327
4. Myers B.D.: Cyclosporin nephrotoxicity. Kidney Int. 1986; 30: 964-974
5. Kahan B.D., Grevel J.: Optimization of cyclosporine therapy in renal transplantation by a pharmacokinetic strategy. Transplantation 1988; 46: 631-644
6. Dieperink H., Leyssac P.P., Kemp E., *et al.*: Nephrotoxicity of cyclosporin A in humans: effects on glomerular filtration and tubular reabsorption rates. Eur. J. Clin. Invest. 1987; 17: 493-496
7. Myers B.D., Ross J., Newton L., Luetscher J., Perlroth M.: Cyclosporin associated chronic nephropathy. N. Engl. J. Med. 1986; 311: 699-705
8. Tegzess A.M.: Ciclosporin and renal function. In: van Joost T.H., Heule F., Bos J.D. (Eds.) *Ciclosporin in Psoriasis*. Actua Sandoz 13, 1988: 128-136
9. Chapman J.R., Marcen R., Arias M., *et al.*: Hypertension after renal transplantation. Transplantation, 1987; 43: 860-864
10. Ciclosporin Hypertension. [Editorial]. Lancet 1988; ii: 1234
11. Murray B.M., Paller M.S., Ferris T.F.: Effect of cyclosporine administration on renal hemodynamics in conscious rats. Kidney Int. 1985; 28: 767-774
12. Myers B.D., Newton L., Boshkos C., *et al.*: Chronic injury of human renal microvessels with low dose cyclosporine therapy. Transplantation 1988; 46: 694-703
13. Bennett W.M., Elzinga L., Kelley V.: Pathophysiology of cyclosporin nephrotoxicity: role of eicosanoids. Transplant. Proc., 1988; 20 (Suppl): 628-633
14. Perico N., Benigni A., Zoja C., Delaini F., Remuzzi G.: Functional significance of exaggerated renal thromboxane A2 synthesis induced by cyclosporin A. Am. J. Physiol. 1986; 251: F581-F587
15. Perico N., Pasini M., Gaspari F., Abbate M., Remuzzi G.: Co-participation of thromboxane A2 and leukotriene C_4 and D_4 in mediating cyclosporine-induced acute renal failure. Transplantation 1991; 52: 873-878
16. Endres S., Ghorbani R., Kelley V.E., *et al.*: The effect of dietary supplementation with n-3 polyunsaturated fatty acids on the synthesis of interleukin-1 and tumor necrosis factor by mononuclear cells. N. Engl. J. Med. 1989; 320: 265-271
17. Meydani S.N., Endres S., Woods M.N., *et al.*: Effect of fish oil supplementation on cytokine production and lymphocyte proliferation in pre- and postmenopausal women. FASEB J. 1990; 4: A795

18. Lee T.H., Hoover R.L., Williams J.D., *et al.*: Effect of dietary enrichment with eicosapentaenoic and docosahexaenoic acids on *in vitro* neutrophil and monocyte leukotriene generation and neutrophil function. N. Engl. J. Med. 1985; 312: 1217-1224
19. Perez R.V., Waymack J.P., Munda R., Alexander W.J.: The effect of donor specific transfusions and dietary fatty acids on rat cardiac allograft survival. J. Surg. Res. 1987; 42: 335-340
20. Otto D.A., Kahn D.R., Hamm M.W., Forrest D.E., Wooten J.T.: Improved survival of heterotopic cardiac allografts in rats with dietary n-3 polyunsaturated fatty acids. Transplantation 1990; 50: 193-198
21. Kelley V.E., Kirkman R.L., Bastos M., Barrett L.V., Strom T.B.: Enhancement of immunosuppression by substitution of fish oil for olive oil as a vehicle for cyclosporine. Transplantation 1989; 48: 98-102
22. Homan van der Heide J.J., Bilo H.J.G., Donker A.J.M., Wilmink J.M., Tegzess A.M.: Effect of dietary fish oil on renal function and rejection in cyclosporin-treated recipients of renal transplants. N. Engl. J. Med. 1993; 329: 769-773
23. Hauser A.C., Derfler K., Stockenhuber F., *et al.*: Effect of calcium-channel blockers on renal function in renal-graft recipients treated with cyclosporine. N. Engl. J. Med. 1991; 324: 1517
24. Feehaly J., Walls J., Mistry N., *et al.*: Does nifedipine ameliorate cyclosporin A nephrotoxicity. Br. Med. J. 1987; 295: 310
25. Weir M.R., Peppler G., Gomolka D., Handwerger B.S.: Additive effect of cyclosporine and verapamil on the inhibition of activation and function of human peripheral blood mononuclear cells. Transplant. Proc. 1988; 20 (Suppl 2): 240-244
26. Donker A.J.M., van der Hem G.K., Sluiter W.J., Beekhuis W.: A radio-isotope method for simultaneous determination of the glomerular filtration rate and the effective renal plasma flow. Neth. J. Med. 1977; 20: 97-103
27. van der Tempel H., Tulleken J.E., Muskiet F.A.J., van Rijswijk M.H.: Effects of fish oil supplementation in RA. Ann. Rheum. Dis. 1990; 49: 76-80
28. Verhagen J., Walstra P., Veldink G.A., Vliegenhart J.F.G., Bruynzeel P.L.B.: Separation and quantitation of leukotrienes by reversed phase high performance liquid chromatography. Prostaglandins Leukotrienes Med. 1984; 13: 15-20
29. Hoving E.B., Jansen G., Volmer M., Doormaal J.J., Muskiet F.A.J.: Profiling of plasma cholesterol esters and triglyceride fatty acids as their methyl esters by capillary gas chromatography, preceded by a separation of lipid classes. J. Chromatogr. Biomed. Appl. 1988; 434: 395-409
30. Dyerberg J., Bang H.O.: Hemostatic function and platelet polyunsaturated fatty acids in eskimos. Lancet 1979; ii: 117-119
31. Hall B.M., Tiller D.J., Duggin G.G., *et al.*: Post-transplant acute renal failure in cadaver renal recipients treated with cyclosporine. Kidney Int. 1985; 28: 178-186
32. Tesi R.J., Elkhammas E.A., Henry M.L., Davies E.A., Salazar A., Ferguson R.M.: Acute rejection episodes: best predictor of long-term primary cadaveric renal transplant survival. Transplant. Proc. 1993; 25: 901-903
33. Jevnikar A.M., Petric R., Holub D.J., Philbrick D.J., Clark W.F.: Effect of cyclosporin on plasma lipids and modification with dietary fish oil. Transplantation 1988; 46: 722-725
34. Bilo H.J.G., Homan van der Heide J.J., Gans R.O.B., Donker A.J.M.: Omega-3 polyunsaturated fatty acids in chronic renal insufficiency. Nephron 1991; 57: 385-393
35. Schmitz P.G., O'Donnell M.P., Kasiske B.M., Keane W.F.: Glomerular hemodynamic effects of dietary polyunsaturated fatty acid supplementation. J. Lab. Clin. Med. 1991; 118: 129-135
36. Düssing R., Struck A., Göbel B.O., Weisser B., Vetter H.: Effects of n-3 fatty acids on renal function and renal prostaglandin E metabolism. Kidney Int. 1990; 38: 315-319
37. Elzinga L., Kelley V.E., Houghton D.C., Bennett W.M.: Modification of experimental nephrotoxicity with fish oil as the vehicle of cyclosporine. Transplantation 1987; 43: 271-274

38. Stoof T.J., Korstanje M.J., Bilo H.J.G., *et al.*: Does fish oil protect renal function in cyclosporin-treated psoriasis patients? J. Int. Med. 1989; 226: 437-441
39. Brouwer R.M.L., Wenting G.J., Pos B., *et al.*: Fish oil ameliorates established cyclosporin A nephrotoxicity after heart transplantation. Kidney Int. 1991; 40: 347-348
40. von Schacky C., Fischer S., Weber P.C.: Long-term effects of dietary marine omega-3 fatty acids upon plasma and cellular lipids, platelet function, and eicosanoid formation in humans. J. Clin. Invest. 1985; 76: 1621-1631
41. Hamberg M.: Transformations of 5,8,11,17-eicosapentaenoic acid in human platelets. Biochim. Biophys. Acta 1980; 618: 389-398
42. Weir M.R., Klasen D.K., Burdick J.F.: A pilot study to assess the ability of an orally available selective thromboxane synthase inhibitor to improve renal function in cyclosporine-treated renal transplant recipients. J. Am. Soc. Nephrol. 1992; 2: 1285-1290
43. Smith S.R., Creech E.A., Schaffer A.V., *et al.*: Effects of thromboxane synthase inhibition with CGS 13080 in human cyclosporine nephrotoxicity. Kidney Int. 1992; 41: 199-205
44. Spurney D.F., Pisetsky D.S., Coffman T.M.: Fish oil (FO) feeding reduces production of biologically active leukotrienes (LTs) in murine lupus nephritis. J. Am. Soc. Nephrol. 1991; 2: 432
45. Kinsella J.E., Lokesh B., Broughton S., Whelan J.: Dietary polyunsaturated fatty acids and eicosanoids: Potential effects on the modulation of inflammatory and immune cells: an overview. Nutrition 1990; 6: 24-44
46. Meydani S.N.: Dietary modulation of cytokine production and biologic functions. Nutrition Rev. 1990; 48: 361-369
47. Simopoulos, A.: Omega-3 fatty acids in health and disease and in growth and development. Am. J. Clin. Nutr. 1991; 54: 438-463
48. Foegh M.L., Alijani M.R., Helfrich G.B., *et al.*: Lipid mediators in organ transplantation. Transplant Proc. 1986; 18 (Suppl 4): 20-24
49. Foegh M.L., Zmudka M., Cooley C., *et al.*: Urine i-TXB_2 in renal allograft rejection. Lancet 1981; ii: 431-434
50. Steinhauer H.B., Wilms H., Ruther M., Schollmeyer P.: Clinical experience with urine TXB_2 in acute renal allograft rejection. Transplant Proc. 1986; 18: 98-103
51. Coffman T.M., Yarger W.E., Klotman P.E.: Functional role of thromboxane production by rejecting renal allografts in rats. J. Clin. Invest. 1985; 75: 1242-1248
52. Coffman T.M., Ruiz P.E., Sanfilippo F., Klotman P.E.: Chronic thromboxane inhibition preserves renal function of rejecting rat renal allografts. Kidney Int. 1989; 35: 24-30
53. Timmer-Bosscha H., Hospers G.A.P., Meijer C., Mulder N.H., Muskiet F.A.J., Martini I.A., Uges D.R.A., de Vries E.G.E.: Influence of docosahexaenoic acid on cisplatin resistance in a human small cell lung carcinoma cell line. J. Natl. Cancer. Inst. 1989; 81: 1069-1075

S.D. Kristensen, E.B. Schmidt, R. De Caterina, S. Endres
n-3 Fatty Acids: Prevention and Treatment in Vascular Disease
Bi & Gi Publishers, Verona - Springer Verlag, London, 1995

15. Effects of n-3 Fatty Acids in IgA Nephropathy

J.V. Donadio Jr.[1], B.J. Holub[2], E.J. Bergstrahl[1] for the Mayo Nephrology Collaborative Group

1. Mayo Clinic and Foundation, Rochester, MN, USA
2. Department of Nutritional Sciences, University of Guelph, Ontario, Canada

Introduction

Idiopathic IgA nephropathy, also known as Berger's disease, is the most commonly encountered glomerular disease worldwide.[1,2] Progressive renal failure develops in 20-25% of patients up to 20 years after diagnosis, although there is considerable variability among different groups of patients.[2-6] IgA nephropathy is an immune complex glomerulonephritis caused by the mesangial deposition of IgA immune complexes, but an understanding of pathogenesis beyond this point is speculative.[7] Likewise, there is no proven effective treatment.[8]

The efficacy of dietary fish oil has been tested in patients with IgA nephropathy with varying results.[9-12] In a recently completed multicentre, placebo-controlled, randomized trial, we reported that treatment with fish oil for 2 years was effective in slowing the rate of renal impairment in patients with progressive IgA nephropathy.[13] The rationale for using fish oil in IgA nephropathy is based on the premise that the net effect of n-3 fatty acids on eicosanoid production, evoked by the initial immunological renal injury, changes the haemostatic balance toward a more vasodilatory state, decreases platelet aggregation, and reduces mesangial cell proliferation and contraction.[14] Here we report experiments determining the proportion of highly unsaturated fatty acids (HUFA) in plasma phospholipids that comprise n-6 eicosanoid precursors in the patients who were enrolled in the clinical trial. The effects of n-3 fatty acids (fish oil) on renal function, determined by measuring changes in the proportion of n-6 eicosanoid precursors, are also reported.

Methods

The sum of the concentrations of n-6 and n-3 HUFA was calculated in order to estimate total HUFA, and the percentage of total HUFA that comprised n-6 eicosanoid precursors was determined by calculating the sum of 20:3 n-6 and 20:4 n-6, before and after supplementation with fish oil and placebo (olive oil) in 97 of the 106 patients who entered the clinical trial.

The fatty acid composition (including n-6 and n-3 HUFA) of plasma phospholipids was measured by capillary gas-liquid chromatography.[15] Plasma phospholipid n-6 HUFA included 20:3 n-6, 20:4 n-6 (arachidonic acid), 22:4 n-6 and 22:5 n-6. The composition of n-3 HUFA included 20:5 n-3 (eicosapentaenoic acid; EPA), 22:5 n-3 and 22:6 n-3 (docosahexaenoic acid; DHA). The following calculations were made:

$$\text{n-6 HUFA} + \text{n-3 HUFA} = \text{total HUFA}$$

where n-6 HUFA and n-3 HUFA are the mean values of groups treated with fish oil and placebo, and total HUFA are expressed in moles percent of fatty acids. Then:

$$\frac{\text{20:3 n-6} + \text{20:4 n-6}}{\text{total HUFA}} = \text{\% n-6 eicosanoid precursors}$$

The percentage of n-6 eicosanoid precursors, namely 20:3 n-6 and 20:4 n-6, may represent a tissues' capacity for synthesizing n-6 eicosanoids.

The percentage of n-6 eicosanoid precursors was determined at baseline, 6 weeks, and 6, 12, 18 and 24 months after supplementation in both treatment groups. Linear regression analysis was used to estimate the annual rate of change in serum creatinine concentration for each patient relative to the percentage of n-6 eicosanoid precursors at 6 weeks.

The cumulative percentage of patients whose serum creatinine concentrations increased by 50% or more during 2 years of treatment was calculated using the Kaplan-Meier method,[16] and was plotted in quartiles of percentage of n-6 eicosanoid precursor changes (after 6 weeks of treatment) in each patient.

Univariate comparisons of the cumulative percentages of patients whose serum creatinine concentrations increased by 50% or more were made using the log-rank test.[17]

The cumulative serum creatinine events in the four groups of percentage of n-6 eicosanoid precursors were also modeled as a linear function and the log likelihood test was used to compare the distribution of the slopes in these four groups.

Results

The composition of plasma phospholipid HUFA was measured in 97 of the 106 patients who entered the clinical trial; 53 of these patients were assigned to receive fish oil and 44 received placebo. Baseline measurements only were made in nine patients (two treated with fish oil and seven treated with placebo) and they were not included in the analysis due to noncompliance with follow-up.

There was a significant and sustained decrease in the percentage of n-6 eicosanoid precursors in the group treated with fish oil and, as expected, there was no change in these two n-6 fatty acids in the placebo-treated group (Fig. 1). The percentage change in n-6 eicosanoid precursors after supplementation in the fish-oil-treated group was similar at each follow-up, and remained unchanged in the placebo group. Thus, renal function changes were related to the percentage of n-6 eicosanoid precursors after 6 weeks of treatment.

The primary renal end-point of the study - an increase of 50% or more in the serum creatinine concentration over 2 years - occurred in 12 patients (27%) in the placebo group, all of whom had treatment levels of n-6 eicosanoid precursors above 60%. This compared with three patients (6%) in the group treated with fish oil who reached the renal end-point. In these patients, the percentage of HUFA that

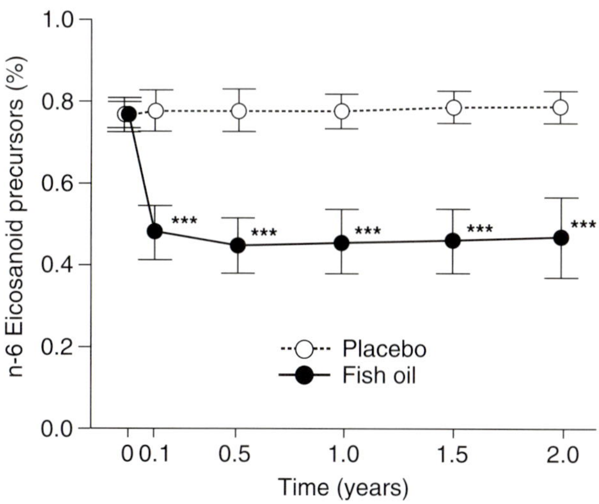

Fig. 1. The percentage of total highly unsaturated fatty acids (HUFA) in plasma phospholipid that comprises n-6 eicosanoid precursors, 20:3 n-6 and 20:4 n-6, was measured in 53 patients with IgA nephropathy treated with fish oil and 44 patients treated with placebo (olive oil) before and after supplementation. Statistical significance of differences from baseline values: ***$p<0.0001$. Data represent mean±SD.

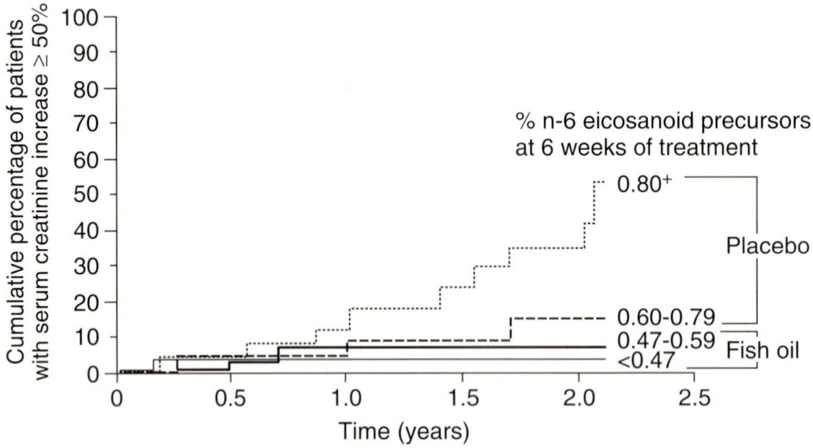

Fig. 2. Cumulative percentage of patients with IgA nephropathy treated with fish oil or placebo, whose serum creatinine increased ≥ 50% during the 2-year treatment period. The cumulative percentage of patients with serum creatinine events is plotted according to the proportion of n-6 eicosanoid precursors maintained in plasma phospholipids after 6 weeks of treatment (χ^2_3=14.75, p=0.002). The percentage of serum creatinine events correlates with the proportion of n-6 eicosanoid precursors modelled as a linear function (χ^2_1=6.72, p=0.001).

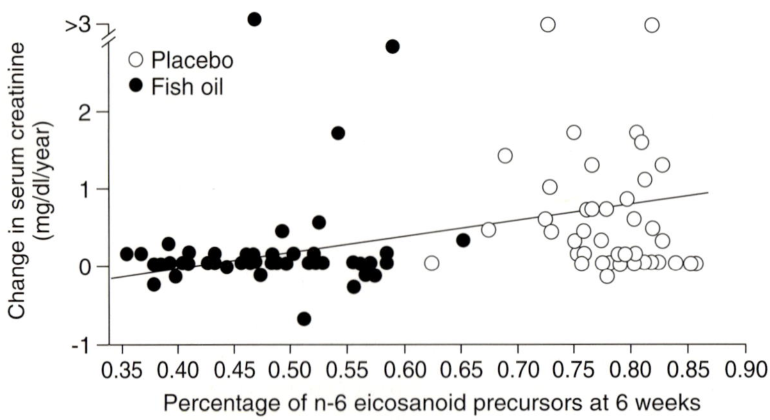

Fig. 3. The annual rates of change (slopes) of serum creatinine in patients with IgA nephropathy treated with fish oil or placebo. The slopes were computed for each patient by linear regression analysis with all results up to and including the 2-year findings. Zero represents no change. Each slope, represented by • (fish oil) and o (placebo), was plotted against the percentage n-6 eicosanoid precursors after 6 weeks of supplementation. r=0.22 and p=0.04 for the pooled data.

comprised n-6 eicosanoid precursors was consistently less than 47-59% after supplementation (χ^2_3=14.75; p=0.002) (Fig. 2).

Renal function was better maintained in the patients in the fish-oil group, as indicated by the median annual changes in serum creatinine concentrations (Fig. 3). The median annual changes in serum creatinine concentrations also correlated with the 6-week treatment values for percentage of n-6 eicosanoid precursors, with the pooled values for fish-oil-treated patients lying below 60% n-6 eicosanoid precursors and the values for placebo-treated patients lying above 60% (Fig. 3).

Discussion

Fish-oil supplementation decreased the proportion of n-6 eicosanoid precursors (20:3 n-6 and 20:4 n-6) in total HUFA in a significant and sustained manner. Fish oil also significantly slowed the rate of loss of renal function in patients with IgA nephropathy, with only 6% of the group treated with fish oil showing an increase in serum creatinine concentration of 50% or more, compared with 27% of the placebo-treated group. In addition, the annual decline in renal function, as estimated by serum creatinine slopes, was less in the fish-oil-treated group as a whole. The renal failure end-points and serum creatinine slopes related to the levels of n-6 eicosanoid precursors, with lower proportions maintained in the fish-oil-treated group, who also had more favourable renal outcomes.

These data support the concept that competition between n-3 and n-6 HUFA can diminish the abundance of n-6 eicosanoid precursors in a tissue, which, in turn, can diminish the intensity of tissue responses that are mediated by n-6 eicosanoids. The mixture of HUFA comprising 20 and 22 carbon atoms maintained in plasma phospholipids is related to dietary intake of linoleic acid (18:2 n-6) and α-linolenic acid (18:3 n-3), precursors of n-6 and n-3 polyunsaturated fatty acids, respectively, by empirical hyperbolic equations in a manner very similar to the relationship reported for laboratory rats.[18] Analysis of volunteers ingesting self-selected diets showed an inter-individual variance in the proportion of n-6 eicosanoid precursors in the fatty acids of plasma phospholipids of about 5%, but the variance among multiple samples taken from the same individual throughout the day was less, and approximated the experimental variance of the analytical procedure (approximately 1%). The reproducibility of these results makes it likely that analysis of the fatty acid composition of plasma lipids can be useful in estimating the diet-related tendencies for severe thrombotic, arthritic or other disorders that are associated with n-6 eicosanoids.

For example, the values reported for populations studied in the USA, Japan and Greenland show the proportion of n-6 eicosanoid precursors in plasma phospholipids to be 75%, 50% and 20%, respectively, which reflect the relative incidence of thromboxane-mediated thrombotic deaths in the USA, Japan and Greenland of approximately 100%, 20% and 10%, respectively.[19,20] Following ingestion of increasing proportions of n-3 HUFA, a downward shift of the hyperbolic curves of n-6 eicosanoid precursors was reported. As the typical American appears to maintain levels of n-6 HUFA in phospholipids near the maximal capacity, it seems useful to consider that the n-6-rich diet in the USA may contribute to the incidence and severity of eicosanoid-mediated diseases, such as coronary thrombosis. Further to this, a careful longitudinal study in the USA showed that people in the upper quintile of n-3 HUFA intake (approximately 0.66 g/day; 0.3%) had 40% fewer cardiovascular deaths during the study than the group who did not ingest polyunsaturated fatty acids in the form of n-3 fatty acids derived from fish.[21]

In other capacities, a component of progressive immune renal disease may be mediated through intermittent bursts of n-6 eicosanoid production in renal tissue after provocative stimuli.[14] In the kidney, thromboxane A_2, derived from 20:4 n-6 (arachidonic acid), induces renal vasoconstriction and mesangial contraction.[22] 20:5 n-3 (EPA) and 22:6 n-3 (DHA) compete with 20:4 n-6 for cyclooxygenase resulting in the production of trienoic eicosanoids that include vasodilatory and platelet anti-aggregating prostacyclin (PGI_3) and non-aggregating, non-vasoconstricting thromboxane A_3. Furthermore, 20:5 n-3 is the preferred substrate for the lipoxygenase pathway of activation resulting in production of inactive leukotriene (LT)B_5. LTB_4, derived from 20:4 n-6, is the major signal for leukocyte and monocyte involvement (*i.e.* cytokine production and phagocytosis) in inflammation.[14]

The substitution of LTB_5 for LTB_4 could downregulate cytokine production and phagocytosis, and have anti-inflammatory consequences.[23]

These biological effects provide a rationale for using fish-oil in IgA nephropathy, the most common immunologically mediated glomerular disease worldwide. The favourable results of our recently completed trial,[13] and the data reported here support the concept that the net result of the intake of n-3 fatty acids, contained in fish oil, is a reduction in n-6 eicosanoid precursors. This in turn, can diminish n-6 eicosanoid production and their effects, including glomerular circulatory contraction, decreased glomerular filtration, platelet aggregation and eventually glomerulosclerosis, the pathological hallmark of progressive IgA nephropathy. These effects appear to have been modified by better maintained renal function in patients with idiopathic IgA nephropathy treated with fish oil than in those treated with placebo.

Summary

Idiopathic IgA nephropathy is the most common glomerular disease in the world and renal failure develops in 20% to 25% of patients up to 20 years after diagnosis. Pathogenesis is poorly understood and there is no effective treatment.

In a recently completed, 2-year randomized, double-blind, placebo-controlled trial, we reported that fish oil effectively retarded the rate of renal impairment in patients with progressive IgA nephropathy.[13] Fifty-five patients were assigned to receive fish oil (12 x 1 g capsules of menhaden oil; 1.7 g eicosapentaenoic acid, 1 g docosahexaenoic acid), and 51 to receive placebo (olive oil).

After 2 years, three patients (5%) in the fish oil group had a serum creatinine concentration increase of ≥ 50% - the primary end point - compared with 14 patients (27%) in the placebo group (95% confidence interval (CI) with a 22% absolute risk reduction, 8.4%–35.6%; p=0.002; relative risk reduction, 81%; number needed to treat, 5; CI: 3-12).

In 97 patients (53 fish oil and 44 placebo), the fatty acid composition of plasma phospholipids was measured using capillary gas-liquid chromatography. The percentage of n-6 eicosanoid precursors (20:3 n-6+20:4 n-6) as a percentage of total highly unsaturated fatty acids (HUFA) decreased significantly after fish oil treatment (p=0.0001). The median annual changes in serum creatinine concentrations (slopes) correlated with the proportions of n-6 HUFA (6-week treatment values) (r=0.22, p=0.04). The primary renal end point occurred more frequently in placebo-treated patients, who had levels of n-6 HUFA between 60% and 80%, than patients supplemented with fish oil, in whom levels of n-6 HUFA were maintained at less than 47% to 59% of total HUFA (X^2_3=14.75; p=0.002).

These data support the premise that n-3 fatty acids reduce the proportion of n-6 eicosanoid precursors which, in turn, reduces n-6 eicosanoid production or action, evoked by the initial immunological injury, favorably altering glomerular contraction, filtration and sclerosis, the consequences of progressive IgA nephropathy. These effects appear to have been modified by better maintained renal function in the fish-oil treated patients than that observed in patients with idiopathic IgA nephropathy treated with placebo.

References

1. D'Amico G.: The commonest glomerulonephritis in the world: IgA nephropathy. Q. J. Med. 1987; 645: 709-727
2. Julian B.A., Waldo F.B., Rifai A., Mestecky J.: IgA nephropathy, the most common glomerulonephritis worldwide: a neglected disease in the United States? Am. J. Med. 1988; 84: 129-132
3. Schmekel B., Svalander C., Bucht H., Westberg N.G.: Mesangial IgA glomerulonephritis in adults: clinical and histopathological observations. Acta. Med. Scand. 1981; 210: 363-372
4. Hood S.A., Velosa J.A., Holley K.E., Donadio J.V. Jr.: IgA-IgG nephropathy: predictive indices of progressive disease. Clin. Nephrol. 1981; 16: 55-62
5. Droz D., Kramer A., Nawar T., Noel L.H.: Primary IgA nephropathy: prognostic factors. Contrib. Nephrol. 1984; 40: 202-207
6. Kusumoto Y., Takebayashi S., Taguchi T., Harada T., Naito S.: Long-term prognosis and prognostic indices of IgA nephropathy in juvenile and in adult Japanese. Clin. Nephrol. 1987; 28: 118-124
7. Emancipator S.N., Lamm M.E.: IgA nephropathy: pathogenesis of the most common form of glomerulonephritis. Lab. Invest. 1989; 60: 168-183
8. Ibels L.S., Győry A.Z.: IgA nephropathy: analysis of the natural history, important factors in the progression of renal disease, and a review of the literature. Medicine 1994; 73: 79-102
9. Hamazaki T., Tateno S., Shishido H.: Eicosapentaenoic acid and IgA nephropathy. Lancet 1984; i: 1017-1018
10. Cheng I.K.P., Chan P.C.K., Chan M.K.: The effect of fish-oil dietary supplement on the progression of mesangial IgA glomerulonephritis. Nephrol. Dial. Transplant. 1990; 5: 241-246
11. Bennett W.M., Walker R.G., Kincaid-Smith P.: Treatment of IgA nephropathy with eicosapentaenoic acid (EPA): a two-year prospective trial. Clin. Nephrol. 1989; 31: 128-131
12. Pettersson E.E., Rekola S., Berglund L., Sundqvist K.G., Angelin B., Diczfalusy U., Björkhem I., Bergström J.: Treatment of IgA nephropathy with omega-3 polyunsaturated fatty acids: a prospective, double-blind, randomized study. Clin. Nephrol. 1994; 41: 183-190

13. Donadio J.V. Jr., Bergstralh E.J., Offord K.P., Spencer D.C., Holley K.E., for the Mayo Nephrology Collaborative Group.: A controlled trial of fish oil in IgA nephropathy. N. Engl. J. Med. 1994; 331: 1194-1949
14. Donadio J.V. Jr.: Omega-3 polyunsaturated fatty acids: A potential new treatment of immune renal disease. Mayo Clin. Proc. 1991; 66: 1018-1028
15. Holub B.J., Skeaff C.M.: Nutritional regulation of cellular phosphatidylinositol. Methods Enzymol. 1987; 141: 234-244
16. Kaplan E.L., Meier P.: Nonparametric estimation from incomplete observations. J. Am. Stat. Assoc. 1958; 53: 457-481
17. Peto R., Peto J.: Asymptomatically efficient rank invariant test procedures. J. R. Stat. Soc. 1972; 135: 185-206
18. Lands W.E.M., Morris A., Libelt B.: Quantitative effects of dietary polyunsaturated fats on the composition of fatty acids in rat tissues. Lipids 1990; 25: 505-516
19. Lands W.E.M., Hamazaki T., Yamazaki K., Okayama H., Sakai K., Goto Y., Hubbard V.S.: Changing dietary patterns. Am. J. Clin. Nutr. 1990; 51: 991-993
20. Lands W.E.M.: Biochemistry and physiology of n-3 fatty acids; FAEB J. 1992; 6: 2530-2536
21. Dolecek T.A., Grandits G.: Dietary polyunsaturated fatty acids and mortality in the Multiple Risk Factor Intervention (MRFIT) study. In: Simpoulos A.P., Kifer R.E., Martin R.R., Barlow S. (Eds.) *World Review of Nutrition and Diet.*, Vol. 66. Basel; Karger Press, 1991: 202-216
22. Scharschmidt L.A., Lianos E., Dunn M.J.: Arachidonate metabolites and the control of glomerular function. Fed. Proc. 1983; 42: 3058-3063
23. Endres S., Ghorbani R, Kelley V.E., Georgilis K., Lonnemann G., van der Meer J.W.M., Cannon J.G., Rogers T.S., Kempner M.S., Weber P.C.: The effect of dietary supplementation with n-3 polyunsaturated fatty acids on the synthesis of interleukin-1 and tumor necrosis factor by mononuclear cells. N. Engl. J. Med. 1989; 320: 265-271

S.D. Kristensen, E.B. Schmidt, R. De Caterina, S. Endres
n-3 Fatty Acids: Prevention and Treatment in Vascular Disease
Bi & Gi Publishers, Verona - Springer Verlag, London, 1995

16. n-3 Fatty Acids in Inflammatory Bowel Disease

S. Endres[1], E. Gröttrup-Wolfers[2], R. Lorenz[3], K. Loeschke[1]

1. *Department of Medicine, Klinikum Innenstadt of Ludwig-Maximilians-University, Munich, Germany*
2. *Virchow Klinikum, Humboldt University, Berlin, Germany*
3. *Institute of Prophylaxis of Vascular Disease, Klinikum Innenstadt of Ludwig-Maximilians-University, Munich, Germany*

Inflammatory Bowel Disease

The aetiology of inflammatory bowel disease (IBD) remains unclear. There is a general consensus that, regardless of the initial stimulus, the immune system contributes to local intestinal inflammation. Little is known about the mechanisms by which inflammatory cells are recruited to the bowel, although it is clear that neutrophils, monocytes, mast cells and lymphocytes are present in increased numbers in the inflamed mucosa.[1] A large number of inflammatory mediators that could contribute to tissue injury and disease activity have also been identified. Elevated concentrations of prostaglandins,[2] of leukotrienes[3] and active oxygen species,[4] as well as antibodies against the colon-epithelium[5] have been demonstrated in IBD patients.

The Cytokine Interleukin-1 and its Antagonist

Cytokines are secreted proteins with central paracrine functions in inflammation and proliferation. Among this large group of proteins is a subgroup whose members were identified initially as products of monocytes and have a similar profile of biological activities. This subgroup comprises the two forms of interleukin (IL)-1, IL-1α and IL-1β, tumour necrosis factor (TNF-α) and, to a certain extent, IL-6. The cytokine IL-1β is a polypeptide mediator produced by mononuclear phagocytes, which has a wide range of biological activities.[6] Aside from its pyrogenic effects, IL-1 influences a wide array of biological functions (Fig. 1).[6] Many of its biological functions are shared by TNF-α.[7] The study of the IL-1 system has gained additional momentum with the discovery of an IL-1-receptor antagonist. This protein was identified as an endogenous inhibitor of IL-1 action. It shares sequence homologies with IL-1α and IL-β, binds to the same receptor as these two proteins, but has no intrinsic activity. Aside from its biological significance, the IL-1-receptor antagonist has proved an excellent experimental tool for demonstrating the important role of IL-1 in certain disease processes.[8] The ability of exogenous IL-1-receptor antagonist to prevent disease in animal models indicates that IL-1 is a necessary intermediate in the disease process. This approach has been used in several disease models, such as septic shock, peritonitis or immune-complex-induced colitis.

IBD and Cytokines

Previous studies of the content of *ex vivo* production of cytokines in IBD have shown elevated levels of IL-1β in biopsies or surgical specimens.[9,10] One study compared the presence of mRNA transcripts of TNF-α and IL-1β with the expression of interleukin-6 mRNA in patients with IBD.[11] These findings are consistent with the findings of Mahida *et al.*,[9] who detected an increase in the production of IL-1β by mononuclear cells isolated from the inflamed mucosa of surgical specimens from patients with Crohn's disease and ulcerative colitis. Similar results have been reported by Ligumsky *et al.*[10] in endoscopic biopsies of

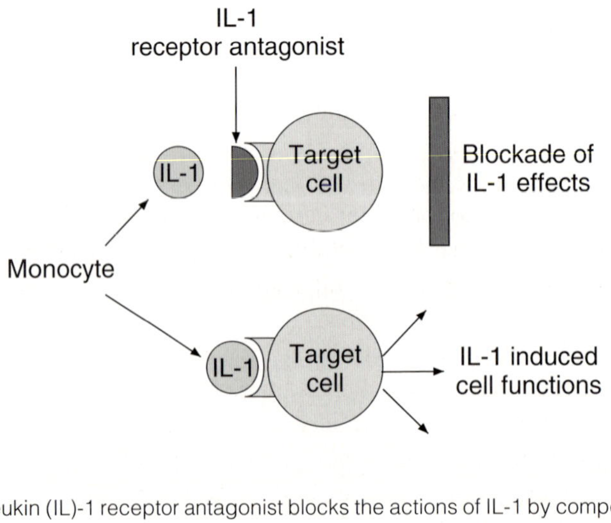

Fig. 1. Interleukin (IL)-1 receptor antagonist blocks the actions of IL-1 by competitive binding to the IL-1 receptor.

the inflamed mucosa of patients with IBD. Stevens *et al.*[11] found that levels of mRNA of TNF-α were not increased in the mucosa of patients with IBD, while mRNA levels of IL-1β and IL-6 were markedly enhanced in active ulcerative colitis. IL-1β mRNA was also found in non-IBD inflamed tissue (such as gastritis or appendicitis), whereas IL-6 mRNA was only present in the inflamed tissue of patients with IBD.

In situ hybridization has been used to detect mRNA transcripts of IL-1β and TNF-α in endoscopic biopsies of patients with IBD.[12] The TNF-α signal was located mainly in the deeper lamina propria, whereas IL-1β was seen in subepithelial macrophages. The study could not conclude with certainty the nature of the cells expressing mRNA for IL-1β and TNF-α, although macrophages seemed to be the most likely candidates. However, these data suggest the existence of a functional heterogeneity within the intestinal macrophage population, with the appearance of at least two subsets of cells with a different secretory repertoire. This is also reflected by the results of conventional immunohistochemistry conducted by Mahida *et al.*,[13] who found two unique subsets of macrophages in the intestine of patients with IBD. It could be argued that the elevation in levels of IL-1β and IL-6 is merely a nonspecific marker of inflammation. However, Cominelli *et al.*[14] studied the effect of intravenous administration of the IL-1-receptor-antagonist on immune-complex-induced rabbit colitis. This specific antagonist caused a significant reduction in tissue inflammation, as assessed by levels of necrosis, oedema or cellular infiltration. The results suggest that elevation of IL-1β in the inflamed intestine is more than a secondary alteration, and it may represent a causative link in the disease process that contributes to the generation and perpetuation of intestinal inflammation.

Modulating the Synthesis of IL-1 by n-3 Polyunsaturated Fatty Acids

The cytokines IL-1 and TNF-α contribute to the pathogenesis of inflammatory diseases and, potentially, atherogenesis. This lends importance to our original observation that dietary supplementation with n-3 fatty acids in healthy volunteers suppresses the capacity of mononuclear cells to synthesize IL-1 and TNF-α. In recent years, further evidence has been obtained to support this hypothesis: first, the suppression of cytokine synthesis by n-3 fatty acids can also be observed in patients with an inflammatory disease (*i.e.* rheumatoid arthritis; Table I); second, the suppression of cytokine synthesis can also be achieved by altering the diet, without using lipid supplements; and third, suppression of cytokine synthesis is probably achieved at the level of transcription, indicated by a decrease in the mRNA levels. The mechanism by which n-3 fatty acids suppress cytokine synthesis remains unknown. This effect may, however, contribute to the beneficial effects of n-3 fatty acids observed in models of chronic inflammatory disease.

Table I. The effect of n-3 fatty acids on cytokine production in humans.

Reference	Model	Cells	n-3 Fatty acid		Suppression of	
			Dose (g/day)	Duration (weeks)	IL-1	TNF-α
Endres *et al.*[22]	Healthy volunteers	MNC	4.6	6	61%↓	40%↓
Kremer *et al.*[23]	Patients with rheumatoid arthritis	MNC	6.7	24	41%↓	
Meydani *et al.*[24]	Healthy volunteers	MNC	2.4	12	50%↓	52%↓
Mølvig *et al.*[25]	Healthy volunteers, diabetics	MNC MPh	1.2	7	30%↓*	No change
Meydani *et al.*[26]	Healthy volunteers	MNC	1.2	24	40%↓	No change
Cooper *et al.*[27]	Healthy volunteers	Whole Blood	1.2	6-8	85%↓**	No change

Abbreviations: MNC=mononuclear cells, MPh=macrophages, IL-1=interleukin-1, TNF-α=tumour necrosis factor-α, *only cell-associated, **only secreted.

n-3 Fatty Acids and IBD

Investigations into the therapeutic effects of n-3 fatty acids in patients with IBD are based on several rationales. One biological effect is the reduced synthesis of pro-inflammatory leukotriene (LT)B_4 after ingestion of n-3 fatty acids. Levels of LTB_4 are increased locally in the mucosa of the inflamed bowel. Inhibition of LTB_4 formation is assumed to be the mechanism of conventional treatment for IBD using lipoxygenase-inhibiting substances, such as 5-aminosalicylic acid. A second rationale is the suppression of local IL-1 formation. As summarized above, this cytokine appears, at least in animal studies, to be a necessary mediator in maintaining colonic inflammation (in a model of immune-complex-induced colitis).

The first prospective, controlled and double-blind study of n-3 fatty acids was published in 1989.[15] This study indicated a beneficial effect of n-3 fatty acids in

Table II. Placebo-controlled trials of n-3 fatty acids in patients with ulcerative colitis.

Ref.	Size	Activity at entry	Conventional therapy	Intervention			Outcome		
				n-3 dose (g/day)	n-3 durat. (months)	Wash-out (months)	Clinical activity	Time to relapse	Steroid sparing
Lorenz *et al.*[15]	10	+ to ++	Minimized and continued	3.2	2x3*	1	(+)		
Stenson *et al.*[18]	24	++	5-ASA continued; steroids adapted	5.4	2x4*	1	(+)		(+)
Aslan *et al.*[19]	11	+ to ++	Adapted	4.2	12*		+		(+)
Hawthorne *et al.*[20]	40/ 56	+/ +++	Continued/ steroids adapted	5.6	12		(+)	±	+

Abbreviations: 5-ASA=5-aminosalicylic acid, *=cross-over design, ± =unchanged, (+)=positive trend, +=significant beneficial effect.

a group of patients with ulcerative colitis, but not in patients with Crohn's disease. Since this study, four more controlled studies and two non-controlled studies have examined the effect of n-3 fatty acids in patients with ulcerative colitis (Table II).[16,17]

In one of the more recent controlled trials, 18 patients completed a cross-over intervention period with n-3 fatty acids (5.4 g/day given for 4 months).[18] The treatment group exhibited significant weight gain (1.7 kg) and demonstrated an improvement in histological findings. Remarkably, in this blinded study, the use of steroids decreased by 50% in the group treated with fish oil, but increased slightly in the control group treated with vegetable oil. In a second study, 11 patients took n-3 fatty acids (4.2 g/day for 8 months).[19] The mean disease activity index decreased by 56% in the fish-oil group and was unchanged in the control group. Again, there was a marked reduction in concurrent medication: 72% of the patients reduced or eliminated anti-inflammatory drugs while on fish-oil treatment. In the largest study, involving a total of 96 patients, fish-oil supplementation also produced a modest steroid sparing effect, but no benefit was seen in maintenance therapy.[20] These three studies[18-20] are in agreement with the earlier positive trial and the two uncontrolled studies, suggesting a beneficial effect of n-3 fatty acids in patients with ulcerative colitis.

Together, these studies draw attention to a large, long-term trial (2 years) in patients with ulcerative colitis that has recently been completed at the University of Munich, Germany.[21] Inclusion criteria for patients with ulcerative colitis were low clinical activity, but at least one flare-up, within the past 2 years. Patients were given either fish-oil capsules at a dose of 5.1 g n-3 fatty acids/day or an equivalent amount of corn-oil as a placebo control. Patients did not take steroids for a least 3 months before entry into the trial and discontinued treatment with 5-aminosalicylic acid after 3 months. The clinical end-point is the absence of relapse for 2 years following a clinically defined relapse. The results from this study will be analysed during 1995.

Acknowledgement

Supported by grant 07ERG037 of the Deutsches Bundesministerium für Forschung und Technologie.

Summary

The aetiology of inflammatory bowel disease is unclear. Local inflammatory mediators, such as metabolites of arachidonic acid and peptide cytokines, appear to contribute to the disease process. The aim of conventional therapy for inflammatory bowel disease is to reduce the local formation of the inflammatory mediator, leukotriene B_4, by inhibiting the activity of lipoxygenases. This therapeutic mechanism provides a rationale for studies of the effects of n-3 fatty acids, which also inhibit leukotriene B_4 formation, on inflammatory bowel diseases. The first study, published in 1989, demonstrated no beneficial effects of n-3 fatty acids in patients with Crohn's disease. However, some clinical improvement, which approached a statistically significant benefit, was detected in patients with ulcerative colitis.

Since this first study, two uncontrolled and four controlled studies have investigated further the therapeutic effects of n-3 fatty acids in patients with ulcerative colitis. The size of the patient population in the controlled studies ranged from 10 to 96 patients. In one of these studies, a significant improvement in clinical activity was demonstrated, while a steroid-sparing effect was detected in another study. The third study demonstrated only a non-significant trend towards improvement, and in the last study, which also included a control group receiving evening primrose oil, no beneficial effect was seen in the 16 patients receiving n-3 fatty acids.

These studies can be compared with a large, long-term trial (2 years) in patients with ulcerative colitis that has recently been completed at the University of Munich. Patients received supplements of n-3 fatty acids or corn oil for a 2-year period. Inclusion criteria for patients with ulcerative colitis were low clinical activity with at least one flare-up within the past 2 years. In this study, the clinical endpoints, relapse or completion of the 2 year study period without clinically defined relapse, are analysed.

References

1. Podolsky D.K.: Inflammatory bowel disease. N. Engl. J. Med. 1991; 325: 928-937
2. Donowitz M.: Arachidonic acid metabolites and their role in inflammatory bowel disease. Gastroenterology 1985; 88: 580-587
3. Sharon P., Stenson W.F.: Enhanced synthesis of leukotriene B4 by colonic mucosa in inflammatory bowel disease. Gastroenterology 1984; 86: 453-460
4. Kitahora T., Suzuki K., Asakura H.: Active oxygen species generated by monocytes and polymorphonuclear cells in Crohn's disease. Dig. Dis. Sci. 1988; 33: 951-955
5. Takahashi F., Das K.M.: Isolation and characterization of a colonic autoantigen specifically recognized by colon tissue-bound immuno-globulin G from idiopathic ulcerative colitis. J. Clin. Invest. 1985; 76: 311-318
6. Dinarello C.A., Wolff S.M.: The role of interleukin-1 in disease. N. Engl. J. Med. 1993; 328: 106-113
7. Vassalli P.: The pathophysiology of tumor necrosis factors. Annu. Rev. Immunol. 1992; 10: 411-452
8. Dinarello C.A.: Interleukin-1 and interleukin-1 antagonism. Blood 1991; 77: 1627-1652
9. Mahida Y.R., Wu K., Jewell D.P.: Enhanced production of interleukin-1ß by mononuclear cells isolated from mucosa with active ulcerative colitis of Crohn's disease. Gut 1989; 30: 835-838
10. Ligumsky M., Simon P.L., Karmeli F., Rachmilewitz D.: Role of interleukin-1 in inflammatory bowel disease - enhanced production during active disease. Gut 1990; 31: 686-689
11. Stevens C., Walz G., Singaram C., Lipman M.L., Zanker B., Muggia A., Antonioli D., Peppercorn M.A., Strom T.B.: Tumor necrosis factor-a, interleukin-1 b, and interleukin-6 expression in inflammatory bowel disease. Dig. Dis. Sci. 1992; 37: 818-826
12. Cappello M., Keshav S., Prince C., Jewell D.P., Gordon S.: Detection of mRNAs for macrophage products in inflammatory bowel disease by *in situ* hybridisation. Gut 1992; 33: 1214-1219
13. Mahida Y.R., Patel S., Gionchetti P., Vaux D., Jewell D.P.: Macrophage subpopulations in lamina propria of normal and inflamed colon and terminal ileum. Gut 1989; 30: 826-834
14. Cominelli F., Nast C.C., Clark B.D., Schindler R., Lierena R., Eysselein V.E., Thompson R.C., Dinarello C.A.: Interleukin 1 (IL-1) gene expression, synthesis, and effect of specific IL-1 receptor blockade in rabbit immune complex colitis. J. Clin. Invest. 1990; 86: 972-980
15. Lorenz R., Weber P.C., Szimnau P., *et al.*: Supplementation of n-3 fatty acids from fish oil in chronic inflammatory bowel disease - a randomized, placebo-controlled, double-blind cross-over trial. J. Intern. Med. 1989; 225 (Suppl. 1): 225-232
16. Salomon P., Kornbluth A.A., Janowitz H.D.: Treatment of ulcerative colitis with fish oil n-3-omega fatty acid: an open trial. J. Clin. Gastroenterol. 1990; 12: 157-161
17. Grimminger F., Führer D., Papavassilis C., Schlotzer E., Mayer K., Heuer K.-U., Kiss L., Walmrath D., Piberhofer S., Lübbecke F., Krämer H.-J., Stevens J., Schütterle G., Seeger W.: Influence of intravenous n-3 lipid supplementation on fatty acid profiles and lipid mediator generation in a patient with severe ulcerative colitis. Eur. J. Clin. Invest. 1993; 23: 706-715
18. Stenson W.F., Cort D., Rodgers J., Burakoff R., De Schryver Kecskemeti K., Gramlich T.L., Beeken W.: Dietary supplementation with fish oil in ulcerative colitis. Ann. Intern. Med. 1992; 116: 609-614
19. Aslan A., Triadafilopoulos G.: Fish oil fatty acid supplementation in active ulcerative colitis: a double-blind, placebo-controlled, crossover study. Am. J. Gastroenterol. 1992; 87: 432-437
20. Hawthorne A.B., Daneshmend T.K., Hawkey C.J., Belluzzi A., Everitt S.J., Holmes G.K., Malkinson C., Shaheen M.Z., Willars J.E.: Treatment of ulcerative colitis with fish oil supplementation: a prospective 12 month randomised controlled trial. Gut 1992; 33: 922-928

21. Loeschke K., Lorenz R., Heldwein W., Endres S., Stufler M., Ewe K.: Effects of n-3 fatty acids in chronic inflammatory bowel disease. In: Goebell, *et al.* (Eds.). *Inflammatory Bowel Disease. Progress in Basic Research and Clinical Implications*. Kluwer Academic Publishers: 456 (Abstract)
22. Endres S., Ghorbani R., Kelley V.E., Georgilis K., Lonnemann G., van der Meer J.W.M., Cannon J.G., Rogers T.S., Klempner M.S., Weber P.C., Schaefer E.J., Wolff S.M., Dinarello L.A.: The effect of dietary supplementation with n-3 polyunsaturated fatty acids on the synthesis of interleukin-1 and tumor necrosis factor by mononuclear cells. N. Engl. J. Med. 1989; 320: 265-271
23. Kremer J., Lawrence D., Jubiz W., Di Giacomo R., Rynes R., Bartholomew L.E., Sherman M.: Dietary fish oil and olive oil supplementation in patients with rheumatoid arthritis. Clinical and immunological effects. Arthritis Rheum. 1990; 33: 810-820
24. Meydani S.N., Endres S., Woods M.M., Goldin B.R., Soo C., Morrill L.A., Dinarello C.A., Gorbach S.L.: Oral (n-3) fatty acid supplementation suppresses cytokine production and lymphocyte proliferation: comparison between young and older women. J. Nutr. 1991; 121: 547-555
25. Mølvig J., Pociot F., Worsaae H., Wogensen L.D., Baek L., Christensen P., Mandrup P.T., Andersen K., Madsen P., Dyerberg J., *et. al.*: Dietary supplementation with omega-3-polyunsaturated fatty acids decreases mononuclear cell proliferation and interleukin-1 beta content but not monokine secretion in healthy and insulin-dependent diabetic individuals. Scand. J. Immunol. 1991; 34: 399-410
26. Meydani S.N., Lichtenstein A.H., Cornwall S., Meydani M., Goldin B.R., Rasmussen H., Dinarello C.A., Schaefer E.J.: Immunologic effects of national cholesterol education panel step-2 diets with and without fish-derived n-3 fatty acid enrichment. J. Clin. Invest. 1993; 92: 105-113
27. Cooper A.L., Gibbons L., Horan M.A., Little R.A., Rothwell N.J.: Effect of dietary fish oil supplementation on fever and cytokine production in human volunteers. Clin. Nutr. 1993; 12: 321-328

S.D. Kristensen, E.B. Schmidt, R. De Caterina, S. Endres
n-3 Fatty Acids: Prevention and Treatment in Vascular Disease
Bi & Gi Publishers, Verona - Springer Verlag, London, 1995

17. Dietary Marine n-3 Fatty Acids in Pregnancy in Relation to Pregnancy Outcome and Child Health and Development: a Brief Overview of Clinically Important Endpoints

S.F. Olsen

Danish Epidemiology Science Centre, State Serum Institute, Artillerivej, Copenhagen, Denmark

Introduction

The n-3 fatty acids are a group of polyunsaturated fatty acids in which the first double bond occurs at the third carbon atom counted from the methyl end of the molecule.[1] Together with the n-6 fatty acids, in which the first double bond occurs at the sixth carbon atom, they constitute two groups of fatty acids designated as essential because they cannot be synthesized *de novo* in higher animals and must therefore be obtained through dietary sources to avoid symptoms of deficiency. The most common dietary source of long-chained (>20 carbon atoms) n-3 fatty acids, eicosapentaenoic acid (20:5 n-3), docosapentaenoic acid (22:5 n-3) and docosahexaenoic acid (22:6 n-3; DHA), are marine animals.

α-linolenic acid (18 carbon atoms) is another n-3 fatty acid that is found in some vegetable oils; desaturation/elongation of α-linolenic acid to the longer chained n-3 fatty acids is possible, but occurs slowly in humans.[2] The current interest in marine n-3 fatty acids was initiated following the suggestion by Dyerberg and Bang in the 1970s that the low incidence of ischaemic heart disease observed in Greenland Eskimos might be due to the high consumption of n-3 fatty acids derived from fish and marine mammals. Since then the n-3 fatty acids have been extensively studied from a biochemical, physiological, and public health point of view.[3-6] Several facts regarding the biochemical and physiological roles of n-3 fatty acids have been well established: first, increasing the intake of n-3 fatty acids leads to an increased formation of the trienoic prostanoids, often at the expense of their dienoic counterparts; second, trienoic prostaglandins often have lower biological activities than their corresponding dienoic counterparts; third, dietary marine n-3 fatty acids lower blood viscosity; and finally, they are important constituents of cell membranes, particularly in neural tissues.

A brief account follows of the possible health-related aspects of the intake of marine n-3 fatty acids in pregnancy, with emphasis on clinically important endpoints and the work of myself and my colleagues.

Postulated Positive Effects of Marine n-3 Fatty Acid Ingested in Pregnancy

Birth weight and complications related to low birth weight

n-3 fatty acids derived from marine animals have been postulated to prevent low birth weight in two different ways.[7] First, they may prolong gestation by altering the balance between the prostaglandins determining the timing of parturition.[8-14] Second, they may increase fetal growth rate by facilitating placental blood flow mediated by reductions in the thromboxane to prostacyclin ratio and blood viscosity.[14-18] Reviews of the epidemiological evidence conclude that dietary marine fat ingested in late pregnancy prolongs the duration of pregnancy and, when ingested in early pregnancy, may stimulate fetal growth. The first notion is better substantiated by the literature, than the latter;[7,19] however, the need for studies that focus on complications related to short gestation and retarded fetal growth, rather than mean duration of pregnancy and birth weight, has been pointed out.[7]

Pre-eclampsia

Physiologically, marine n-3 fatty acids might reduce the risk of pre-eclampsia by mechanisms similar to those mentioned above in relation to fetal growth, as impaired placental blood flow is believed to be essential in the aetiology of pre-eclampsia.[6,20,21] However, conclusive epidemiological evidence in favour of this possibility is very meagre.

Fetal neurodevelopment

Several different lines of evidence support the view that dietary provision of marine n-3 fatty acids is essential to ensure that the growing foetus/infant reaches its full potential for brain development. Apart from essential amino acids, n-3 fatty acids constitute the largest component of the cerebral cortex and retina that can only be obtained from the diet.[22] Two series of intervention studies have provided evidence that two indices of visual system function, visual acuity and the electroretinogram, develop more slowly in very premature infants fed standard milk formulas that lack longer chain n-3 fatty acids than in those fed formulas supplemented with marine-oil sources of DHA.[23-28] The question of whether ingestion of DHA during pregnancy is an absolute requirement in order to secure normal fetal/infant neurodevelopment, or whether this need can be met through maternal elongation/desaturation of α-linolenic acid, which is present in a number of different foods, to DHA and/or through a longer lasting pre-conceptional accretion of n-3 fatty acids into maternal body stores remains unresolved.

Cardiovascular diseases in the child

Recent evidence indicates that people who had a low birth weight have increased risk of hypertension and other cardiovascular diseases later in life.[29] It has been suggested that a low maternal intake of marine n-3 fatty acids in pregnancy could lead to retarded fetal growth and simultaneously induce a propensity in the foetus for hypertension and other cardiovascular diseases later in life.[19]

Postulated Adverse Effects of Marine n-3 Fatty Acid Ingested in Pregnancy

Bleeding complications in pregnancy

It is well established that oils rich in long-chain n-3 fatty acids prolong the bleeding time (a laboratory measure), but this has not been matched by an increased occurrence of bleeding complications in groups of (non-pregnant) subjects receiving fish oil. However, pregnancy and delivery is a period in which both the foetus/child and the mother are particularly vulnerable to bleeding complications.[7,30]

Complications related to postmaturity and prolonged labour

High intake of marine n-3 fatty acids may potentially increase the risk of complications related to high birth weight and/or prolonged pregnancy, and may theoretically also inhibit the process of delivery by interacting with prostaglandin metabolism.[7]

Methodological Considerations Regarding Future Studies

When studied epidemiologically, the endpoints discussed above require very large sample sizes and/or very efficient designs. A randomized, controlled trial would be the first method of choice in epidemiological aetiological research. If focused on particular risk groups and if undertaken on a multicentre basis, it may be possible to acquire enough statistical power to render such trials conclusive. Observational studies rely on methods for assessing dietary patterns in large groups, which is, in general, difficult, although the methodology of nutritional epidemiology has improved much within the last few years. A second choice for epidemiological studies would be observational cohort studies with prospective data collection; however, these cohorts would need to be extremely large if undertaken in the general population. Case-control studies would probably be the quickest and cheapest to perform, but inherent in these would be the interpretational problems that relate to obtaining an unbiased and sufficiently precise assessment of previous dietary patterns in individuals after the disease or complication status is manifest.

Summary

This paper provides a brief account of possible health-related aspects of marine n-3 fatty acid intake in pregnancy, with emphasis on clinically important endpoints and the work by myself and my colleagues. The results addressed here include the findings that intake of marine n-3 fatty acids in pregnancy could protect against complications related to preterm delivery and intrauterine growth retardation, preeclampsia, and impaired neurodevelopment and hypertension in the child, but that a high intake of marine n-3 fatty acids in pregnancy could increase the risk of bleeding complications in pregnancy, postmaturity and prolonged labour.

References

1. Hansen H.S.: Dietary essential fatty acids and *in vivo* prostaglandin production in mammals. World. Rev. Nutr. Diet 1983; 42: 102-134
2. Tinoco J.: Dietary requirements and functions of α-linolenic acid in animals. Prog. Lipid. Res. 1982; 21: 1-45
3. Dyerberg J.: Linolenate-derived polyunsaturated fatty acids and prevention of atherosclerosis. Nutr. Res. 1986; 44: 125-134
4. Leaf A., Weber P.C.: Cardiovascular effects of n-3 fatty acids. N. Engl. J. Med. 1988; 318: 549-557
5. Gibson R.A.: The effect of diets containing fish and fish oils on disease risk factors in humans. Aust. N.Z. J. Med. 1988; 18: 713-722
6. Sanders T.A.: Marine oils: metabolic effects and role in human nutrition. Proc. Nutr. Soc. 1993; 52: 457-472
7. Olsen S.F.: Consumption of marine n-3 fatty acids during pregnancy as a possible determinant of birth weight. A review of the current epidemiologic evidence. Epidemiol. Rev. 1993; 15: 399-413 [Erratum appeared in Am. J. Epidemiol 1994; 139: 856]
8. Olsen S.F., Hansen H.S., Sorensen T.I., *et al.*: Intake of marine fat, rich in (n-3)-polyunsaturated fatty acids, may increase birthweight by prolonging gestation. Lancet 1986; 2: 367-369
9. Olsen S.F., Sorensen J.D., Secher N.J., *et al.*: Randomised controlled trial of effect of fish-oil supplementation on pregnancy duration. Lancet 1992; 339: 1003-1007
10. Olsen S.F., Hansen H.S., Jensen B.: Fish oil *versus* arachis oil food supplementation in relation to pregnancy duration in rats. Prostagland. Leuk. Essen. Fatty Acids 1990; 40: 255-260

11. Olsen S.F., Secher N.J.: A possible preventive effect of low-dose fish oil on early delivery and pre-eclampsia: indications from a 50-year-old controlled trial. Br. J. Nutr. 1990; 64: 599-609
12. Olsen S.F., Hansen H.S., Sommer S., *et al.*: Gestational age in relation to marine n-3 fatty acids in maternal erythrocytes: a study of women in the Faroe Islands and Denmark. Am. J. Obstet. Gynaecol. 1991; 164: 1203-1209
13. Olsen S.F., Hansen H.S., Sandström M., Jensen B.: Erythocyte levels compared with reported dietary intake of marine n-3 fatty acids in pregnant women. Br. J. Nutr. 1996; 73: 387-395
14. Olsen S.F., Hansen H.S., Secher N.J., Jensen B., Sandström B.: Gestation length and birth weight in relation to intake of marine n-3 fatty acids. Br. J. Nutr. 1995; 73: 397-404
15. Andersen H.J., Andersen L.F., Fuchs A.R.: Diet, pre-eclampsia and intrauterine growth retardation. Lancet 1989; 1: 1146
16. Sorensen J.D., Olsen S.F., Pedersen A.K., Boris J., Secher N.J., FitzGerald G.A.: Effect of fish oil supplementation in the third trimester of pregnancy on prostacyclin and thromboxane production. Am. J. Obstet. Gynaecol. 1993; 168: 915-922
17. Olsen S.F., Grandjean P., Weihe P., Videro T.: Frequency of seafood intake in pregnancy as a determinant of birth weight: evidence for a dose dependent relationship. J. Epidemiol. Commun. Health 1993; 47: 436-440
18. Olsen S.F., Olsen J., Frische G.: Does fish consumption during pregnancy increase fetal growth? A study of the size of the newborn, placental weight and gestational age in relation to fish consumption during pregnancy. Int. J. Epidemiol. 1990; 19: 971-977
19. Olsen S.F.: Further on the association between retarded fetal growth and adult cardiovascular disease. Could low intake of marine diets be a common cause? J. Clin. Epidemiol. 1994; 47: 565-569
20. Secher N.J., Olsen S.F.: Fish-oil and pre-eclampsia. Br. J. Obstet. Gynaecol. 1990; 97: 1077-1079
21. Dyerberg J., Bang H.O.: Pre-eclampsia and prostaglandins. Lancet 1985; i: 1267
22. Connor W.E., Neuringer M., Reisbick S.: Essential fatty acids: the importance of n-3 fatty acids in the retina and brain. Nutr. Rev. 1992; 50: 21-29
23. Uauy R., Birch D.G., Peirano P.: Visual and brain function measurements in studies of n-3 fatty acid requirements of infants. J Pediatr. 1992; 120: S168-180 [Erratum appeared in J. Pediatr. 1992; 121: 329]
24. Carlson S.E., Werkman S.H., Peeples J.M., Wilson W.M.: Long-chain fatty acids and early visual and cognitive development of preterm infants. Eur. J. Clin. Nutr. 1994; 48: S27–S30
25. Birch E.E., Birch D.G., Hoffman D.R., Uauy R.: Dietary essential fatty acid supply and visual acuity development. Invest. Ophthalmol. Vis. Sci. 1992; 33: 3242–3253
26. Carlson S.E., Werkman S.H., Rhodes P.G., Tolley E.A.: Visual-acuity development in healthy preterm infants: effect of marine-oil supplementation. Am. J. Clin. Nutr. 1993; 58: 35-42
27. Hoffman D.R., Birch E., Birch D., Uauy R.D.: Effects of supplementation with omega-3 long-chain polyunsaturated fatty acids on retinal and cortical development in premature infants. Am. J. Clin. Nutr. 1993; 57: 807S-812S
28. Birch D.G., Birch E., Hoffman D., Uauy R.D.: Retinal development in very-low-birth-weight infants fed diets differing in omega-3 fatty acids. Invest. Ophthalmol. Vis. Sci. 1992; 33: 2365-2376
29. Barker D.J., Glukman P.D., Godfrey K.M., Harding J.E., Owens J.A., Robinson J.S.: Fetal nutrition and cardiovasular disease in adult life. Lancet 1993; 341: 938-941
30. Secher N.J., Olsen S.F., Sorensen J.D.: Fish-oil and pre-eclampsia (Correspondence). Br. J. Obstet. Gynaecol. 1991; 98: 738-740

S.D. Kristensen, E.B. Schmidt, R. De Caterina, S. Endres
n-3 Fatty Acids: Prevention and Treatment in Vascular Disease
Bi & Gi Publishers, Verona - Springer Verlag, London, 1995

18. Safety Aspects of Dietary n-3 Fatty Acids

E.B. SCHMIDT[1], J. MØLLER[2], N. SVANEBORG[1], J. DYERBERG[3]

1. Department of Medicine and Endocrinology, Aalborg Hospital, Aalborg, Denmark
2. Department of Gastroenterology, Aalborg Hospital, Aalborg, Denmark
3. Medi-Lab a.s., Copenhagen, Denmark

Introduction

Interest in the therapeutic effects of long-chain n-3 fatty acids (FA) is growing. Research in this area has evolved from cardiovascular prophylaxis and treatment to several other disciplines, including renal diseases, inflammatory disorders (arthritis, psoriasis, colitis), asthma, infectious diseases, and cancer.[1-3]

Adverse effects have been reported occasionally after supplementation of the diet with n-3 FA, but few papers have focused on the tolerability, side-effects or safety of n-3 FA in humans. In this paper, findings from the literature and from our own studies of dietary supplementation with n-3 FA will be discussed in relation to these issues.

Source of n-3 FA

Some safety issues may relate to the source of n-3 FA (fish, cod liver oil, fish-oil concentrates of various types) rather than to the effects of n-3 FA *per se*. Thus, concern has been expressed about the possible intake of heavy metals and pesticides from contaminated fish,[4] although the risk of such an event is probably minimal. However, in a recently published study from Finland, intake of non-fatty fish (but not of sea water fish) was correlated with an increased risk of ischaemic heart disease (IHD).[5] This was believed to be caused by a high content of mercury in non-fatty fish, promoting lipid peroxidation. It is potentially possible that toxic compounds from fish could be present in fish-oil concentrates, but they are usually removed during industrial processing. However, bottled cod liver oil and other fish oils should be stored in the cold and consumed within a reasonably short time period to reduce the risk of *in vitro* oxidation.[6] The composition of the fish oil may also be important, as the effects, and potentially also the side-effects, of the two major long-chained n-3 FA, eicosapentaenoic acid (EPA; 20:5) and docosahexaenoic acid (DHA; 22:6), may differ.

Lipid Peroxidation

There is accumulating evidence that lipid peroxidation, in particular oxidation of low-density-lipoproteins (LDL), may play a pivotal role in atherogenesis.[7] Highly unsaturated n-3 FA from any source are susceptible to oxidation. However, epidemiological and experimental data indicate no increase in the incidence of atherosclerosis induced by n-3 FA,[2] which suggests that either n-3 FA oxidation does not occur to any important extent *in vivo*, or that it is outweighed by the beneficial effects of the fatty acids. It should also be mentioned that some of the beneficial effects of n-3 FA, including reduced production of platelet-derived growth factor from endothelial cells[8] and impairment of smooth muscle cell proliferation,[9] may actually be counteracted by antioxidants.

The effect of n-3 FA on plasma levels of vitamin E and on lipid peroxidation in humans is shown in Table I. In several studies, vitamin E was added in small amounts to the n-3 supplement as an antioxidant. However, Table I only indicates studies in which vitamin E was given in high pharmacological doses. As can be seen from Table I, the effect of n-3 FA on plasma levels of vitamin E or on lipid peroxidation was not consistent.

The level of vitamin E in platelets and red blood cells decreased in 40 healthy men given n-3 FA, 10 g/day for 10 weeks. However, this effect was reversed when α-tocopherol (200 mg) was added to the supplement for a further 8 weeks.[26] In other studies, vitamin E levels increased in platelets[15] and red blood cells[24] following supplementation with n-3 FA.

Bleeding Risk

Although stroke is more common in Greenland Eskimos (Inuit) than in Western populations, it is unknown whether strokes in the Inuit population are of thrombotic or haemorrhagic origin.[29] In contrast, the incidence of cerebrovascular disease does not differ between Alaskan Eskimos and other Alaskans,[30] and, in Japan, is lower[31] or unaltered[32] in fish-consuming populations compared with populations that have a low intake of seafood (and n-3 FA).

In some studies, the platelet count has been reduced by dietary supplementation

Table I. The effect of dietary n-3 fatty acids (FA) on levels of serum vitamin (S-vit) E and lipid peroxides in humans.

Study	Design	n	Daily dose of n-3 FA (g)	Duration of treatment (weeks)	S-vit. E	Lipid peroxides	Additional vit. E
Knapp *et al.*[10]	Open	6	15	4	→		
Olivieri *et al.*[11]	Open	20	3	8	→	↓	
Bach *et al.*[12]	Controlled	15	1.3	5	↓		
		15	2.5	5	→		
Corrocher *et al.*[13]	Open	13	7	8	→	↓	
Hänninen	Open	43	1	15	→		
et al.[14]	Controlled	100	0.3-1.1	12	→		
Croset *et al.*[15]	Controlled	8	0.1	8	→		
Brown *et al.*[16]	Open	11	4.5	4	→	→	No
		11	4.5	4	↑	→	+400 IU
Nozaki *et al.*[17]	Open	14	2.7	26		→	
Nenseter *et al.*[18]	Controlled	12	5.4	16		→	
Meydani *et al.*[19]	Open	25	2.4	12	→	↑	
Shapiro *et al.*[20]	Open	10	4.8	6	↑		
Harats *et al.*[21]	Controlled	42	3	4	→	↑	
Haglund *et al.*[22]	Open	12	12	3	↓	→	+0.3 IU/g
		12	12	3	→	→	+1.5 IU/g
Sanders *et al.*[23]	Open	9	3	6	↓		
Berlin *et al.*[24]	Controlled	40	15	10	→		
Nelson *et al.*[25]	Controlled	9	6	6		↑	
Nair *et al.*[26]	Controlled	40	10	10	↓	↑	No
		40	10	8	↑	↓	+200 mg
Frankel *et al.*[27]	Open	9	5.1	6	→	→	
Schmidt *et al.*[28]	Open	71	4-6	6	→		

Abbreviations: →=no change; ↑=increase; ↓=decrease; n=number of subjects in study.

with n-3 FA, although levels have never reached those associated with an increased risk of bleeding.[33] In one study, in which hyperlipidaemic adolescents were supplemented with a low dose of n-3 FA/day (1.5 g/day for 6 months), 8 of 11 patients experienced epistaxis.[34]

In patients treated with percutaneous transluminal coronary angioplasty (PTCA), a non-significant increase in bleeding episodes occurred in patients receiving n-3 FA (6 g/day for 6 months) (four episodes) compared with control patients who received olive oil (no bleeding episodes).[35] All patients received aspirin, dipyridamole and heparin perioperatively in addition to the oils. In another study of a similar type, no bleeding episodes were reported.[36]

No spontaneous bleeding or excessive bleeding after delivery, surgery or trauma has been reported after dietary supplementation with n-3 FA. Furthermore, no clinically significant bleeding has been reported in studies in which n-3 FA were given in combination with aspirin.[37,38] One minor episode of epistaxis occurred during supplementation with n-3 FA (3.4 g/day for 4 weeks) in 22 patients treated with warfarin.[39]

Immune Incompetence

Immune reactivity is reduced by n-3 FA.[2,40] While this is likely to be beneficial in some conditions, it could potentially be detrimental under other circumstances, increasing the risk of infectious diseases and cancer. However, there is no evidence that the intake of n-3 FA is associated with an increased risk of cancer. In contrast, experimental evidence suggests that n-3 FA may have a beneficial influence on certain cancer types.[1,4]

It is difficult to evaluate whether dietary n-3 FA increase the risk of infections, but no case of severe infection has been reported to occur in subjects participating in clinical trials of n-3 FA. In experimental models, n-3 FA have been reported to enhance,[41,42] decrease[43-45] or have no effect[46] on susceptibility to infectious agents.

Other Effects

In a controlled study, 83 men from The Netherlands and Norway received a 6-week dietary supplement of mackerel (delivering 4.7 g of EPA and DHA) or meat.[47] In subjects receiving the mackerel diet, there was a mean decrease in the platelet count of approximately 15 x 10^9/l, but no changes in renal function, liver function or other safety parameters were noticed. Other investigators have detected minor alterations in liver parameters induced by dietary n-3 FA,[48] but no clinically important changes in liver function have been reported after supplementation with n-3 FA.

One single case of intoxication with vitamin A has been reported in a 35-year old man, who took 30-50 capsules/day of various fish-oil products.[49]

Finally, body weight may increase if n-3 FA are taken as a supplement to the regular diet.

Adverse Biochemical Effects of n-3 FA

The main risks associated with an increased intake of n-3 FA are increased plasma low density lipoprotein (LDL) cholesterol, increased oxidation of LDL, deterioration of glycaemic control in non-insulin dependent diabetes (NIDDM) and impairment of fibrinolysis. An increase in plasma LDL cholesterol has been noted in some normolipidaemic individuals supplemented with n-3 FA, and, more commonly, in patients with hypertriglyceridaemia.[50] It should be emphasized that, in hypertriglyceridaemia, levels of LDL are often low and are usually only raised slightly (and to 'normal' levels) by n-3 FA. Glycaemic control may deteriorate in NIDDM, especially after high doses of n-3 FA,[51] and in some patients this has been of clinical relevance.[52] Apparently, metabolic control is not altered in patients with insulin-dependent diabetes mellitus (IDDM).[51] Finally, there is evidence that n-3 FA may increase plasma levels of plasminogen activator inhibitor-1,[53] which may impair overall fibrinolysis and increase the risk of cardiovascular disease.[54]

Long-Term Studies

It should be emphasized strongly that the results presented above have been obtained after dietary substitution or supplementation with n-3 FA for short-term periods of a few weeks or months. In contrast, Saynor *et al.*[55] studied a group of 365 subjects with IHD and/or hyperlipidaemia, who received supplements of n-3 FA (3 g/day for up to 7 years). They studied 258 subjects for 1 year, 109 for 4 years and 40 for 7 years. The supplement was given as 10-20 ml of a bottled fish-oil concentrate (Maxepa®). Seventy-five subjects withdrew from the study, mainly for geographical reasons, or because they disliked the taste of fish oil. The authors reported no clinically relevant adverse effects on levels of haemoglobin, creatinine, albumin or bilirubin, and found no cause for concern in the long-term use of the supplement.

We have studied the effect of dietary supplementation with the n-3 FA, Pikasol® (Lube, Denmark, made as EPAX 5500^{TG} by Pronova Biocare, Norway) (4 g/day for 9 months) in 24 healthy volunteers.[28] All subjects completed the study without experiencing subjective side-effects, and no clinically relevant biochemical changes in safety parameters were noted in any of the individuals. There were small decreases in the erythrocyte volume fraction and albumin levels, and a small increase in plasma aspartate aminotransferase levels. These changes were statistically significant, but were not considered to be of clinical importance. Renal function, serum levels of vitamin E and the platelet count were unaltered during supplementation. A small, but statistically significant, decrease in the level of plasma uric acid was detected. This could be important, as the level of uric acid may correlate with the risk of IHD.[56] However, no decreases in plasma uric acid have been found in other studies.[47,55]

Details of Own Studies

The following section gives details of the studies conducted by our own group.

Methodology

A re-esterified triglyceride preparation of a fish-oil concentrate has been used in human studies for more than 6 years. The composition of this encapsulated re-esterified triglyceride preparation (Pikasol®) is shown in Table II. The effect of supplementation with this oil has been studied in healthy subjects and in more than 300 patients with various disorders (IHD, hyperlipidaemia, IDDM, hypertension and rheumatoid arthritis).

The results of these studies, in which a number of safety parameters were measured after supplementation with a moderately high dose (4-6 g/day) of n-3 FA for 6 weeks, are presented in Table III.

The level of vitamin E in serum was determined by high performance liquid chromatography (HPLC), while other laboratory measurements were made using standard methods. As several components were measured, it may be appropriate to use the Bonferroni correction to reduce the risk of mass significance. However, as the issue is one of safety, the results are discussed in terms of conventional statistical significance ($p<0.05$; two-tailed test).

Table II. Composition of the fish-oil concentrate, Pikasol®

Fatty acids	**% of Total Fat**
Total n-3 FA	68
Eicosapentaenoic acid	34
Docosahexaenoic acid	19
n-6 Fatty Acid	<2
Monounsaturated fatty acids	17
Saturated fatty acids	5
General	
Peroxide value (meq/kg)	<1
Vitamin E (IU/g)	2
Vitamin A (IU/g)	<1
Vitamin D (IU/g)	<1
Cholesterol (mg/g)	<1

Overall experience

Compliance was excellent, as judged by interviews and by incorporation of EPA and DHA into platelet and leukocyte membranes. Mild gastrointestinal side-effects occurred, but often disappeared following continued intake of n-3 FA. No bleeding episodes, infections or serious adverse effects occurred in individual study participants.

Haematology

The leukocyte count decreased slightly after dietary supplementation with n-3 FA (Table III). This result is of potential interest, because several studies have suggested that the leukocyte count is positively correlated with the risk of cardiovascular disease.[57] It should be stressed that the lower number of leukocytes in peripheral blood counts after dietary supplementation with n-3 FA do not increase the risk of infection.

There was a significant decrease in the erythrocyte volume fraction, but the magnitude of this decrease cannot be considered to be clinically important. In view of the normal levels of haemoglobin and the reduction in levels of albumin, these data may suggest that n-3 FA increase the plasma volume (and thus decrease blood viscosity).

The platelet count was unaltered by n-3 FA, a finding which is in agreement with most studies conducted to investigate moderate doses of n-3 FA.[33] Following n-3 supplementation, the platelet count did not decrease in any patients to levels below the reference interval ($140 \times 10^9/l$) of our laboratory.

Renal and liver function

Levels of serum creatinine increased slightly after a 6-week supplement with n-3 FA (Table III), but the increase was not of clinical relevance. Statistically significant increases in levels of liver enzymes (aspartate aminotransferase and lactate dehydrogenase) were seen after 6 weeks (Table III).

The decrease in albumin levels observed was moderate and may have been due to plasma dilution, as the synthesis of other liver proteins, such as coagulation factors, was not reduced. Although the changes detected were small and no enzyme levels increased to above the reference interval, these findings highlight the possible risk of liver disease during long-term use of fish-oil preparations.

Serum vitamin E

No changes were observed in vitamin E levels after dietary supplementation with n-3 FA. It should be mentioned that the fish-oil preparation used was enriched with vitamin E (2 IU/capsule; Table II).

Table III. The effect of dietary supplementation with n-3 fatty acids, 4-6 g/day for 6 weeks, n=71 on safety parameters. Values are given before (b) and after (a) the supplement.

		Median	**Median difference**	**95% confidence interval of median difference**	**p value**
B-leukocytes	b	5.7	1.0	0.8-1.3	0.02
(10 g/l)	a	5.2			
B-haemoglobin	b	8.8	0.4	0.3-0.5	0.004
(mmol/l)	a	8.6			
B-erythrocyte volume fraction	b	0.42	0.02	0.2-0.03	0.0002
	a	0.41			
B-platelet count	b	236	17	14-21	0.88
(10 g/l)	a	238			
S-albumin	b	43	2	2-3	<0.00001
(mmol/l)	a	41			
S-magnesium	b	0.86	0.06	0.05-0.08	0.06
(mmol/l)	a	0.85			
S-alkaline phosphatase	b	136	15	12-18	0.73
(mmol/l)	a	142			
S-uric acid	b	0.30	0.04	0.02-0.04	0.19
(mmol/l)	a	0.28			
S-bilirubin	b	9	2	2-3	0.02
(μmol/l)	a	10			
S-albumin corrected calcium	b	2.35	2.30	2.30-2.35	0.0002
(mmol/l)	a	240			
S-creatinine	b	84	6	5-8	0.01
(μmol/l)	a	88			
S-asparate amino-transferases (U/l)	b	17	4	3-5	0.002
	a	19			
S-lactate dehydrogenase	b	244	32	25-41	0.02
(U/l)	a	259			
S-vitamin E (α-tocopherol)	b	35	4.5	3.5-6.5	0.99
(μmol/l)	a	34			

Conclusions

Following short-term intake of fish-oil concentrates, gastrointestinal side-effects are common, but there have been few reports of clinically important adverse effects or toxicity. Experience of the use of fish-oil concentrates is limited, but seafood has been consumed for centuries without apparent toxic effects. Nevertheless, it should be mandatory that toxic compounds, such as heavy metals and pesticides, are removed during industrial processing of fish-oil concentrates.

The major area of concern surrounding the ingestion of fish-oil concentrates (especially in high doses) is increased oxidation of LDL. It is, however, unclear whether n-3 FA lead to a clinically relevant increase in the *in vivo* oxidation of LDL or to the formation of other harmful oxidation products, and whether this may be prevented by the addition of antioxidants. It seems appropriate, therefore, at present to recommend a high dietary intake of antioxidants in conjunction with fish-oil concentrates, and it is preferable to use fish-oil products with added antioxidants. In our view, the bleeding risk is minimal, but the risk of immune incompetence, although hypothetical, should be kept in mind.

Our studies have revealed that Pikasol® is well tolerated without major adverse effects. Although short-term studies of fish-oil concentrates have revealed no serious side-effects, their safety and tolerability need to be documented in long-term clinical trials.

Acknowledgements

Pikasol® was kindly supplied by LUBE A/S, Denmark and Pronova Biocare A/S, Norway. The Authors also wish to thank technicians Inge Aardestrup and Else Marie Overby for their skilled and dedicated work.

Summary

Minor gastrointestinal side-effects are common, but otherwise there is little indication from the literature of clinically important side-effects or toxicity after short-term intake of fish oil concentrates. The experience with the use of fish oil concentrates on a long-term basis is limited, but fish has been consumed in the history of mankind without apparent toxic effects. It should, however, be mandatory that toxic compounds, like heavy metals and pesticides, are removed during industrial processing of fish oil concentrates.

The main area of concern during intake of fish oil concentrates (especially high doses) is increased oxidation of LDL, although it is unclear whether n-3 fatty acids (FA) lead to a clinically relevant increased oxidation of LDL or other harmful oxidation products *in vivo*, and whether this may be prevented by added antioxidants. However, it seems at present appropriate to recommend a diet rich in antioxidants together with fish oil concentrates and preferable to use fish oil products with antioxidants added. In our view, the bleeding risk is minimal, while the risk of immune incompetence, although hypothetical, should be kept in mind.

Concerning our own studies with Pikasol®, a re-esterified triglyceride preparation, this has been well tolerated without serious adverse effects. Although short-term studies have revealed no serious side-effects of fish oil concentrates, their safety and tolerability need to be documented during long-term clinical trials.

References

1. Simopoulos A.P.: Omega-3 fatty acids in health and disease and in growth and development. Am. J. Clin. Nutr. 1991; 54: 438-463
2. Schmidt E.B., Dyerberg J.: n-3 fatty acids: Current status in cardiovascular medicine. Drugs 1994; 47: 405-424
3. De Caterina R., Endres S., Kristensen S.D., Schmidt E.B.: n-3 fatty acids and renal diseases. Am. J. Kidney Dis. 1994; 24: 397-415
4. Svensson B-G., Nilsson A., Hansson M., *et al.*: Exposure to dioxins and dibenzofurans through the consumption of fish. N. Engl. J. Med. 1991; 324: 8-12
5. Tisdale M.J.: Cancer and omega-3 fatty acids. In: Drevon C.A., Baksaas I., Krokan H.E. (Eds). *Omega-3 Fatty Acids: Metabolism and Metabolic Effects*. Birkhäuser Verlag, 1993: 335-341
6. Piché L.A., Draper H.H., Cole P.D.: Malondialdehyde excretion by subjects consuming cod liver oil vs a concentrate of n-3 fatty acids. Lipids 1988; 23: 370-371
7. Witzkum J.L., Steinberg D.: Role of oxidized low density lipoprotein in atherogenesis. J. Clin. Invest. 1991; 88: 1785-1792
8. Fox P.L., DiCorleto P.E.: Fish oils inhibit endothelial cell production of platelet-derived growth factor-like protein. Science 1988; 241: 453-456
9. Shiina T., Terano T., Saito J., Tamura Y., Yoshida S.: Eicosapentaenoic acid and docosahexaenoic acid suppress the proliferation of vascular smooth muscle cells. Atherosclerosis 1993; 104: 95-103
10. Knapp H.R., Reilly I.A.G., Alessandrini P., *et al.*: *In vivo* indexes of platelet and vascular function during fish-oil administration in patients with atherosclerosis. N. Engl. J. Med. 1986; 314: 937-942
11. Olivieri O., Negri M., De Gironcoli M., *et al.*: Effects of dietary fish oil on malondialdehyde production and glutathione peroxidase activity in hyperlipidaemic patients. Scand. J. Clin. Lab. Invest. 1988; 48: 659-665
12. Bach R., Schmidt U., Jung F., *et al.*: Effects of fish oil capsules in two dosages on blood pressure, platelet functions, haemorheological and clinical chemistry parameters in apparently healthy subjects. Ann. Nutr. Metab. 1989; 33: 359-367
13. Corrocher R., Ferrari S., de Gironcoli M., *et al.*: Effect of fish oil supplementation on erythrocyte lipid pattern, malondialdehyde production and gluthathione-peroxidase activity in psoriasis. Clin. Chim. Acta. 1989; 179: 121-132
14. Hänninen O., Aagren J.J. Effects of moderate freshwater fish diet on lipid metabolism of Finnish students. J. Intern. Med. 1989; 225 (Suppl. 1): 77-81
15. Croset M., Véricel E., Rigaud M., *et al.*: Functions and tocopherol content of blood platelets from elderly people after low intake of purified eicosapentaenoic acid. Thromb. Res. 1990; 57: 1-12
16. Brown J.E, Wahle K.W.J.: Effect of fish-oil and vitamin E supplementation on lipid peroxidation and whole-blood aggregation in man. Clin. Chim. Acta. 1990; 193: 147-156
17. Nozaki S., Matsuzawa Y., Hirano K-I., Sakai N., Kubo M., Tarui S.: Effects of purified eicosapentaenoic acid ethyl ester on plasma lipoproteins in primary hypercholesterolemia. Int. J. Vitam. Nutr. Res. 1992; 62: 256-260
18. Nenseter M.S., Rustan A.C., Lund-Katz S., *et al.*: Effect of dietary supplementation with n-3 polyunsaturated fatty acids on physical properties and metabolism of low density lipoprotein in humans. Arterioscler. Thromb. 1992; 12: 369-379
19. Meydani M., Natiello F., Goldin B., *et al.*: Effect of long-term fish oil supplementation on vitamin E status and lipid peroxidation in women. J. Nutr. 1991; 121: 484-491

20. Shapiro A.C., Meydani S.N., Meydani M., *et al.*: The effect of fish oil supplementation on plasma a-tochopherol, retinol, lipid and lipoprotein levels in normolipidemic subjects. Nutr. Res. 1991; 11: 539-548
21. Harats D., Dabach Y., Hollander G., *et al.*: Fish oil ingestion in smokers and nonsmokers enhances peroxidation of plasma lipoproteins. Atherosclerosis 1991; 90: 127-139
22. Haglund O., Luostarinen R., Wallin R., *et al.*: The effects of fish oil on triglycerides, cholesterol, fibrinogen and malondialdehyde in humans supplemented with vitamin E. J. Nutr. 1991; 121: 165-169
23. Sanders T.A.B., Hinds A.: The influence of a fish oil high in docosahexaenoic acid on plasma lipoprotein and vitamin E concentrations and haemostatic function in healthy male volunteers. Br. J. Nutr. 1992; 68: 163-173
24. Berlin E., Bhathena S.J., Judd J.T., *et al.*: Effects of omega-3 fatty acid and vitamin E supplementation on erythrocyte membrane fluidity, tocopherols, insulin binding, and lipid composition in adult men. J. Nutr. Biochem. 1992; 3: 392-400
25. Nelson G.J., Morris V.C., Schmidt P.C., Levander O.: The urinary excretion of thiobarbituric acid reactive substances and malondialdehyde by normal adult males after consuming a diet containing salmon. Lipids 1993; 28: 757-761
26. Nair P.P., Judd J.T., Berlin E., Taylor P.R., Shami S., Sainz E., *et al.*: Dietary fish oil-induced changes in the distribution of a-tocopherol, retinol, and ß-carotene in plasma, red blood cells, and platelets: modulation by vitamin E. Am. J. Clin. Nutr. 1993; 58: 98-102
27. Frankel E.N., Parks E.J., Xu R., Schneeman B.O., Davis P.A., German J.B.: Effects of n-3 fatty acid-rich fish oil supplementation on the oxidation of low density lipoproteins. Lipids 1994; 29: 233-236
28. Schmidt E.B., Møller J.M., Svaneborg N., Dyerberg J.: Safety aspects of fish oils. Experiences with an n-3 concentrate of reesterified triglycerides (Pikasol®). Drug Invest. 1994; 7: 215-220
29. Bjerregaard P., Dyerberg J.: Mortality from ischaemic heart disease and cerebrovascular disease in Greenland. Int. J. Epidemiol. 1988; 17: 514-519
30. Middaugh J.P.: Cardiovascular deaths among Alaskan natives 1980-86. Am. J. Public Health 1990; 80: 282-285
31. Hirai A., Terano T., Tamura Y., *et al.*: Eicosapentaenoic acid and adult diseases in Japan: Epidemiological and clinical aspects. J. Intern. Med. 1989; 225 (Suppl.1): 69-75
32. Hamazaki T., Urakaze M., Sawazaki S., *et al.*: Comparison of pulse wave velocity of the aorta between inhabitants of fishing and farming villages in Japan. Atherosclerosis 1988; 73: 157-160
33. Kristensen S.D., Schmidt E.B., Dyerberg J.: Dietary supplementation with n-3 polyunsaturated fatty acids and human platelet function: A review with particular emphasis on implications for cardiovascular disease. J. Intern. Med. 1989; 225 (Suppl. 1): 141-150
34. Clarke J.T.R., Cullen-Dean C., Regelink E., *et al.*: Increased incidence of epistaxis in adolescents with familial hypercholesterolemia treated with fish oil. J. Pediatr. 1990; 116: 139-141
35. Reis G.J., Sipperly M.E., McCabe C.H., *et al.*: Randomised trial of fish oil for prevention of restenosis after coronary angioplasty. Lancet 1989; ii: 177-181
36. Dehmer G.J., Popma J.J., Van Den Berg E.K., *et al.*: Reduction in the rate of early restenosis after coronary angioplasty by a diet supplemented with n-3 fatty acids. N. Engl. J. Med. 1988; 319: 733-740
37. Thorngren M., Gustafson A.: Effects of 11-week increase in dietary eicosapentaenoic acid on bleeding time, lipids, and platelet aggregation. Lancet 1981; ii: 1190-1193
38. Harris W.S., Silveira S., Dujovne C.A.: The combined effects of n-3 fatty acids and aspirin on hemostatic parameters in man. Thromb. Res. 1990; 57: 517-526
39. Smith P., Arnesen H., Opstad T., *et al.*: Influence of highly concentrated n-3 fatty acids on serum lipids and hemostatic variables in survivors of myocardial infarction receiving either oral anticoagulants or matching placebo. Thromb. Res. 1989; 53: 467-474

40. Meydani S.N., Lichtenstein A.H., Cornwall S., *et al.*: Immunologic effects of national cholesterol education panel step-2 diets with and without fish-derived n-3 fatty acid enrichment. J. Clin. Invest. 1993; 92: 105-113
41. D'Ambola J., Aeberhard E.E., Trang N., *et al.*: Effect of dietary (n-3) and (n-6) fatty acids on *in vivo* pulmonary bacterial clearance by neonatal rabbits. J. Nutr. 1991; 121: 1262-1269
42. Chang H.R., Dulloo A.G., Vladoianu I.R., *et al.*: Fish oil decreases natural resistance of mice to infection with salmonella typhimurium. Metabolism 1992; 41: 1-2
43. Levander O.A., Ager Jr A.L., Morris V.C., *et al.*: Plasmodium yoelli: Comparative antimalarial activities of dietary fish oils and fish oil concentrates in vitamin-E deficient mice. Exp. Parasitol. 1990; 70: 323-329
44. Kumaratilake L.M., Robinson B.S., Ferrante A., *et al.*: Antimalarial properties of n-3 and n-6 polyunsaturated fatty acids: *In vitro* effects on *Plasmodium falciparum* and *in vivo* effects on *P. berghei*. J. Clin. Invest. 1992; 89: 961-967
45. Blok W.L., Vogels M.T.E., Curfs J.H.A.J., *et al.*: Dietary fish-oil supplementation in experimental gram-negative infection and in cerebral malaria in mice. J. Infect. Dis. 1992; 165: 898-903
46. Rubin R.H., Wilkinson R.A., Xu L., *et al.*: Dietary marine lipid does not alter susceptibility of (NZBxNZW)F_1 mice to pathogenic microorganisms. Prostaglandins 1989; 38: 251-262
47. van Houwelingen R., Nordøy A., van der Beek E., Houtsmuller U., de Metz M., Hornstra G.: Effect of a moderate fish intake on blood pressure, bleeding time, hematology, and clinical chemistry in healthy males. Am. J. Clin. Nutr. 1987; 46: 424-436
48. Inagaki M., Harris W.S.: Changes in lipoprotein composition in hypertriglyceridemic patients taking cholesterol-free fish oil supplements. Atherosclerosis 1990; 82: 237-246
49. Grupp B.P.: Hypervitaminosis A following long-term use of high-dose fish oil supplements. Chest 1990; 97: 1260
50. Schmidt E.B., Kristensen S.D., De Caterina R., Illingworth D.R.: The effects of n-3 fatty acids on plasma lipids and lipoproteins and other cardiovascular risk factors in patients with hyperlipidemia. Atherosclerosis 1993; 103: 107-121
51. Malasanos T.H., Stacpoole P.W.: Biological effects of w-3 fatty acids in diabetes mellitus. Diabetes Care 1991; 14: 1160-1179
52. Stacpoole P.W., Alig J., Kilgore L.L., *et al.*: Lipodystrophic diabetes mellitus. Investigations of lipoprotein metabolism and the effects of omega-3 fatty acid administration in two patients. Metabolism 1988; 37: 944-951
53. Schmidt E.B.: n-3 fatty acids and fibrinolysis. In: De Caterina R.D., Kristensen S.D., Schmidt E.B. (Eds.). *Fish Oil and Vascular Disease*. Verona; Bi and Gi Publishers 1992: 73-77
54. Jespersen J., Munkvad S., Gram J.B.: The fibrinolysis and coagulation systems in ischaemic heart disease. Risk markers and their relation to metabolic dysfunction of the arterial intima. Dan. Med. Bull. 1993; 40: 495-502
55. Saynor R., Gillott T.: Changes in blood lipids and fibrinogen with a note on safety in a long term study on the effects of n-3 fatty acids in subjects receiving fish oil supplements and followed for seven years. Lipids 1992; 27: 533-538
56. Frohlich E.D.: Uric acid. A risk factor for coronary heart disease. JAMA 1993; 270: 378-379
57. Kannel W.B., Anderson K., Wilson P.W.F.: White blood cell count and cardiovascular disease. JAMA 1992; 267: 1253-1256

S.D. Kristensen, E.B. Schmidt, R. De Caterina, S. Endres
n-3 Fatty Acids: Prevention and Treatment in Vascular Disease
Bi & Gi Publishers, Verona - Springer Verlag, London, 1995

19. Parenteral Administration of n-3 Fatty Acids: Indications, Experience and Perspectives

Y.A. Carpentier[1], C. Simoens[1], V. Siderova[1], I. El Nakadi[1], M. Richelle[1], D. Dubois[1], R.J. Deckelbaum[2]

1. *L. Deloyers Laboratory for Experimental Surgery, Université Libre de Bruxelles, Brussels, Belgium*
2. *Institute of Human Nutrition, Columbia University, New York, USA*

Biological Activities of n-3 Fatty Acids

n-3 fatty acids (FA) represent an important component of cell-membrane phospholipids with a substantial potential to influence physical properties, receptor and enzyme activity, as well as secondary messenger production.[1] In addition, eicosapentaenoic acid (EPA, 20:5 n-3), and to a lesser extent docosahexaenoic acid (DHA, 22:6 n-2), may inhibit the formation of eicosanoids from arachidonic acid (AA), and EPA can be competitively used as a precursor for the formation, through the same enzymatic pathways (*e.g.* cyclooxygenase and lipoxygenases), of less potent inflammatory and thrombotic mediators.

Finally, incorporation of n-3 FA into cell-membrane phospholipids appears to reduce cell responses to inflammatory, aggregatory and catabolic mediators.

Experimental and recent clinical studies suggest a role for n-3 FA in the primary and secondary prevention of cardiovascular accidents, not only through their effect on plasma lipids, but mainly because of their potential to markedly decrease interactions between endothelial cells, leukocytes and platelets[2] as well as their antiarrhythmic properties.[3-5] Other potential areas for the use of n-3 FA involve several immune diseases (including renal pathologies and graft rejections) and inflammatory disorders.[6]

Experimental investigations have also reported a protective effect in conditions associated with a large release of inflammatory cytokines, such as septic shock.[7,8]

Intravenous Administration of Lipids

Intravenous (i.v.) administration of n-3 FA will rapidly supply free FA to the cell's metabolic pool and induce changes in membrane composition much faster than FA supplied by dietary supplementation.[9] Lipid emulsions have been used in parenteral nutrition for more than 25 years, both as an energy supply and a source of essential FA.[10] The first well-tolerated preparation was developed using the chylomicron model and consisted of soybean triacylglycerols emulsified with egg yolk phospholipids. This preparation can supply 30-40% of a patient's calorie intake but provides very large amounts of C18 polyunsaturated fatty acids (PUFA), mainly as linoleate (C18:2 n-6, 53-55 mol%) and, to a much lesser extent, as α-linolenate (C18:3 n-3, 7-9 mol%). Infusion of these emulsions in animals[11,12] and in man[13] over a period of 2 weeks or more results in the accumulation of linoleate in plasma and in cell membrane phospholipids, together with a reduction of arachidonate and long-chain polyunsaturated (LCP) n-3 FA. For the past 10 years, another emulsion has been available in which 50% of the soybean triacylglycerols (TAGs) are replaced by medium-chain TAGs (MCT) derived from coconut oil (Fig. 1).

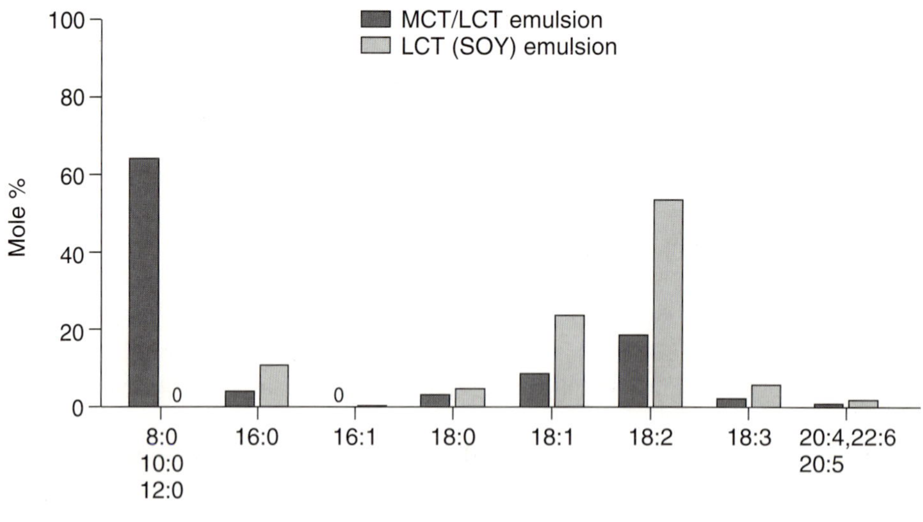

Fig 1. This figure compares the fatty acid (FA) composition of triacylglycerols present in two different lipid emulsions used in parenteral nutrition. FA pattern is expressed in mole per cent. One emulsion contains exclusively long-chain triacylglycerols (LCT) derived from soybean oil (LCT (SOY)) and is particularly rich in polyunsaturated fatty acids such as linoleic (18:2 n-6) and α-linolenic (18:3 n-3) acids. The other emulsion (MCT/LCT) contains a 1:1 (wt:wt) mixture of medium-chain triacylglycerols (MCT) and soybean LCT and is particularly rich in caprylic (C8:0), capric (C10:0) and lauric (C12:0) acids.

Use of this new emulsion allows the maintenance of a more balanced FA pattern in cell membranes.[13] However, an increased supply of LCP n-3 FA may be of interest either in the field of parenteral nutrition (*e.g.* in premature infants, in surgical patients and in those requiring intensive care) or as a means of quickly modifying the membrane or the intracellular pools of n-3 FA.[14]

Intravenous Administration of n-3 FA in Animals

Emulsions containing ethyl ester n-3 FA, TAGs derived from fish oil, or reconstituted TAGs with an enriched content of either EPA or DHA, as tri-EPA or tri-DHA, have been evaluated. An important contribution to this area of research was made by Hamazaki and his colleagues.[15-19]

These investigators have performed several animal studies, starting with infusions of tri-EPA or tri-DHA in rabbits, looking at changes in the EPA and DHA content of plasma and blood cell phospholipids, as well as changes in ADP- and collagen-induced platelet aggregation. Tri-EPA infusion resulted in an increased content of EPA in plasma and platelet phospholipids, together with decreased platelet aggregation. In contrast, tri-DHA infusion induced an increase in EPA and DHA content in platelet and red blood cell phospholipids without affecting platelet aggregation.[15,16]

In another study in rabbits, these authors showed increased leukotriene (LT)B_5 and decreased LTB_4 production by polymorphonuclear leukocytes in response to 10 mM of the calcium ionophore A23187, after only 1 hour following an infusion of tri-EPA at a dose of 0.2 g TAGs/kg.[17] Changes in eicosanoid balance were more pronounced after 6 hours, and a dose-dependent effect (up to the upper dose of 0.8 g TAGs/kg) was demonstrated. Although more limited, changes in the production of LTB_4 and LTB_5 were also observed after infusions of different doses of tri-DHA (0.2-0.8 g TAGs/kg).[18]

These studies were followed by an experiment in which the composition of heart lipids and tolerance to ischaemia-reperfusion were assessed in isolated rat heart pre-infused for 10 minutes with a 10% preparation of either tri-EPA (90% pure) or tri-DHA (97% pure).[19]

No, or only minor, incorporation of EPA was observed in heart phospholipids; however, there was a substantial increase in infused n-3 FA (EPA>DHA) in free FA in the heart.

This was not associated with a protective effect of cardiac function during ischaemia-reperfusion; on the contrary, a deterioration of cardiac function was observed after tri-DHA administration. In fact, it seems that the amount of α-tocopherol (0.02%) added to these preparations was too low to prevent peroxidative damage in the emulsions, as indicated by the high levels of dialdehydes detected in the effluates.

Intravenous Administration of Almost Pure n-3 FA in Man

Hamazaki *et al.*[20] reported the first i.v. infusion of n-3 FA in man. This consisted of 30 ml (i.e. 3 g tri-EPA) and was infused over 10 min to two healthy volunteers. Following the infusion, an increased urinary excretion of prostaglandin I_3 and thromboxane B_3, and also of prostaglandin I_2 and thromboxane B_2 (which probably resulted from the small amount of arachidonate in the preparation) was observed. One subject experienced a reaction (fever and muscle pain) 2 hours after the infusion. This probably calls for a better understanding of the intravascular metabolism and the pathways of delivery to tissues of these particular FA in order to define the most appropriate form of administration and infusion rate in man.

Metabolism of Infused TAGs

The classical view on tissue delivery of FA contained in TAG-rich particles (Fig. 2) takes into account the extrahepatic hydrolysis of the majority of particle TAGs by lipoprotein lipase (LPL), followed by uptake of the remnant particles by the liver.[21] Of interest, *in vitro* studies have shown fish oil TAGs (containing 44% LCP n-3 FA) to be a poor substrate for LPL, when compared with soybean TAGs.[22] In addition, hydrolysis by LPL releases EPA and DHA at a much slower rate than the other FA contained in fish oil. Finally, addition of fish oil to soybean TAGs substantially inhibits total TAG hydrolysis by LPL, the effect being particularly marked at a relative concentration of LCP n-3 FA of 10% or more. In agreement with these *in vitro* data, infusions of chylomicrons enriched with n-3 FA to rats deliver only small amounts of EPA and DHA to extrahepatic tissues.[23] These FA remain in higher concentrations in particle remnants that are preferentially removed by the liver.

A large proportion of n-3 FA are recycled into phospholipids and released in endogenous very low density lipoproteins. Hence, if a marked rise in plasma TAGs is to be avoided, n-3 FA preparations derived from fish oil should be infused at a relatively slow rate or mixed in low proportions relative to other TAGs. We tested the possibility of supplementing lipid emulsions currently provided to patients receiving parenteral nutrition with 10% fish oil, *i.e.* 4.4% LCP n-3 FA. During a 2-week period of exclusive parenteral nutrition in dogs, which provided 50% of non-protein calories (~ 45 Kcal/kg/day) as lipids, animals were randomly allocated to receive a soybean long-chain TAG (LCT) or a mixed MCT/LCT emulsion with or without 10% fish oil supplementation (providing 0.2 g n-3 FA/kg/day).[24] At this ratio, *in vivo* supplementation with fish oil did not cause any impairment in the elimination of infused TAGs, in spite of a progressive rise in EPA (and to a lesser extent of DHA) concentration in plasma TAGs, which confirmed the slower release of these FA from infused TAGs. The supply of fish oil by an i.v. route was

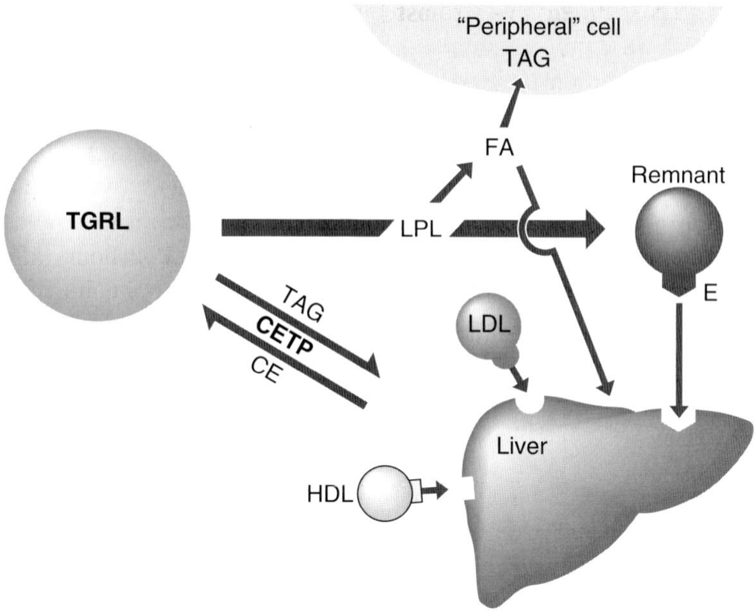

Fig 2. Intravascular metabolism of triacylglycerol-rich lipoproteins (TGRLs). At the endothelial site of peripheral tissues, a substantial proportion of triacylglycerols (TAGs) contained in the particle undergo hydrolysis by lipoprotein lipase (LPL). This releases fatty acids (FA), which are largely taken up by peripheral cells to be oxidized or reesterified into TAGs. Remaining FA are released into the circulation as albumin-bound free FA, which may be removed by different tissues including the liver. Under the regulation of cholesteryl ester transfer protein (CETP), another (smaller) part of TAGs is transferred to low-density lipoproteins (LDL) and high-density lipoproteins (HDL), in exchange for cholesteryl esters (CEs). These processes lead to the formation of remnant particles with a reduced size and an enriched content of CEs. ApoE (E) contained on these remnants allows for their binding and uptake by specific hepatic receptors, which are different from HDL and LDL receptors.

associated with a substantial incorporation of n-3 FA into plasma[11] and tissue (liver>muscle) phospholipids, but no detectable storage in adipose tissue and muscle TAGs.[24]

I.V. Administration of Emulsions Containing n-3 FA in Man

In man, the effect of i.v. fish oil supplementation was assessed using a hypertriglyceridaemic clamp.[25] This model, which has been developed by our group, is based on the same principle as the hyperglycaemic clamp used in studies of carbohydrate metabolism. In our model, the contribution of endogenous lipid stores to the plasma pool is minimized by a constant infusion of glucose and amino acids. Infusion of a lipid emulsion is superimposed after 3 hours, first at a high rate to raise plasma TAGs rapidly to the desired level and thereafter at a rate adjusted so that TAG concentration is maintained at a stable level over a period of at least 4 hours. In such conditions, plasma lipid removal is equal to the amount of exogenous lipids infused. Using the hyptertriglyceridaemic clamp, six healthy volunteers received an LCT emulsion derived from soybean without and with 10% fish oil. Fish oil supplementation did not significantly decrease TAG elimination and did not affect free FA levels or exchanges of neutral lipids with low-density lipoprotein (LDL) and high-density lipoprotein (HDL) (see below).[26]

In a subsequent experiment, supplementation of a mixed MCT/LCT emulsion with 10% fish oil TAGs (providing<2 g EPA and 2 g DHA/day) did not alter plasma TAG elimination, measured by an hypertriglyceridaemic clamp over 4 consecutive days.[27] Of interest, changes in the pattern of FA (i.e. increased EPA and DHA, decreased AA content) were documented, not only in plasma but also in platelet (Table I) and white blood cell phospholipids (Table II) after only one or two infusions.

Recent advances in our understanding of the tissue uptake of FA and their intracellular metabolic fate has led to the possibility of optimizing the delivery of

Table I. The effect on platelet fatty acid content of repeated infusions of medium-chain triacylglycerols/long-chain triacylglycerols with (upper line) and without (lower line) 10% fish oil in man (n=2).

	Platelet fatty acid content (%)				
Fatty acid	**Day 1**	**Day 2**	**Day 3**	**Day 4**	**Day 5**
18:2 n-6	6.3	6.5	6.4	6.8	6.8
	5.5	5.7	5.7	6.0	6.1
20:4 n-6	24.1	23.8	23.7	23.3	22.8
	26.0	25.9	25.5	25.5	25.1
20:5 n-3	0.4	0.6	0.7	0.7	0.9
	0.4	-	0.4	-	0.4
22:5 n-3	2.5	2.5	2.6	2.6	2.7
	2.2	2.2	2.2	2.0	2.0
22:6 n-3	1.9	2.0	2.1	2.1	2.2
	2.1	2.0	2.0	2.0	2.1
Σ n-3	4.8	5.1	5.4	5.4	5.8
	4.7	4.2	4.6	4.0	4.5
20:4 n-6/Σ n-3	5.02	4.67	4.39	4.31	3.93
	5.53	6.17	5.54	6.38	5.58

n-3 FA to specific organs. In addition to the pathway described above, a proportion of TAG FA is transferred to cholesterol-rich LDL and HDL via exchange processes regulated by cholesteryl ester transfer protein.[28] Furthermore, our groups recently showed that, dependent on their sizes, emulsion particles could be taken up by cells via receptor pathways involving apolipoprotein E, or even directly through a non-receptor-mediated pathway.[29]

Finally, exchanges of FA between particle surface phospholipids and cell membrane phospholipids, directly or after exchange with endogenous lipoprotein surface phospholipids, should also be considered. Also, the high susceptibility of PUFA to peroxidative attack remains a matter of concern and reinforces the need for an adequate supply of antioxidants when providing n-3 FA.[19]

Conclusions

It is important to realize that the intracellular trafficking and the metabolic fate of FA may vary depending on their mechanism of uptake. This was shown recently in endothelial cell cultures supplemented with oleate, provided as an oleate–

Table II. The effect on white blood cell fatty acid content of repeated infusions of medium-chain triacylglycerols/long-chain triacylglycerols with (upper line) and without (lower line) 10% fish oil in man (n=2).

	White blood cell fatty acid content (%)				
Fatty acid	**Day 1**	**Day 2**	**Day 3**	**Day 4**	**Day 5**
18:2 n-6	9.1	9.6	9.8	10.1	10.1
	8.6	8.8	9.6	9.2	9.9
20:4 n-6	17.4	16.4	16.1	15.8	15.9
	17.7	17.6	17.2	17.7	16.7
20:5 n-3	0.5	0.8	0.9	0.9	1.0
	0.4	0.2	-	0.2	0.4
22:5 n-3	3.3	3.4	3.5	3.6	3.8
	2.1	2.1	2.1	2.0	2.0
22:6 n-3	2.7	2.8	2.9	3.0	3.0
	2.6	2.2	2.3	2.1	2.3
Σ n-3	6.5	7.0	7.3	7.5	7.8
	5.1	4.5	4.4	4.5	4.7
20:4 n-6/Σ n-3	2.68	2.34	2.21	2.11	2.04
	3.47	3.91	3.91	3.93	3.55

albumin complex, as tri-oleate or as cholesteryl oleate, in reconstituted LDL.[27] Thus, delivery of FA to tissues is dependent not only on efficient extracellular hydrolysis of circulating TAGs by lipoprotein lipase at the endothelial site, but may also be achieved by direct particle uptake or by exchange with emulsion surface phospholipids. This may clear the way for new approaches that enhance delivery of n-3 FA and target specific tissues by using more appropriate vehicles.

Acknowledgements

Studies from our laboratories reported here have been performed with the support of grants no. 3.4632.92 and 3.4695.95 from the Belgian Fonds de la Recherche Scientifique Médicale and grant no. HL-40404 from the U.S. National Institutes of Health. Generous supply of Omegavenoes and financial support from Fresenius AG are gratefully acknowledged. We wish to express our deep appreciation to Ms. N. Van Laer and Ms. S. Mulongo for their tremendous secretarial help.

Summary

n-3 fatty acids (FA) are an important component of cell membrane phospholipids and have a substantial potential for influencing physical properties, receptor and enzyme activity and secondary messenger production. In addition, eicosapentaenoic acid (EPA) (20:5 n-3), and to a lesser extent, docosahexaenoic acid (DHA) (22:6 n-3), may inhibit the formation of eicosanoids from arachidonic acid (AA). Furthermore, EPA can be used as a precursor for the formation, through the same enzyme pathways (i.e. cyclooxygenases and lipoxygenases), of much less potent mediators of inflammatory and thrombotic events. Finally, incorporation of n-3 FA into cell membrane phospholipids appears to reduce the response of cells to inflammatory, aggregatory and catabolic mediators. Experimental studies have suggested a role for n-3 FA in the prevention of cardiovascular and inflammatory disorders, and in the treatment of several immune disorders, including graft rejections. The aim of intravenous administration of n-3 FA is to supply available free FA directly to a cell's metabolic pool, and to induce changes in membrane composition much faster than dietary supplementation would allow. Emulsions containing ethyl ester n-3 FA or triacylglycerols (TAGs) (tri-EPA and tri-DHA, derived from fish oil) have been evaluated experimentally. TAGs containing n-3 FA represent a poor substrate for lipoprotein lipase *in vitro*, and the addition of n-3 FA in excess of 10% (mol%) may impede the hydrolysis of soybean-derived TAGs. In a variety of animal species, enrichment of chylomicrons or artificial particles with n-3 FA is associated with a low degree of extrahepatic lipolysis, and the formation of n-3 FA-rich remnants, presumably destined for the liver. Thus, in order to avoid a marked rise in plasma TAGs, n-3 FA preparations should be infused at a relatively slow rate, or should be mixed in low proportions with other TAGs. A 2-week regimen of exclusive parenteral nutrition in dogs (0.2 g n-3 FA/kg/day) was associated with the substantial incorporation of n-3 FA into plasma and tissue phospholipids. No storage was detectable in adipose tissue or muscle. In humans, supplementation of a mixed emulsion (50% w/w medium-chain triglycerides and 50% w/w long-chain triglycerides) with 10% fish oil TAG (approximately 2% EPA and 2% DHA) did not alter plasma TAG elimination, measured over 4 consecutive days using a hypertriglyceridaemic clamp. After two infusions, changes in the pattern of FA (increased EPA and DHA content and decreased AA content) were detected not only in the plasma, but also in platelet and white blood cell phospholipids. Changes in eicosanoid balance, immune response and platelet aggregation have been reported to occur rapidly after such infusions, and the results of preliminary clinical studies are encouraging. However, the sensitivity of polyunsaturated FA to peroxidative attack should be kept in mind, and an adequate supply of antioxidants must be provided.

References

1. Simopoulos A.P., Koletzko B., Anderson R.E., Hornstra G., Mensink R.P., Weksler B.B., Harris W.S., De Caterina R., Muggli R., Sprecher H.: The 1st Congress of the International Society for the Study of Fatty Acids and Lipids (ISSFAL): Fatty acids and lipids from cell biology to human disease. J. Lipid Res. 1994; 35: 169-173
2. De Caterina R., Cybulsky M.I., Clinton S.K., Gimbrone M.A. Jr., Libby P.: The omega-3 fatty acid docosahexaenoate reduces cytokine-induced expression of proatherogenic and proinflammatory proteins in human endothelial cells. Arterioscler. Thromb. 1994; 14: 1829-1836
3. Kang J.X., Leaf A.: Effects of long-chain polyunsaturated fatty acids on the contraction of neonatal rat cardiac myocytes. Proc. Natl. Acad. Sci. USA 1994; 91: 9886-9890
4. Billman G.E., Hallaq H., Leaf A.: Prevention of ischemia-induced ventricular fibrillation by omega-3 fatty acids. Proc. Natl. Acad. Sci. USA 1994; 91: 4427-4430
5. McLennan P.L.: Relative effects of dietary saturated, monounsaturated, and polyunsaturated fatty acids on cardiac arrhythmias in rats. Am. J. Clin. Nutr. 1993; 57: 207-212
6. Grimble R.F.: Dietary manipulation of the inflammatory response. Proc. Nutr. Soc. 1992; 51: 285-294
7. Murray M.J., Svingen B.A., Holman R.T., Yaksh T.L.: Effects of a fish oil diet on pigs' cardiopulmonary response to bacteremia. JPEN 1991; 15: 152-158
8. Pscheidl E.M., Wan J.M., Blackburn G.L., Bistrian B.R., Istfan N.W.: Influence of ω-3 fatty acids on splanchnic blood flow and lactate metabolism in an endotoxemic rat model. Metabolism 1992 41: 698-705
9. Carpentier Y.A., Siderova V.S., Simoens C., Richelle M., Dubois D., Deckelbaum, R.J.: Immunoregulatory role of lipids. In: Cynober L., Fürst P., Lawin P. (Eds.): *Pharmacological Nutrition, Immune Nutrition.* München; W. Zuckschwerdt Verlag GmbH, 1995: 33-41
10. Wretlind A.: Development of fat emulsions. JPEN 1981; 5: 230-235
11. Rössle C.: Intravascular metabolism of a fish oil-supplemented lipid emulsion in an experimental dog model: effects on plasma and liver lipids, lipoproteins and incorporation of long-chain n-3 fatty acids into plasma lipids. Clin. Nutr. 1993; 12: 118-120
12. Carpentier Y.A., Richelle M., Rössle C., Simoens C., Derluyn M., Crabbe V., Deckelbaum R.J.: Tissue fatty acid composition of dogs during total parenteral nutrition (TPN) with MCT/LCT supplemented with fish oil. Clin. Nutr. 1993; 12 (Suppl.): 3 (Abstract)
13. Dahlan W., Richelle M., Kulapongse S., Rössle C., Deckelbaum R.J., Carpentier Y.A.: Effects of essential fatty acid content of lipid emulsions on erythrocyte polyunsaturated fatty acid composition in patients on long-term parenteral nutrition. Clin. Nutr. 1992; 11: 262-268
14. Harris W.S.: The benefits and pathologies from excesses and deficiencies of dietary fatty acids. Curr. Opin. Endocrinol. Diabetes 1994; 260-266
15. Urakaze M., Hamazaki T., Soda Y., Miyamoto A., Ibuki F., Yano S., Kumagai A: Infusion of emulsified trieicosapentaenoyl-glycerol into rabbits - the effects on platelet aggregation, polymorphonuclear leucocyte adhesion, and fatty acid composition in plasma and platelet phospholipids. Thromb. Res. 1986; 44: 673-682
16. Hamazaki T., Urakaze M., Yano S., Soda Y., Miyamoto A., Kubota K., Ibuki F.: Injection of tridocosahexaenoyl-glycerol emulsion and fatty acid composition of blood cells. Lipids 1987; 22: 1031-1034
17. Sawazaki S., Nakamura N., Hamazaki T., Yamazaki K., Urakaze M., Yano S.: Intravenous infusion of trieicosapentaenoyl-glycerol and LTB_4 and LTB_5 production by leukocytes of rabbits. Am. J. Physiol. 1992; 262: 1711-1718

18. Nakamura N., Hamazaki T., Yamazaki K., Taki H., Kobayashi M., Yazawa K., Ibuki F.: Intravenous infusion of tridocosahexaenoyl-glycerol emulsion into rabbits. Effects on leukotriene B4/5 production and fatty acid composition of plasma and leukocytes. J. Clin. Invest. 1993; 92: 1253-1261

19. Schjött J., Brekke O-L., Jynge P., Bjerve K.S., Hamazaki T.: Infusion of EPA and DHA lipid emulsions: effects on heart lipids and tolerance to ischaemia-reperfusion in the isolated rat heart. Scand. J. Clin. Lab. Invest. 1993; 53: 873-882

20. Hamazaki T., Fischer S., Schweer H., Meese C.O., Urakaze M., Yokoyama A., Yano S.: The infusion of trieicosapentaenoyl-glycerol into humans and the *in vivo* formation of prostaglandin I_3 and thromboxane A_3. Biochem. Biophys. Res. Commun. 1988; 151: 1386-1394

21. Carpentier Y.A.: Intravascular metabolism of fat emulsions. Clin. Nutr. 1989; 8: 115-125

22. Oliveira F., Carpentier Y.A., Hansen I., Deckelbaum R.J.: Triglyceride hydrolysis of soy vs fish oil LCT emulsions. Clin. Nutr. 1992; 11 (Suppl.): 44

23. Melin T., Qi C., Bengtsson-Olivecrona G., Akesson B., Nilsson A.: Hydrolysis of chylomicron polyenoic fatty acid esters with lipoprotein lipase and hepatic lipase. Biochim. Biophys. Acta 1991; 1075: 259-266

24. Simoens C., Richelle M., Rössle C., Derluyn M., Deckelbaum R.J., Carpentier Y.A.: Manipulation of tissue fatty acid profile by i.v. lipids in dogs. Clin. Nutr. 1995; 14: 177-185

25. Carpentier Y.A., Kinney J.M., Siderova V.S., Richelle M., Nishiwaki H., Olivecrona T., Deckelbaum R.J.: Hypertriglyceridaemia clamp: a new model for studying lipid metabolism. Clin. Nutr. 1990; 9 (Suppl.): 1 (Abstract)

26. Richelle M., Carpentier Y.A., Siderova V., Deckelbaum R.J.: Does fish oil (FO) supplementation affect the intravascular metabolism of LCT emulsion in man? Clin. Nutr. 1993; 12 (Suppl): 2

27. Richelle M.: Effet de la composition des deux constituants principaux (triglycérides et phospholipides) sur le métabolisme intravasculaire des émulsions lipidiques. Ph.D. Thesis Université Libre de Bruxelles 1995: 108-120

28. Richelle M., Deckelbaum R.J., Carpentier Y.A.: Long chain vs medium chain triacylglycerol intravenous emulsions in lipid exchange processes with human plasma low density lipoprotein. Biochemistry 1994; 33: 4872-4878

29. Schwiegelsohn B., Presley J.F., Gorecki M., Vogel T., Carpentier Y.A., Maxfield F.R., Deckelbaum R.J.: Effects of apoprotein E on intracellular metabolism of model triglyceride-rich particles are distinct from effects on cell particle uptake. J. Biol. Chem. 1995; 270: 1761-1769

S.D. Kristensen, E.B. Schmidt, R. De Caterina, S. Endres
n-3 Fatty Acids: Prevention and Treatment in Vascular Disease
Bi & Gi Publishers, Verona - Springer Verlag, London, 1995

20. Bioavailability of n-3 Fatty Acid Formulations

J. DYERBERG[1], P. MADSEN[2], J. MØLLER[3], I. AARDESTRUP[2], E.B. SCHMIDT[4]

1. *Medi-Lab a.s., Copenhagen, Denmark*
2. *Department of Clinical Chemistry, Aalborg Hospital, Aalborg, Denmark*
3. *Department of Gastroenterology, Aalborg Hospital, Aalborg, Denmark*
4. *Department of Medicine and Endocrinology, Aalborg Hospital, Aalborg, Denmark*

Introduction

Since our original observations in Greenland Eskimos of an association between dietary intake of marine long-chain polyunsaturated n-3 fatty acids (FA) and biological and cellular functions,[1,2] much interest has been focused on the potential health benefits of marine n-3 FA and the amount of seafood in the diet. Supplementation with various n-3 FA formulations has been the primary tool used to obtain an exact dose of n-3 FA and to perform blinded, controlled studies. Initially, deodorized crude fish oils; *e.g.*, cod liver oil (CLO) and whole fish body oils, were used. In these preparations, the n-3 FA are natural triglycerides (TGs). Problems of patient compliance due to the large amounts of such oils that had to be ingested in order to reach relatively high levels of n-3 FA, prompted the development of more concentrated compounds. Thus, concentrates of n-3 FA containing large amounts of eicosapentaenoic acid (EPA) and docosahexaenoic acid (DHA) have been developed. Such formulations, which contain 30-90% total FA in the form of EPA and DHA, have been used. The n-3 FA are present in these formulations mainly as free fatty acids (FFA), ethyl esters (EE) or reesterified TGs (rTGs).

Some conflicting results have arisen from the few studies that have dealt with the absorption of EPA and DHA from the various concentrated n-3 FA formulations. El Boustani *et al.*[3] reported a delayed and reduced incorporation of EPA into plasma TGs when administered as EE, compared with the incorporation of EPA administered as natural TGs or as FFA. Lawson and Hughes,[4] compared the time course for the appearance of and increase in concentration of EPA in plasma TG relative to the maximal rise in α-linolenic acid, and found nearly 100% absorption of EPA and DHA as FFA, whereas only 68% and 20% of EPA as natural TG or EE, respectively, were absorbed.

More recent data generally point to an equal absorption of n-3 FA, in the form of either TG or EE.[5-7] Thus, Luley *et al.*[5] compared the absorption of EPA and DHA from natural fish oil TG with that from EE, at two different levels of EPA and DHA (54% and 85%) and found no difference in absorption. Nordøy *et al.*[6] compared the content of n-3 FA in chylomicron TG and the increase in chylomicron TG after a test meal that included a large dose of n-3 FA provided either as rTG or as EE. These authors found a similar absorption of n-3 FA irrespective of whether the supplement was rTG or EE. In spite of different rates of hydrolyses of FA from triacylglycerols by lipase *in vitro*, Krokan *et al.*[7] found that the absorption of EPA and DHA from synthetic EEs rich in EPA and DHA was fully comparable to that from natural triacylglycerols containing smaller amounts of these FA. In a study by Hansen *et al.*,[8] volunteers were given EPA and DHA either as natural TG or as EE at a dose of approximately 3.5 g/day for 7 weeks. They found equal incorporation of EPA and DHA into plasma phospholipids from the two formulations. The incorporation of EPA into plasma cholesteryl esters from EE was, however, significantly lower than that from natural TG.

The lack of a controlled study comparing the five commonly used fish oil supplements (natural TG in fish body oil and CLO, EEs, FFA and rTGs) led us to undertake the present blinded, placebo-controlled study in 72 healthy volunteers. The enrichment of EPA and DHA in plasma TGs, cholesterol esters and phospholipids was examined after intake of five different n-3 FA formulations or placebo oil (corn oil) for 2 weeks.

Methods

Subjects

Seventy-two healthy subjects (36 women aged 21-56 years and 36 men aged 23-55 years) volunteered for the study. Any volunteer who had taken CLO or other fish oil preparations within 2 months prior to the study was excluded. The volunteers were instructed to avoid acetylsalicylic acid 2 weeks prior to and during the study, and to abstain from alcoholic beverages for 1 day before study visits. The study was approved by the local Ethics Committee.

Experimental design

The volunteers were randomized to six groups: four double-blinded groups given concentrated fish oils or placebo, each person taking five capsules twice daily at meal times for 2 weeks; and two single-blinded groups given CLO or fish body oil capsules twice daily for 2 weeks. The single-blinded design in the two natural fish oil groups was due to the different number of capsules in these groups. All supplements were from Pronova Biocare, Sandefjord Norway: EPAX 5500 TG, consisting of rTGs; EPAX 6000 FA, consisting of FFA; EPAX 5500 EE, consisting of EE; EPAX 3000 TG, consisting of a refined fish body oil, CLO; and corn oil (CO) as placebo.

The composition and amounts of the supplements are given in Table I. The daily supplement of EPA plus DHA was 3.1-3.6 g. The subjects were examined at baseline and after 2 weeks of supplementation. Each examination was made in the morning after an overnight fast.

Blood was drawn from an antecubital vein with minimal stasis. Serum was prepared by clotting whole blood for 1 hour at room temperature and centrifugation at 2000 G for 15 minutes. Serum was transferred to plastic tubes and stored at -70°C until analysis. All analytical work was performed before breaking the randomization code.

Table I. Dose and composition of capsules and relative and absolute amounts of EPA and DHA given in the six study groups.

	Re-Ester. Triglycer.	**Free FA**	**Ethyl Esters**	**Fish body oil**	**Cod liver oil**	**Corn oil**
Weight of capsules (mg)	650	650	650	1000	500	650
Capsules/day	5 + 5	5 + 5	5 + 5	6 + 7	17 + 17	5 + 5
EPA (%)	28.5	33.5	28.8	15.7	8.1	0
DHA (%)	19.8	21.5	21.4	11.4	11.0	0
n-6 FA (%)	4.0	2.2	3.9	2.5	2.2	56.7
Monounsaturated FA (%)	13.3	12.1	15.7	25.9	51.8	29.0
Saturated FA (%)	1.0	2.8	6.0	27.5	16.0	13.4
Tocopherols (mg/g)	3.7	3.5	3.9	1.1	1.0	2.8
EPA (g/day)	1.85	2.18	1.87	2.04	1.38	0
DHA (g/day)	1.29	1.40	1.39	1.48	1.87	0
EPA + DHA (g/day)	3.1	3.6	3.3	3.5	3.2	0

Abbreviations: EPA=eicosapentaenoic acid, DHA=docosahexaenoic acid, FA=fatty acids.

Fatty acid analysis

Total lipids were extracted from serum according to Bligh and Dyer.[9] Serum (400 μl) was mixed briefly with 500 μl chloroform ($CHCl_3$) containing internal standards (diheptadecanoyl phosphatidylcholine, cholesteryl heptadecanoate and triheptadecanoin) and 1000 ml methanol containing butylated hydroxytoluene as antioxidant.

After addition of 500 ml $CHCl_3$ and 500 μl H_2O and brief mixing, the tubes were centrifuged at 1000 G for 2 minutes for phase separation; 550 ml of the $CHCl_3$ phase was transferred to a SepPak NH_2 column (Waters Corporation, Milford, MA, USA), which had been prewashed with hexane. Lipid classes were separated into phospholipids (PL), cholesterol esters (CE) and monoglycerides, diglycerides and TGs as described by Kaluzny *et al.*,[10] except that the glycerides were collected as a single class. The extracted lipids were dried under nitrogen (N_2) and redissolved in 100 μl toluene. Transmethylation was carried out overnight at 45°C under N_2 after addition of 200 ml methanolic sulphuric acid 1%.[11] The methylated FA were extracted after addition of 500 μl NaCl 5% and 1500 μl hexane. The hexane phase was washed with 2% $NaHCO_3$, dried under N_2 and redissolved in 60 μl dichloromethane. Gas chromatography was performed isothermally at 220°C on an HP 5700 gas chromatograph (Hewlett Packard, Avondale, PA, USA) supplied with a 25 m x 0.53 mm FFAP-CB capillary column (Chrompack, Middelburg, The Netherlands) with N_2 as the carrier gas (2 ml/minute).

Statistics

The SPSS for Windows statistical software package, version 6.1, was applied. Statistical comparisons between groups at baseline and after 2 weeks of supplementation were made using the Mann-Whitney U-test. A two-sided p value < 0.05 was considered statistically significant.

Results

The results of the increase in the amounts of EPA and DHA in plasma CE, PL and TG, and in the sum of EPA and DHA in each lipid class are given in Table II. The total increases in EPA, DHA and in EPA plus DHA are illustrated in Figure 1.

Each n-3 FA preparation produced a significant increase in both EPA and DHA in all lipid classes compared with placebo oil. When comparing the different n-3 FA preparations, it should be borne in mind that despite the fact that the total amounts of EPA plus DHA given to the volunteers were almost equal (see Table I), the relative amounts of EPA and DHA varied to some extent; for example, between FFA and CLO. This is illustrated in Figure 1, which shows that the total increase

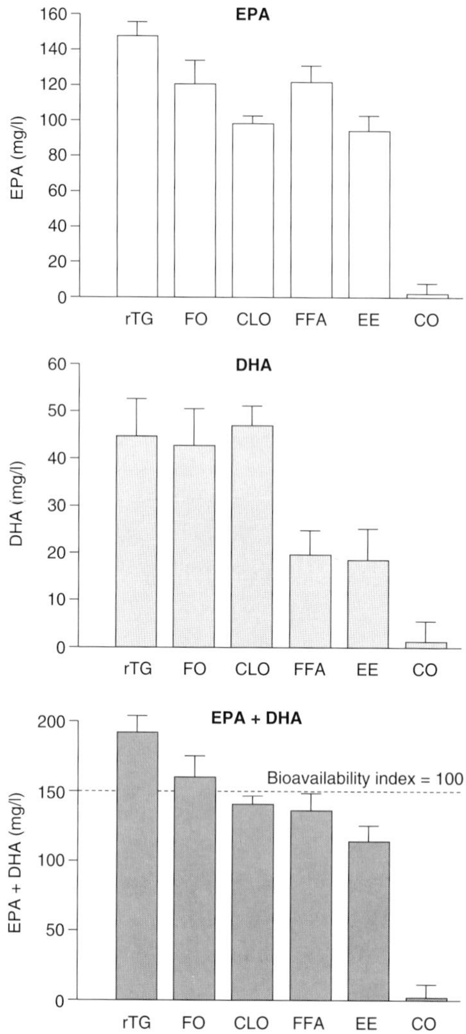

Fig. 1. Difference between end of study and baseline values in eicosapentaenoic acid (EPA), docosahexaenoic acid (DHA) and EPA plus DHA in the sum of serum lipid fractions (cholesterol esters plus triglycerides plus phospholipids). A bioavailability index of 100 is indicated in the EPA plus DHA plot, corresponding to the mean value of increases after natural fish oils: fish body oil (FO) and cod liver oil (CLO). Values are means±SEM.

in EPA after giving CLO was fourth in magnitude, whereas CLO produced the greatest increase in DHA. The volunteers in the CLO group received approximately 0.5 g less EPA and approximately 0.5 g more DHA per day compared with the other groups. Consequently, the sum of EPA and DHA gives a more accurate picture of differences in bioavailability. However, considering EPA and DHA individually in CE, PL and TG, calculating the sums of EPA plus DHA in each class of plasma lipid individually, and using the grand total as a measure of bioavailability, in this study, EE was the formulation giving the lowest assimilation. The differences in the grand total of EPA plus DHA (Fig. 1) were significant when comparing EE with rTG

Table II. Mean difference between baseline and end of study regarding the amount of eicosapentaenoic acid (EPA) and docosahexaenoic acid (DHA) in serum lipids. Values are given in mg/l.

	CE			PL			TG		
	EPA	DHA	EPA+ DHA	EPA	DHA	EPA+ DHA	EPA	DHA	EPA+ DHA
rTG	71.0	4.8	75.8	60.5	27.1	87.6	15.9	12.8	28.7
FFA	53.1	3.5	56.6	52.8	5.6	58.4	15.4	11.0	26.4
EE	46.3	3.2	49.5	37.3	6.9	44.2	10.4	8.4	18.8
FO	55.0	4.2	59.2	53.7	25.9	79.6	11.7	12.0	23.7
CLO	48.4	5.6	54.0	38.8	21.2	60.0	11.8	20.1	31.9
CO	2.7	1.5	4.2	0.4	0.3	0.7	-1.2	-0.9	-2.1

Abbreviations: rTG=re-esterified triglycerides, FFA=free fatty acids, EE=ethyl esters, FO=fish body oil, CLO=cod liver oil, CO=corn oil, CE=cholesterol esters, PL=phospholipids, TG=triglycerides.

(p=0.0001) and EE with fish body oil (p=0.024), but not when comparing EE with CLO (p=0.13) and EE with FFA (p=0.29).

Comparing the assimilation of the other preparations (rTG, fish body oil, CLO and FA), again using the grand total sums of EPA plus DHA as an index, the bioavailability of rTG was significantly better than that of FA (p=0.006) and of CLO (p=0.002), whereas it did not differ from fish body oil (p=0.24). However, it should be noted that there was only a modest difference in bioavailability between fish body oil and CLO (Fig. 1). There were no significant differences between fish body oil, CLO and the FA preparations.

Discussion

This study set out to resolve the hitherto conflicting data on the bioavailability of EPA and DHA from various preparations of fish oil.[3-5] It also aimed to address whether the stereochemistry of EPA and DHA in the acylglycerol molecule influenced FA assimilation, as other authors have raised the question of whether structural differences in TGs influence their bioavailability.[12,13]

The hypothesis that marine n-3 FA may have beneficial effects arose from studies in Eskimos, who obtain their n-3 FA mainly from marine mammal TGs. The long-chained n-3 FA of these TGs are located in the sn-1/3 position, as distinct from fish oils, in which n-3 FA are found mainly in the sn-2 position. Lingual and pancreatic lipases stereospecifically liberate FA from the 1 and 3 positions of triglycerides, leaving the 2-monoglyceride intact.[14,15] The n-3 FA are consequently absorbed either as sn-2-monoglycerides or as FFA, depending on the molecular structure of the dietary triglycerides.

Taking the mean of the increase in EPA plus DHA in all three plasma lipid classes (grand total) for the two natural fish oils (fish body oil and CLO) as unity (100%), the mean relative bioavailability, unadjusted for dosage, of EPA plus DHA from EE was 73%, from FFA 91% and from rTG 124%. Adjusted for dosage, the results were 76%, 86% and 134%, respectively. This finding of an equal or lower bioavailability of EPA plus DHA from FFA compared with natural TGs is in contrast with the findings of Lawson *et al.*[4] from an 8-hour absorption study, and those of Beckermann *et al.*[16] using a 1-week crossover design. Both studies included eight volunteers and both found an increased bioavailability of FFA compared with natural TG. However, comparing FFA, TG and EE in a 24-hour absorption study in eight volunteers, El Boustani *et al.*[3] found an equal absorption of EPA from FFA and natural TG. All three studies demonstrated a reduced bioavailability of EE preparations when compared with natural TGs. In contrast to these studies in humans, de Schrijver *et al.*[17] found a decreased assimilation of fish oil-derived FFA in rats, compared with natural fish oil.

The explanation for the differences in FFA absorption in the above mentioned studies could be due to interactions between the n-3 FA preparations and the normal diet. FFA form insoluble salts, *e.g.* with Ca (Ca soaps), that influence their assimilation.

The discrepant results regarding FFA bioavailability preparations do not allow definitive conclusions to be drawn, although they indicate that FFA preparations have a bioavailability in man comparable to that of natural TGs. There may, however, be a problem with tolerability, as FFA are locally irritative and may give rise to a higher incidence of side-effects.[16]

Our findings of a lower bioavailability of EPA and DHA from EE than from FFA or TG are in accordance with the demonstration that pancreatic lipase hydrolyses EEs to a lesser degree than TGs[3,4] and at a slower rate.[7] They are also in accordance with some studies that have examined the bioavailability of n-3 EE,[3,4,8,16] but not with findings of other studies.[5-7] As discussed below, the relationship between the intake of the capsules and the normal diet could offer an explanation for these discrepancies. Thus, in the study by Nordøy *et al.*,[6] who found an equally good absorption of n-3 FA from EE and TG, the n-3 FA were given as part of a lipid-rich meal. Also, Lawson *et al.*[18] found that the absorption of EPA and DHA from EE was increased substantially by co-ingestion with a high-fat meal. The assimilation of EEs may be enhanced when given as part of a (lipid-rich) meal.

The question of whether the stereochemistry of acylglycerols of fish oil may influence assimilation of EPA and DHA was addressed in the present study by using a randomized rTG, thus enabling us to study both the effect of concentrated fish oil preparations and the effect of stereoisometry. In the re-esterification process, which adds, on average, one extra n-3 FA to each TG molecule, the positioning of EPA and DHA in the glyceride molecule is at random. Thus, the sn-1/3 and sn-2 positions are equally esterified by EPA and DHA in the glycerol molecule.

Our results showed that the randomization of EPA and DHA in acylglycerols has no negative bearing on the bioavailability of long-chain n-3 FA in man. These findings are in accordance with those of de Schrijver *et al.*[17] in rats. In a 24-day balance study, these authors found an equal bioavailability of natural fish oil and randomized fish oil compared with soya bean oil, whereas the absorption of FFA derived from fish oil was moderately lower when compared with the other fish oil supplements. Christensen *et al.*[19] reached the same conclusion when comparing the absorption patterns over 24 hours in rats fed either fish oil or seal oil. They found an initially better absorption of n-3 FA from fish oil than from seal oil, but the overall effects of the structure of the dietary triacylglycerols on n-3 FA assimilation were negligible. The finding that the molecular structure of glycerides does not influence FA assimilation is in accordance with the fact that, although Eskimos consume marine mammal TGs with n-3 FA localized predominantly in the sn-1/3 position, which differs from the Western seafood fish diet in which n-3 FA are mainly in the sn-2 position, this habit is equal to that of the marine mammals obtaining their n-3 FA from fish. The fact that organ FA stereochemistry is independent of the structure of the dietary acylglycerols has been further documented by Christensen and Høy[20] who found no difference in organ lipid content and composition of n-3 FA between two groups of rats fed either seal oil or fish oil for 17 days.

Interestingly, we found an even higher index of bioavailability (124%) of rTGs than of natural TGs (fish body oil and CLO), although it should be stressed that this difference was only significant when compared with CLO. A tentative explanation for this finding could be that besides TGs, rTG also contains both diglycerides and monoglycerides. This imitates the normal acylglyceride absorption conditions in the intestine. The monoglycerides and diglycerides may facilitate normal micellar formation, in which the sn-2-monoglycerides from dietary TG are absorbed and preserved by reacylation of TG in the enterocyte, and subsequently secreted as lymphatic chylomicrons. The volunteers were asked to take their capsules along with their morning and evening meals, but some volunteers may have taken their capsules at other times. Lawson and Hughes[18] found that absorption of fish oil FA from EE was increased substantially by co-ingestion with a high-fat meal. Also, Silverman *et al.*[21] found that the relative absorption of EPA from tuna fish meat was significantly higher than from fish oil. The findings by Nordøy *et al.*[6] that n-3 FA as rTG and as EE were equally well absorbed could likewise be due to the fact that they were given as part of a lipid-rich meal. This again emphasizes the effect of meal conditions on n-3 FA absorption.

In conclusion, our results demonstrate that bioavailability may differ between the commonly used types of concentrated fish oil preparations. rTGs have superior bioavailability, whereas EE may have a lower bioavailability. FFA have medium bioavailability, which is not different from that of natural fish oil TGs. Our study further documents that the isometry of n-3 FA in the glyceride molecule does not influence the assimilation of EPA plus DHA in man. It should, however, be stressed that these conclusions are based on relatively short-term (2 weeks) studies at a fixed daily n-3 FA dose of approximately 3.5 g.

Summary

The use of marine n-3 polyunsaturated fatty acids (FA) as food supplements has prompted the development of concentrated formulations to overcome patient compliance problems related to the natural, rather low concentrated fish oils. Conflicting data on the bioavailability of these preparations initiated the present study, which compares three concentrated n-3 FA preparations - ethyl esters, free fatty acids and reesterified triglycerides - with placebo oil in a double-blinded design. Two single blinded arms with natural fish body oil and cod liver oil were also included in the study. The study comprised 72 volunteers divided into six groups who were given approximately 3.3 g of eicosapentaenoic acid (EPA) plus docosahexaenoic acid (DHA) daily for 2 weeks. The increase from baseline in absolute amounts of EPA and DHA in fasting serum triglycerides, cholesterol esters and phospholipids was examined. Consistent patterns for the three serum lipid fractions were observed. The bioavailability of EPA + DHA from reesterified triglycerides was superior (124%) compared with natural fish oil triglycerides, whereas the bioavailability of EPA + DHA from ethyl esters was inferior (73%). Free fatty acid bioavailability (91%) did not differ substantially from natural triglycerides. The study further demonstrated that fatty acid stereochemistry of the acylglycerols does not influence the bioavailability of EPA and DHA in man.

References

1. Dyerberg J., Bang H.O.: Haemostatic function and platelet polyunsaturated fatty acids in Eskimos. Lancet 1979; ii: 433-435
2. Dyerberg J., Bang H.O., Stoffersen E., Moncada S., Vane J.R.: Eicosapentaenoic acid and prevention of thrombosis and atherosclerosis. Lancet 1978; ii: 117-119
3. El Boustani S.E., Colette C., Monnier L., Descomps B., de Paulet A.C., Mendy F.: Enteral absorption in man of eicosapentaenoic acid in different chemical forms. Lipids 1987; 22: 711-714
4. Lawson L.D., Hughes G.: Human absorption of fish oil fatty acids as triacylglycerols, free acids, or ethyl esters. Biochim. Biophys. Res. Comm. 1988; 152: 328-335
5. Luley C., Wieland H., Gruwald J.: Bioavailability of omega-3 fatty acids: ethylester preparations are as suitable as triglyceride preparations. Akt. Ernaehr-Med. 1990; 15: 122-125
6. Nordøy A., Barstad L., Connor W.E., Hatcher L.: Absorption of the n-3 eicosapentaenoic and docosahexaenoic acids as ethyl esters and triglycerides by humans. Am. J. Clin. Nutr. 1991; 53: 1185-1190

7. Krokan H.E., Bjerve K.S., Moerk E.: The enteral bioavailability of eicosapentaenoic acid and docosahexaenoic acid is as good from ethyl esters as from glycerol esters in spite of lower hydrolytic rates by pancreatic lipase *in vitro*. Biochim. Biophys. Acta 1993; 1168: 59-67
8. Hansen J.-B., Olsen J.-O., Wilsgaard L., Lyngmo V., Svensson B.: Comparative effects of prolonged intake of highly purified fish oils as ethyl ester or triglyceride on lipids, haemostasis and platelet function in normolipaemic men. Eur. J. Clin. Nutr. 1993; 47: 497-507
9. Bligh E.G., Dyer W.J.: A rapid method of total lipid extraction and purification. Can. J. Biochem. Physiol. 1959; 37: 911-917
10. Kaluzny M.A., Duncan L.A., Merritt M.V., Epps D.E.: Rapid separation of lipid classes in high yield and purity using bonded phase columns. J. Lipid Res. 1985; 26: 135-140
11. Christie W.W.: Gas Chromatography and Lipids: a Practical Guide. Ayr; The Oily Press Ltd., 1989
12. Ackman R.G.: The absorption of fish oils and concentrates. Lipids 1992; 27: 858-862
13. Nelson G.J., Ackman R.G.: Absorption and transport of fat in mammals with emphasis on n-3 polyunsaturated fatty acids. Lipids 1988; 23: 1005-1014
14. Tso P., Hayashi H.: The physiology and regulation of the intestinal absorption and transport of omega-3 and omega-6 fatty acids. Adv. Prostaglandin Thromboxane Leukotriene Res. 1989; 19: 623-626
15. Borgström B.: In: Smith D.H. (Ed.) *Biomembranes*. Vol. 4B. New York; Plenum Press, 1974: 555-620
16. Beckermann B., Beneke M., Seitz I.: Vergleich der Bioverfügbarkeit von Eicosapentaensäure und Docosahexaensäure aus Triglyceriden, freien Fettsäuren und Ethylestern bei Probanden. Arzneim Forsch Drug Res. 1990; 40: 700-704
17. de Schrijver R., Vermeulen D., Backx S.: Digestion and absorption of free and esterified fish oil fatty acids in rats. Lipids 1991; 26: 400-404
18. Lawson L.D., Hughes B.G.: Absorption of eicosapentaenoic acid and docosahexaenoic acid from fish oil triacylglycerols or fish oil ethyl esters co-ingested with a high-fat meal. Biochim. Biophys. Res. Comm. 1988; 156: 960-963
19. Christensen M.S., Høy C.-E., Redgrave T.G.: Lymphatic absorption of n-3 polyunsaturated fatty acids from marine oils with different intramolecular fatty acid distribution. Biochim. Biophys. Acta 1994; 1215: 198-204
20. Christensen M.S., Høy C.-E.: Time related incorporation of (n-3) polyunsaturated fatty acids from seal oil or fish oil into rat tissue phospholipids. Nutr. Res. 1992; 12: 1141-1154
21. Silverman D.I., Ware J.A., Sacks F.M., Pasternak R.C.: Comparison of the absorption and effect on platelet function of a single dose of n-3 fatty acids given as fish or fish oil. Am. J. Clin. Nutr. 1991; 53: 1165-1170

Subject Index

R

S

T

V